Radiate Science knowledge with CGP...

OK, so there's a lot to learn in GCSE Combined Science — it is worth two GCSEs, after all.

Not to worry. This chunky CGP book explains all the facts, theory and practical skills you'll need, with essential exam practice questions on every page. It's a beautiful thing.

How to access your free Online Edition

This book includes a free Online Edition to read on your PC, Mac or tablet.
To access it, just go to **cgpbooks.co.uk/extras** and enter this code...

By the way, this code only works for one person. If somebody else has used this book before you, they might have already claimed the Online Edition.

CGP — still the best! ☺

Our sole aim here at CGP is to produce the highest quality books —
carefully written, immaculately presented and dangerously close to being funny.

Then we work our socks off to get them out to you
— at the cheapest possible prices.

Contents

Published by CGP.

From original material by Richard Parsons.

Editors: Sarah Armstrong, Mary Falkner, Katherine Faudemer, Robin Flello, Emily Garrett, Sharon Keeley-Holden, Chris Lindle, Duncan Lindsay, Rachael Rogers, Sophie Scott, Camilla Simson, Charlotte Whiteley and Sarah Williams.

Contributor: Paddy Gannon.

ISBN: 978 1 78294 570 3

With thanks to Susan Alexander, Barrie Crowther, Mark Edwards, Emily Howe, Rachel Kordan, Glenn Rogers and Hayley Thompson for the proofreading.

Printed by Elanders Ltd, Newcastle upon Tyne.
Clipart from Corel®

Illustrations by: Sandy Gardner Artist, email sandy@sandygardner.co.uk

The Scientific Method

This section <u>isn't</u> about how to 'do' science — but it does show you the way <u>most scientists</u> work.

Science is All About Testing Hypotheses

Scientists make an observation.

1) Scientists <u>OBSERVE</u> (look at) something they don't understand, e.g. an illness.
2) They come up with a <u>possible explanation</u> for what they've observed.
3) This explanation is called a <u>HYPOTHESIS</u>.

Hundreds of years ago, we thought demons caused illness.

They test their hypothesis.

4) Next, they test whether the hypothesis is <u>right or not</u>.
5) They do this by making a <u>PREDICTION</u> — a statement based on the hypothesis that can be tested.
6) They then <u>TEST</u> this prediction by carrying out <u>experiments</u>.
7) If their prediction is <u>right</u>, this is <u>EVIDENCE</u> that their <u>hypothesis might be right</u> too.

Other scientists test the hypothesis too.

8) Other scientists <u>check</u> the evidence — for example, they check that the experiment was carried out in a <u>sensible</u> way. This is called <u>PEER-REVIEW</u>.
9) Scientists then <u>share their results</u>, e.g. in scientific papers.
10) Other scientists carry out <u>more experiments</u> to test the hypothesis.
11) Sometimes these scientists will find <u>more evidence</u> that the <u>hypothesis is RIGHT</u>.
12) Sometimes they'll find <u>evidence</u> that shows the <u>hypothesis is WRONG</u>.

Then we thought it was caused by 'bad blood' (and treated it with leeches).

The hypothesis is accepted or rejected.

13) If <u>all the evidence</u> that's been found <u>supports</u> the <u>hypothesis</u>, it becomes an <u>ACCEPTED THEORY</u> and goes into <u>textbooks</u> for people to learn.
14) If the <u>evidence</u> shows that the hypothesis is <u>wrong</u>, scientists must:
- <u>Change the hypothesis</u>, OR
- Come up with a <u>new hypothesis</u>.

Now we know that illnesses that can be spread between people are due to microorganisms.

Theories Can Involve Different Types of Models

1) A <u>model</u> is a <u>simple way</u> of <u>describing</u> or <u>showing</u> what's going on in <u>real life</u>.
2) Models can be used to <u>explain ideas</u> and <u>make predictions</u>. For example:

> The <u>Bohr model</u> of an <u>atom</u> (see page 83) is a simple <u>picture</u> of what an atom looks like. It can be used to explain <u>trends</u> in the <u>periodic table</u>.

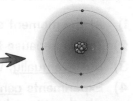

3) All models have <u>limits</u> — a single model <u>can't explain</u> everything about an idea.

I'm off to the zoo to test my hippo-thesis...

You can see just how much testing has to be done before something gets accepted as a theory. If scientists aren't busy testing their own hypothesis, then they're busy testing someone else's. Or just playing with their models.

Communication & Issues Created by Science

Scientific developments can be great, but they can sometimes <u>raise more questions</u> than they answer...

It's Important to Tell People About Scientific Discoveries

1) Scientific discoveries can make a big difference to <u>people's lives</u>.
2) So scientists need to <u>tell the world</u> about their discoveries.
3) They might need to tell people to <u>change their habits</u>, e.g. stop smoking to protect against lung cancer.
4) They might also need to tell people about new <u>technologies</u>. For example:

> <u>Genetic engineering</u> (see p.66) is used to produce <u>genetically modified crops</u>. Information about these crops needs to be communicated to <u>farmers</u>, so they can decide whether to <u>grow</u> them, and to the <u>general public</u>, so they can make <u>informed decisions</u> about the food they buy and eat.

Scientific Evidence can be Presented in a Biased Way

1) <u>Reports</u> about scientific discoveries in the <u>media</u> (e.g. newspapers or television) can be <u>misleading</u>.
2) The data might be <u>presented</u> in a way that's <u>not quite right</u> — or it might be <u>oversimplified</u>.
3) This means that people may not <u>properly understand</u> what the scientists found out.
4) People who want to make a point can also sometimes <u>present data</u> in a <u>biased way</u> (in a way that's <u>unfair</u> or <u>ignores</u> one side of the argument). For example:

- A <u>scientist</u> may talk a lot about <u>one particular relationship</u> in the data (and not mention others).
- A <u>newspaper article</u> might describe data <u>supporting</u> an idea without giving any evidence <u>against</u> it.

Scientific Developments are Great, but they can Raise Issues

1) Scientific developments include <u>new technologies</u> and <u>new advice</u>.
2) These developments can create <u>issues</u>. For example:

<u>Economic (money) issues:</u> Society <u>can't</u> always <u>afford</u> to do things scientists recommend, like spending money on green energy sources.

<u>Social (people) issues:</u> Decisions based on scientific evidence affect <u>people</u> — e.g. should alcohol be banned (to prevent health problems)?

<u>Personal issues:</u> Some decisions will affect <u>individuals</u> — e.g. some people might be upset if a <u>wind farm</u> is built next to their house.

<u>Environmental issues:</u> <u>Human activity</u> can affect the <u>environment</u> — e.g. some people think that <u>genetically modified crops</u> (see page 66) could cause <u>environmental problems</u>.

Science Can't Answer Every Question — Especially Ethical Ones

1) At the moment scientists <u>don't agree</u> on some things — like what the universe is made of.
2) This is because there <u>isn't</u> enough <u>data</u> to <u>support</u> the scientists' hypotheses.
3) But <u>eventually</u>, we probably <u>will</u> be able to answer these questions once and for all.
4) Experiments <u>can't tell us</u> whether something is <u>ethically right or wrong</u>. For example, whether it's right for people to use new drugs to help them do better in exams.
5) The best we can do is make a decision that <u>most people</u> are more or less happy to live by.

Tea to milk or milk to tea? — Totally unanswerable by science...

Science can't tell you whether or not you should do something. That's for you and society to decide. But there are tons of questions science might be able to answer, like where life came from and where my superhero socks are.

Risk

By reading this page you are agreeing to the <u>risk</u> of a paper cut...

Nothing is Completely Risk-Free

1) A <u>hazard</u> is something that could <u>cause harm</u>.

2) All hazards have a <u>risk</u> attached to them — this is the <u>chance</u> that the hazard will cause harm.

3) <u>New technology</u> can bring <u>new risks</u>. For example:

> When <u>nuclear power stations</u> first appeared they brought <u>new risks</u> with them. They produce <u>nuclear waste</u> and if there's an <u>accident</u> they could release <u>dangerous substances</u> into the environment. These risks need to be thought about <u>along with</u> the <u>benefits</u> of nuclear power (see page 211).

4) To make a <u>decision</u> about activities that involve <u>hazards</u>, we need to think about:

   • the <u>chance</u> of the hazard causing harm,

   • how <u>bad</u> the <u>outcome</u> (consequences) would be if it did.

People Make Their Own Decisions About Risk

1) Not all risks have the same <u>consequences</u>. For example, if you chop veg with a sharp knife you risk <u>cutting your finger</u>, but if you go scuba-diving you risk <u>death</u>.

2) Most people are happier to accept a risk if the consequences <u>don't last long</u> and <u>aren't serious</u>.

3) People tend to think <u>familiar</u> activities are <u>low-risk</u>. They tend to think <u>unfamiliar</u> activities are <u>high-risk</u>. But this <u>isn't always true</u>. For example:

> • Cycling on roads is often <u>high-risk</u>. But it's a <u>familiar</u> activity, so many people are happy to do it.
> • Air travel is actually pretty <u>safe</u>, but a lot of people think it is <u>high-risk</u>.

4) The best way to <u>estimate</u> the <u>size of a risk</u> is to look at <u>data</u>. E.g. you could estimate the risk of a driver crashing by recording <u>how many people</u> in a group of 100 000 drivers crashed their cars over a year.

Investigations Can Have Hazards

1) Hazards from science experiments include things like:

<u>microorganisms</u>
(e.g. bacteria)

<u>chemicals</u>

<u>electricity</u>

<u>fire</u>

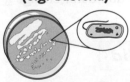 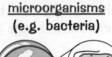   

2) When you <u>plan</u> an investigation you need to make sure that it's <u>safe</u>.

3) You should <u>identify</u> all the hazards that you might come across.

4) Then you should think of ways of <u>reducing the risks</u>. For example:

> • If you're working with <u>sulfuric acid</u>, always wear gloves and safety goggles. This will reduce the risk of the acid <u>burning</u> your skin and eyes.
> • If you're using a <u>Bunsen burner</u>, stand it on a heat proof mat. This will reduce the risk of starting a fire.

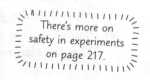
There's more on safety in experiments on page 217.

Not revising — an unacceptable exam hazard...

The world is a dangerous place. You need to look out for hazards and find ways to reduce their risks.

Designing Investigations

Dig out your lab coat and dust down your safety goggles... it's <u>investigation time</u>.
Investigations include <u>lab experiments</u> and <u>studies</u> done in the <u>real world</u>.

Investigations Produce Evidence to Support or Disprove a Hypothesis

1) Scientists <u>observe</u> things and come up with <u>hypotheses</u> to explain them (see page 1).
   You need to be able to do the same. For example:

   > <u>Observation</u>: People have big feet and spots. <u>Hypothesis</u>: Having big feet causes spots.

2) To <u>find out</u> if your hypothesis is <u>right</u>, you need to do an <u>investigation</u> to gather evidence.

3) To do this, you need to use your hypothesis to make a <u>prediction</u> — something you think <u>will happen</u>
   that you can <u>test</u>. E.g. people who have bigger feet will have more spots.

4) Investigations are used to see if there are <u>patterns</u> or <u>relationships</u> between <u>two variables</u>.

To Make an Investigation a Fair Test You Have to Control the Variables

1) In a lab experiment you usually <u>change one thing</u> (a variable) and <u>measure</u> how it affects <u>another thing</u>
   (another variable).

   > **EXAMPLE:** you might <u>change</u> the <u>temperature</u> of an enzyme-controlled
   > reaction and <u>measure</u> how it affects the <u>rate of reaction</u>.

2) <u>Everything else</u> that could affect the results needs to <u>stay the same</u>.
   Then you know that the thing you're <u>changing</u> is the <u>only</u> thing that's affecting the results.

   > **EXAMPLE** <u>continued</u>: you need to keep the pH the same. If you don't, you won't know if any
   > change in the rate of reaction is caused by the change in temperature, or the change in pH.

3) The variable that you **CHANGE** is called the **INDEPENDENT** variable.

4) The variable you **MEASURE** is called the **DEPENDENT** variable.

5) The variables that you **KEEP THE SAME** are called **CONTROL** variables.

6) Because you can't always control all the variables,
   you often need to use a **CONTROL EXPERIMENT**.

   > **EXAMPLE** <u>continued:</u>
   > Independent = temperature
   > Dependent = rate of reaction
   > Control = pH, concentration
   > of enzyme used, etc.

7) This is an experiment that's kept under the <u>same conditions</u> as the rest of the investigation, but <u>doesn't</u>
   have anything <u>done</u> to it. This is so that you can see what happens when you don't change <u>anything</u>.

Evidence Needs to be Repeatable, Reproducible and Valid

1) <u>REPEATABLE</u> means that if the <u>same person</u> does the experiment again, they'll get <u>similar results</u>.
   To check your results are repeatable, <u>repeat</u> the readings
   <u>at least three times</u>. Then check the repeat results are all similar.

2) <u>REPRODUCIBLE</u> means that if <u>someone else</u> does the experiment,
   the results will still be <u>similar</u>. To make sure your results are
   reproducible, get <u>another person</u> to do the experiment too.

   > If data is repeatable and
   > reproducible, it's reliable and
   > scientists are more likely to trust it.

3) <u>VALID results</u> come from experiments that were designed to be a <u>fair test</u>.
   They're also repeatable and reproducible.

This is no high street survey — it's a designer investigation...

You need to be able to plan your own investigations. You should also be able to look at someone else's plan and
decide whether or not it needs improving. Those examiners are pretty demanding.

Collecting Data

Ah ha — now it's time to get your hands mucky and <u>collect some data</u>.

The Bigger the Sample Size the Better

1) Sample size is <u>how many things you test</u> in an investigation, e.g. 500 people or 20 types of metal.

2) The <u>bigger</u> the sample size the <u>better</u> — to <u>reduce</u> the chance of any <u>weird results</u>.

3) But scientists have to be <u>sensible</u> when choosing how big their sample should be.
E.g. if you were studying how lifestyle affects weight it'd be great to study everyone in the UK
(a huge sample), but it'd take ages and cost loads. So the sample size should be <u>big</u>, but not <u>too big</u>.

Your Data Should be Accurate and Precise

1) <u>ACCURATE</u> results are results that are <u>really close</u> to the <u>true answer</u>.

2) The accuracy of your results usually depends on your <u>method</u>.
You need to make sure you're measuring the <u>right thing</u>.

3) You also need to make sure you <u>don't miss anything</u> that
should be included in the measurements. For example:

> If you're measuring the <u>volume of gas</u> released by
> a reaction, make sure you <u>collect all the gas</u>.

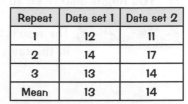

Repeat	Data set 1	Data set 2
1	12	11
2	14	17
3	13	14
Mean	13	14

Data set 1 is more precise
than data set 2 — the results are all
close to the mean (not spread out).

4) <u>PRECISE</u> results are ones where the data is <u>all really close</u> to the <u>mean</u> (average) of your repeated results.

Your Equipment has to be Right for the Job

1) The <u>measuring equipment</u> you use has to be able to <u>accurately</u> measure the
chemicals you're using. E.g. if you need to measure out 11 cm³ of a liquid,
use a <u>measuring cylinder</u> that can measure to 1 cm³ — not 5 or 10 cm³.

2) You also need to <u>set up the equipment properly</u>. For example, make sure
your <u>mass balance</u> is set to <u>zero</u> before you start weighing things.

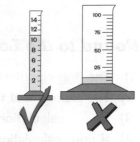

You Need to Look out for Errors and Anomalous Results

1) The results of your experiment will always <u>vary a bit</u> because of <u>RANDOM ERRORS</u> —
for example, mistakes you might make while <u>measuring</u>.

2) You can <u>reduce</u> the effect of random errors by taking <u>repeat readings</u> and finding the <u>mean</u>.
This will make your results <u>more precise</u>.

3) If a measurement is wrong by the <u>same amount every time</u>, it's called a <u>SYSTEMATIC ERROR</u>.
For example:

> If you measure from the <u>very end</u> of your <u>ruler</u> instead of from the
> <u>0 cm mark</u> every time, <u>all</u> your measurements would be a bit <u>small</u>.

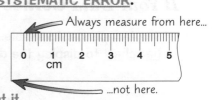

Always measure from here...

...not here.

4) If you know you've made a systematic error, you might be able to <u>correct it</u>.
For example, by adding a bit on to all your measurements.

5) Sometimes you get a result that <u>doesn't fit in</u> with the rest. This is called an <u>ANOMALOUS RESULT</u>.

6) You should try to <u>work out what happened</u>. If you do (e.g. you find out that
you measured something wrong) you can <u>ignore</u> it when processing your results.

The bigger the better — what's true for cakes is true for samples...

Make sure you take lots of care when collecting data — there's plenty to watch out for, as you can see.

Processing and Presenting Data

Processing your data means doing <u>calculations</u> with it so it's <u>more useful</u>. Then you get to draw pretty graphs...

Data Needs to be Organised

1) <u>Tables</u> are useful for <u>organising data</u>.
2) When you draw a table <u>use a ruler</u>.
3) Make sure <u>each column</u> has a <u>heading</u> (including the <u>units</u>).

Test tube	Repeat 1 (cm³)	Repeat 2 (cm³)
A	28	37
B	47	51

You Might Have to Find the Mean and the Range

1) When you've done repeats of an experiment you should always calculate the <u>mean</u> (a type of average).
2) You might also need to calculate the <u>range</u> (how spread out the data is).

EXAMPLE: The results of an experiment to find the volume of gas produced in a reaction are shown in the table below. Calculate the mean volume and the range.

Volume of gas produced (cm³)		
Repeat 1	Repeat 2	Repeat 3
28	37	32

You should ignore anomalous results when calculating the mean or range.

1) To calculate the <u>mean</u>, <u>add together</u> all the data values. Then <u>divide</u> by the <u>total number</u> of values in the sample. $(28 + 37 + 32) \div 3 = 32 \text{ cm}^3$

2) To calculate the <u>range</u>, <u>subtract</u> the <u>smallest</u> number from the <u>largest</u> number. $37 - 28 = 9 \text{ cm}^3$

Round to the Lowest Number of Significant Figures

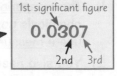

1st significant figure

$$0.0307$$

2nd   3rd

1) The <u>first significant figure</u> of a number is the first digit that's <u>not zero</u>.
2) The second and third significant figures come <u>straight after</u> (even if they're zeros).
3) In <u>any</u> calculation, you should round the answer to the <u>lowest number of significant figures</u> (s.f.) given.
4) If your calculation has more than one step, <u>only</u> round the <u>final</u> answer.

EXAMPLE: The mass of a solid is 0.24 g and its volume is 0.715 cm³. Calculate the density of the solid.

Density = 0.24 g ÷ 0.715 cm³ = 0.33566... = 0.34 g/cm³ (2 s.f.) — Final answer should be rounded to 2 s.f.

2 s.f.   3 s.f.

If Your Data Comes in Categories, Present It in a Bar Chart

If the independent variable comes in <u>clear categories</u> (e.g. blood group, types of metal) you should use a <u>bar chart</u> to display the data. There are some <u>golden rules</u> you need to follow for <u>drawing</u> bar charts:

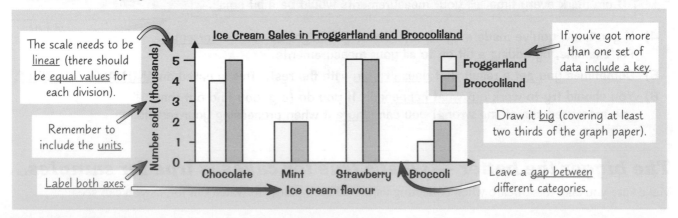

The scale needs to be <u>linear</u> (there should be <u>equal values</u> for each division).

Remember to include the <u>units</u>.

<u>Label both axes</u>.

Ice Cream Sales in Froggartland and Broccoliland

Number sold (thousands)

Ice cream flavour

Chocolate   Mint   Strawberry   Broccoli

If you've got more than one set of data <u>include a key</u>.

☐ Froggartland
◼ Broccoliland

Draw it <u>big</u> (covering at least two thirds of the graph paper).

Leave a <u>gap between</u> different categories.

Working Scientifically

If Your Data is Continuous, Plot a Graph

If both variables can have any value <u>within a range</u> (e.g. length, volume) use a <u>graph</u> to display the data.

Here are the rules for plotting points on a graph:

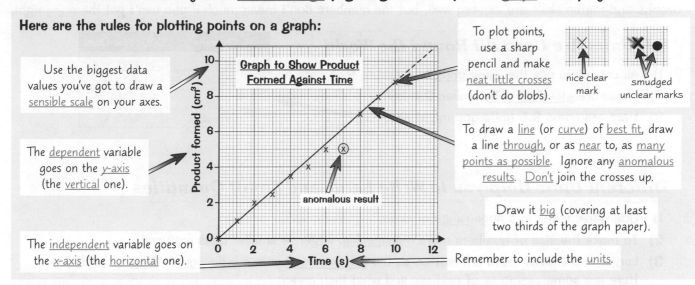

Use the biggest data values you've got to draw a <u>sensible scale</u> on your axes.

The <u>dependent</u> variable goes on the <u>y-axis</u> (the <u>vertical</u> one).

The <u>independent</u> variable goes on the <u>x-axis</u> (the <u>horizontal</u> one).

Graph to Show Product Formed Against Time

anomalous result

To plot points, use a sharp pencil and make <u>neat little crosses</u> (don't do blobs).

nice clear mark

smudged unclear marks

To draw a <u>line</u> (or <u>curve</u>) of <u>best fit</u>, draw a line <u>through</u>, or as <u>near</u> to, as <u>many points as possible</u>. Ignore any <u>anomalous results</u>. <u>Don't</u> join the crosses up.

Draw it <u>big</u> (covering at least two thirds of the graph paper).

Remember to include the <u>units</u>.

You Can Calculate the Rate of a Reaction from the Gradient of a Graph

1) This is the <u>formula</u> you need to calculate the <u>gradient</u> (slope) of a graph:

2) You can use it to work out the <u>rate of a reaction</u> (how <u>quickly</u> the reaction happens).

$$gradient = \frac{change\ in\ y}{change\ in\ x}$$

EXAMPLE:

The graph shows the volume of gas produced in a reaction against time. Calculate the rate of reaction.

1) To calculate the <u>gradient</u>, pick <u>two points</u> on the line that are easy to read. They should also be a <u>good distance</u> apart.

2) Draw a line <u>down</u> from one of the points. Then draw a line <u>across</u> from the other, to make a <u>triangle</u>.

3) The line drawn <u>down the side</u> of the triangle is the <u>change in y</u>. The line <u>across the bottom</u> is the <u>change in x</u>.

4) Read points <u>off the graph</u> to work out the change in y and the change in x:

Change in y = 6.8 − 2.0 = 4.8 cm^3 Change in x = 5.2 − 1.6 = 3.6 s

5) Then put these numbers in the formula above to find the rate of the reaction:

Rate = gradient = $\frac{change\ in\ y}{change\ in\ x}$ = $\frac{4.8\ cm^3}{3.6\ s}$ = 1.3 cm^3/s

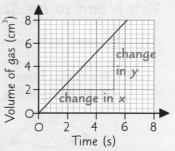

change in y

change in x

To calculate a rate, the graph must have time on the x-axis.

Graphs Show the Relationship Between Two Variables

1) You can get <u>three</u> types of <u>correlation</u> (relationship) between variables:

2) A correlation <u>doesn't mean</u> the change in one variable is <u>causing</u> the change in the other (see page 9).

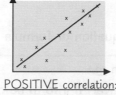

<u>POSITIVE</u> correlation: as one variable <u>increases</u> the other <u>increases</u>.

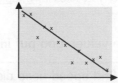

<u>INVERSE</u> (negative) correlation: as one variable <u>increases</u> the other <u>decreases</u>.

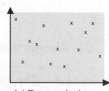

<u>NO</u> correlation: <u>no relationship</u> between the two variables.

I love eating apples — I call it core elation...

Science is all about finding relationships between things. And I don't mean that chemists gather together in corners to discuss whether or not Devini and Sebastian might be a couple... though they probably do that too.

Units

Graphs and maths skills are all very well, but the numbers don't mean much if you can't get the <u>units</u> right.

S.I. Units Are Used All Round the World

1) All scientists use the same <u>units</u> to measure their data.

2) These are <u>standard units</u>, called S.I. units.

3) Here are some S.I. units you might see:

Quantity	S.I. Base Unit
mass	kilogram, kg
length	metre, m
time	second, s
temperature	kelvin, K

Different Units Help you to Write Large and Small Quantities

1) Quantities come in a huge <u>range</u> of sizes.

2) To make the size of numbers more <u>manageable</u>, larger or smaller units are used.

3) Larger and smaller units are written as the <u>S.I. base unit</u> with a <u>little word</u> in <u>front</u> (a prefix).
Here are some <u>examples</u> of <u>prefixes</u> and what they mean:

prefix	mega (M)	kilo (k)	deci (d)	centi (c)	milli (m)	micro (μ)
how it compares to the base unit	1 000 000 times bigger	1000 times bigger	10 times smaller	100 times smaller	1000 times smaller	1 000 000 times smaller

Kilogram is an exception. It's an S.I. unit with the prefix already on it.

E.g. 1 <u>kilometre</u> is <u>1000</u> metres.

E.g. there are <u>1000</u> <u>millimetres</u> in 1 metre.

You Need to be Able to Convert Between Units

1) You need to know how to <u>convert</u> (change) one unit into another. Here are some useful conversions:

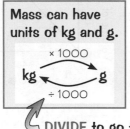

Mass can have units of kg and g.

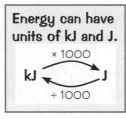

Energy can have units of kJ and J.

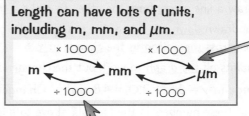

Length can have lots of units, including m, mm, and μm.

MULTIPLY to go from a <u>bigger unit</u> to a <u>smaller unit</u>.

DIVIDE to go from a <u>smaller unit</u> to a <u>bigger unit</u>.

EXAMPLE: A car has travelled 0.015 kilometres. How many metres has it travelled?

1) 1 km = 1000 m.

2) So to convert from km (a bigger unit) to m (a smaller unit) you need to <u>multiply</u> by 1000.

0.015 km × 1000 = 15 m

2) Always make sure the values you put into an equation or formula have the <u>right units</u>. For example:

- The equation to find speed uses distance in <u>m</u>.
- If your distance is in <u>cm</u>, you'll have to <u>convert</u> it into m before you put it into the equation.

I wasn't sure I liked units, but now I'm converted...

It's easy to get in a muddle when converting between units, but there's a handy way to check you've done it right. If you're moving from a smaller unit to a larger unit (e.g. g to kg) the number should get smaller, and vice versa.

Drawing Conclusions

Congratulations — you've made it to the <u>final step</u> of an investigation — <u>drawing conclusions</u>.

You Can Only Conclude What the Data Shows and NO MORE

1) To come to a conclusion, <u>look at your data</u> and <u>say what pattern you see</u>.

<u>EXAMPLE:</u> The table on the right shows the heights of pea plant seedlings grown for three weeks with different fertilisers.

Fertiliser	Mean growth / mm
A	13.5
B	19.5
No fertiliser	5.5

<u>CONCLUSION:</u> <u>Pea plant</u> seedlings grow taller over a <u>three week</u> period with fertiliser B than with fertiliser A.

2) It's important that the conclusion <u>matches the data</u> it's based on — it <u>shouldn't go any further</u>.

<u>EXAMPLE</u> <u>continued</u>: You can't conclude that <u>any other type of plant</u> would grow taller with fertiliser B than with fertiliser A — the results could be totally different.

3) You also need to be able to <u>use your results</u> to <u>justify your conclusion</u> (i.e. back it up).

<u>EXAMPLE</u> <u>continued</u>: The pea plants grew 6 mm more on average with fertiliser B than with fertiliser A.

4) When writing a conclusion you need to say whether or not the data <u>supports</u> the <u>original hypothesis</u>:

<u>EXAMPLE</u> <u>continued</u>: The hypothesis might have been that adding different types of fertiliser would affect the growth of pea plants by different amounts. If so, the data <u>supports</u> the hypothesis.

Correlation DOES NOT Mean Cause

1) If two things are <u>correlated</u>, there's a <u>relationship</u> between them — see page 7.
2) But a correlation <u>doesn't always</u> mean that a change in one variable is <u>causing</u> the change in the other.
3) There are <u>three possible reasons</u> for a correlation:

1 CHANCE

There is <u>no scientific reason</u> for the correlation — it just happened <u>by chance</u>. Other scientists <u>wouldn't</u> get a correlation if they carried out the same investigation.

2 LINKED BY A 3rd VARIABLE

There's <u>another factor</u> involved.

E.g. there's a correlation between water temperature and shark attacks. They're linked by a <u>third variable</u> — the number of people swimming (more people swim when the water's hotter, which means you get more shark attacks).

3 CAUSE

Sometimes a change in one variable does <u>cause</u> a change in the other. You can only conclude this when you've <u>controlled all the variables</u> that could be affecting the result.

I conclude that this page is a bit dull...

In the exams you could be given a conclusion and asked whether some data supports it — so make sure you understand how far conclusions can go. And remember, correlation does not mean cause.

Uncertainties and Evaluations

Hurrah! The end of another investigation. Well, now you have to work out all the things you did <u>wrong</u>.

Uncertainty is the Amount of Error Your Measurements Might Have

1) Measurements you make will have some <u>uncertainty</u> in them (i.e. they won't be completely perfect).

2) This can be due to <u>random errors</u> (see page 5). It can also be due to <u>limits</u> in what your <u>measuring equipment</u> can measure.

3) This means that the <u>mean</u> of your results will have some uncertainty to it.

4) You can <u>calculate</u> the uncertainty of a <u>mean result</u> using this equation:

5) The <u>less precise</u> your results are, the <u>higher</u> the uncertainty will be.

6) Uncertainties are shown using the '±' symbol.

The range is the largest value minus the smallest value (see (p.6).

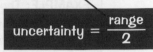

$$\text{uncertainty} = \frac{\text{range}}{2}$$

 **EXAMPLE:** The table below shows the results of an experiment to find the speed of a trolley. Calculate the uncertainty of the mean.

Repeat	1	2	3	mean
Speed (m/s)	2.02	1.98	2.00	2.00

1) First work out the <u>range</u>:
Range = 2.02 − 1.98
= 0.04 m/s

2) Use the range to find the uncertainty:
Uncertainty = range ÷ 2 = 0.04 ÷ 2 = 0.02 m/s   So, uncertainty of the mean = 2.00 ± 0.02 m/s

Evaluations — Describe How it Could be Improved

I'd value this E somewhere in the region of 250-300k.

In an evaluation you look back over the whole investigation.

1) You should comment on the <u>method</u> — was it <u>valid</u>? Did you control all the other variables to make it a <u>fair test</u>?

2) Comment on the <u>quality</u> of the <u>results</u> — was there <u>enough evidence</u> to reach a valid <u>conclusion</u>? Were the results <u>repeatable</u>, <u>reproducible</u>, <u>accurate</u> and <u>precise</u>?

3) Were there any <u>anomalous</u> results? If there were <u>none</u> then <u>say so</u>. If there were any, try to <u>explain</u> them — were they caused by <u>errors</u> in measurement?

4) You should comment on the level of <u>uncertainty</u> in your results too.

5) Thinking about these things lets you say how <u>confident</u> you are that your conclusion is <u>right</u>.

6) Then you can suggest any <u>changes</u> to the <u>method</u> that would <u>improve</u> the quality of the results, so you could have <u>more confidence</u> in your conclusion.

7) For example, taking measurements at <u>narrower intervals</u> could give you a <u>more accurate result</u>. E.g.

- Say you do an experiment to find the <u>temperature</u> at which an enzyme <u>works best</u>.
- You take measurements at <u>30 °C</u>, <u>40 °C</u> and <u>50 °C</u>. The results show that the enzyme works best at <u>40 °C</u>.
- To get a more accurate result, you could <u>repeat</u> the experiment and take <u>more measurements</u> <u>around 40 °C</u>. You might then find that the enzyme actually works best at <u>42 °C</u>.

8) You could also make more <u>predictions</u> based on your conclusion. You could then carry out <u>further experiments</u> to test the new predictions.

Evaluation — next time, I'll make sure I don't burn the lab down...

So there you have it — Working Scientifically. Make sure you know this stuff like the back of your hand. It's not just in the lab that you'll need to know how to work scientifically. You can be asked about it in the exams as well.

Cells and Microscopy

Biology's all about <u>living stuff</u>. And all living stuff is made of <u>cells</u>. So let's make a <u>start</u> with cells...

Cells Can be Eukaryotic or Prokaryotic

1) <u>Eukaryotic</u> cells are <u>complex</u>. All <u>animal</u> and <u>plant</u> cells are eukaryotic.
2) <u>Prokaryotic</u> cells are <u>smaller</u> and <u>simpler</u>. <u>Bacteria</u> are prokaryotic cells.
3) Both types of cells contain <u>sub-cellular structures</u> — parts of cells that each have a <u>specific function</u>.

You Need to Learn the Structures Within Eukaryotic Cells...

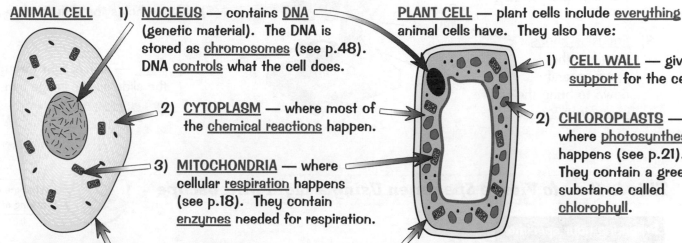

<u>ANIMAL CELL</u>

1) <u>NUCLEUS</u> — contains <u>DNA</u> (genetic material). The DNA is stored as <u>chromosomes</u> (see p.48). DNA <u>controls</u> what the cell does.

2) <u>CYTOPLASM</u> — where most of the <u>chemical reactions</u> happen.

3) <u>MITOCHONDRIA</u> — where cellular <u>respiration</u> happens (see p.18). They contain <u>enzymes</u> needed for respiration.

<u>PLANT CELL</u> — plant cells include <u>everything</u> animal cells have. They also have:

1) <u>CELL WALL</u> — gives <u>support</u> for the cell.

2) <u>CHLOROPLASTS</u> — where <u>photosynthesis</u> happens (see p.21). They contain a green substance called <u>chlorophyll</u>.

4) <u>CELL MEMBRANE</u> — <u>controls</u> what goes <u>in and out</u> of the cell by being a <u>selective barrier</u> (see p.26). They also contain <u>receptor molecules</u>. These are needed so that molecules (e.g. hormones — see p.37) can <u>communicate</u> with the cell.

...and Within Prokaryotic Cells

A bacterial cell

1) <u>CHROMOSOMAL DNA</u> — <u>one</u> long circular strand of DNA.
2) <u>PLASMIDS</u> — <u>small loops</u> of <u>extra DNA</u>.
3) <u>CELL MEMBRANE</u>

Cells are Studied Using Microscopes

1) Microscopes use lenses to <u>magnify</u> objects (make them <u>look bigger</u>).
2) They also increase the <u>resolution</u> of an image. This means they <u>increase the detail</u> you can see.
3) <u>Light microscopes</u> let us see things like a cell's <u>nucleus</u> and <u>chloroplasts</u>.
4) <u>Electron microscopes</u> (e.g. transmission electron microscopes) were <u>invented after</u> light microscopes.
5) They have a <u>higher magnification</u> and <u>resolution</u> than light microscopes. This means they let us see much <u>smaller things</u> in <u>more detail</u>.
6) Electron microscopes have given us a <u>better understanding</u> of <u>sub-cellular structures</u>.

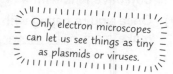

Only electron microscopes can let us see things as tiny as plasmids or viruses.

Cell structures — become an estate agent...

The number of some structures will depend on the cell's function, e.g. muscle cells, which respire lots, will have lots of mitochondria. Also, plant cells that are underground (so don't get any light) won't have chloroplasts.

Q1   Give two functions of the cell membrane in an animal cell.   [2 marks]

 **PRACTICAL**

Light Microscopy

Ah, the light microscope — that great invention that lets us see really small things. Here's how to use one...

You Need to Know What the Main Parts of a Light Microscope Do...

1) Eyepiece lens — looked through to see the image. It also magnifies the image.

2) Stage — supports the slide (see below).

3) Focusing knobs — move the stage up and down to bring the image into focus.

Coarse adjustment knob

Fine adjustment knob

4) Objective lenses — magnify the image. Usually there are three different objective lenses to choose from.

5) Clip — holds the slide in place.

6) Lamp — shines light through the slide so the image can be seen more easily.

This is How to View a Specimen Using a Light Microscope

What are you looking at?

Preparing your specimen

1) Take a thin slice of your specimen (the thing you're looking at).

2) Take a clean slide and use a pipette to put one drop of water in the middle of it.

3) Then use tweezers to place your specimen on the slide.

4) If your specimen is colourless, you might need to add a drop of stain to make your specimen easier to see. Stains can also be used to highlight different structures or tissues.

5) Carefully lower a cover slip onto the slide using a mounted needle. Try not to trap any bubbles under the cover slip.

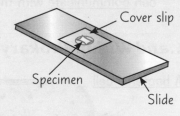

Cover slip

Specimen

Slide

Viewing your specimen

1) Clip the slide onto the stage.

2) Select the objective lens with the lowest power (magnification).

3) Use the coarse adjustment knob to move the stage up to just underneath the objective lens.

4) Look down the eyepiece, then move the stage down until the specimen is nearly in focus.

5) Move the fine adjustment knob, until you get a clear image.

6) If you want to make the image bigger, use an objective lens with a higher power (and refocus).

7) Once you're happy with what you can see, you can make a scientific drawing of your specimen (see p.220).

A higher magnification isn't always a good thing — if your specimen is big you might not be able to see the whole thing. It can also be difficult to focus at high magnifications.

I take my microscope everywhere — good job it's a light one...

There's lots of important stuff here about how to use a light microscope to view specimens — so get learning.

Q1 A student has a thin piece of onion skin. She wants to view it under a light microscope.
Describe the steps she could take to prepare a slide containing the onion skin. [3 marks]

More on Light Microscopy

Sometimes you need to do a bit of <u>maths</u> with microscope images. It's time to get your <u>numbers head on</u>...

Magnification is How Many Times Bigger the Image is

1) You can work out the <u>total magnification</u> of an image under a microscope using this formula:

total magnification = eyepiece lens magnification × objective lens magnification

 **EXAMPLE:**

What's the total magnification of an image viewed with an eyepiece lens magnification of × 10 and an objective lens magnification of × 40?

total magnification = 10 × 40 = × 400

2) You can also work out the magnification of an image if you <u>don't know</u> what <u>lenses</u> were used.

3) You need to be able to <u>measure the image</u>. You also need to know the <u>real size</u> of the specimen.

4) This is the <u>formula</u> you need:

$$\text{magnification} = \frac{\text{image size}}{\text{real size}}$$

Both measurements should have the same units. If they don't, you'll need to convert them first (see p.8).

 **EXAMPLE:**

The width of a specimen is 0.02 mm. The width of its image under a microscope is 8 mm. What magnification was used to view the specimen?

magnification = 8 mm ÷ 0.02 mm = × 400

5) You can find the <u>image size</u> or the <u>real size</u> of an object using this <u>formula triangle</u>.

6) <u>Cover</u> the thing you want to find. The parts you can <u>see</u> are the formula you need to use.

 **EXAMPLE:**

The width of a specimen's image under a microscope is 3 mm. The magnification is × 100. What is the real width of the specimen?

Cover up '<u>real size</u>' on the formula triangle. This leaves the formula: image size ÷ magnification

So, the real width = 3 mm ÷ 100 = 0.03 mm

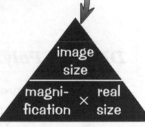

You Can Write Numbers in Standard Form

Standard form is useful for writing <u>very big</u> or <u>very small</u> numbers in a <u>simpler</u> way. It looks like this:

<u>A</u> is a number between <u>1 and 10</u>. $A \times 10^n$ <u>n</u> is the number of places the <u>decimal point moves</u>.

EXAMPLE: Write 0.0025 mm in standard form.

1) The first number needs to be <u>between 1 and 10</u> so the decimal point needs to move after the '2'.

0.0025

2) The decimal point has moved <u>three places</u> to the <u>right</u>, so n will be <u>−3</u>.

2.5 × 10⁻³

n is <u>positive</u> if the decimal point moves to the <u>left</u>.
n is <u>negative</u> if the decimal point moves to the <u>right</u>.

Mi-cros-copy — when my twin gets annoyed...

Keep an eye on the units for these magnification equations — if they're not the same they just won't work.

Q1   Calculate the magnification of an image viewed with a ×8 eyepiece lens and a ×15 objective lens. [1 mark]

14

DNA

DNA is a big, big deal in biology. It acts as a <u>code</u> — it tells the body which <u>proteins</u> to make.
You need to know about the <u>structure</u> of DNA, so here goes...

DNA is a Double Helix

1) <u>DNA</u> contains all of an organism's <u>genetic material</u> —
   the chemical <u>instructions</u> it needs to grow and develop.

2) A DNA molecule has <u>two strands coiled together</u>.
   They make a <u>double helix</u> (a double-stranded spiral).

3) Each DNA strand is made up of lots of molecules called <u>nucleotides</u>.

4) Each nucleotide contains a small molecule called a "<u>base</u>".

5) Each base <u>joins</u> to a base on the other strand.
   This keeps the two DNA strands <u>tightly wound together</u>.

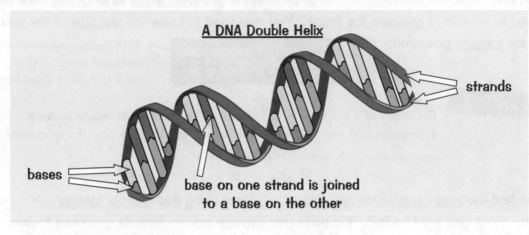

A DNA Double Helix

strands

bases

base on one strand is joined
to a base on the other

DNA is a Polymer

1) Monomers are <u>small</u>, <u>basic</u> molecules.

2) <u>Polymers</u> are large, complex molecules.
   They are made from <u>long chains</u> of <u>monomers</u> joined together.

3) <u>DNA</u> is a <u>polymer</u> made up of <u>nucleotide monomers</u>.

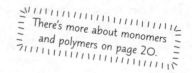
There's more about monomers
and polymers on page 20.

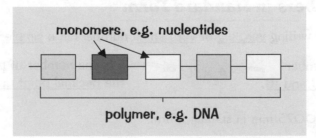

monomers, e.g. nucleotides

polymer, e.g. DNA

DNA — a very important twisty molecule...

Every living organism has to have DNA — it contains the instructions that make each organism work.

Q1   Which one of the following describes the structure of DNA?

    A A double helix made from two nucleotides.   **C** A double helix made from two strands.

    B A triple helix made from three nucleotides.   **D** A triple helix made from three strands.   [1 mark]

Q2   Why can DNA be described as a polymer?   [1 mark]

Topic B1 — Cell Level Systems

Enzymes

Chemical reactions are what make you work. And enzymes are what make them work.

Enzymes Control Cell Reactions

1) Cells have thousands of different chemical reactions going on inside them all the time.
Together these reactions make up the cell's metabolism.

2) Enzymes help the reactions of metabolism to happen quickly.

3) This is because enzymes are biological catalysts. A catalyst is a substance that speeds up a reaction.

4) Every different biological reaction has its own enzyme especially for it.

Enzymes are Very Specific

1) A substrate is a molecule that gets changed in a chemical reaction.

2) Every enzyme has an active site — the part where it joins on to its substrate to catalyse the reaction.

3) Enzymes are substrate specific — this means that they usually only work with one substrate.

4) This is because the substrate has to fit into the active site for the enzyme to work.

5) If the substrate's shape doesn't match the active site's shape, then the reaction won't be catalysed.

6) This is called the 'lock and key' hypothesis. The substrate fits into the enzyme just like a key fits into a lock.

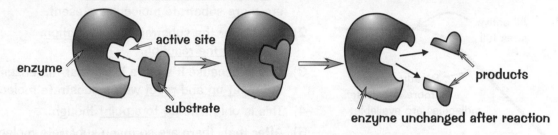

Temperature Affects Enzyme Shape and Activity

1) Different factors (e.g. temperature) affect how well enzymes can work.

2) A higher temperature increases the rate of an enzyme-catalysed reaction at first.

3) This is because the enzymes and the substrate move about more, so they're more likely to meet up and react.

4) But if it gets too hot, some of the bonds holding the enzyme together break.

5) This changes the shape of the enzyme's active site. This means the substrate won't fit any more.

6) If this happens, the enzyme is said to be denatured. It can't catalyse the reaction at all.

7) All enzymes have an optimum temperature — this is the temperature that they work best at.

8) The optimum temperature for the most important human enzymes is about 37 °C — the same temperature as our bodies.

There's more about factors that affect enzyme activity on the next page.

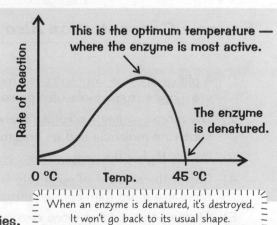

When an enzyme is denatured, it's destroyed. It won't go back to its usual shape.

If the lock and key mechanism fails, there's always the window...

Enzymes aren't just useful for controlling chemical reactions in the body — we even put them in things like biological washing powders to catalyse the breakdown of nasty stains (like tomato ketchup). Useful, eh?

Q1   Name the part of an enzyme that joins on to a substrate.   [1 mark]

More on Enzymes

On the previous page you saw how <u>temperature</u> can affect enzyme activity.
Well here are <u>three more factors</u> that can affect the <u>rate</u> of an <u>enzyme-controlled reaction</u>...

pH Can Affect Enzyme Shape and Activity

1) If pH is <u>too high</u> or <u>too low</u>, it affects the <u>bonds</u> holding the active site together.

2) This changes the <u>shape</u> of the <u>active site</u> and <u>denatures</u> the enzyme.

3) All enzymes have an <u>optimum pH</u> that they work best at.

4) The optimum pH is often <u>neutral pH 7</u>, but <u>not always</u>.

5) E.g. <u>pepsin</u> is an enzyme in the <u>stomach</u>. It works best at <u>pH 2</u>.

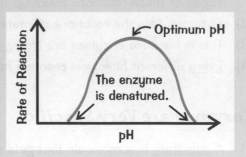

Substrate Concentration Affects the Rate of Reaction

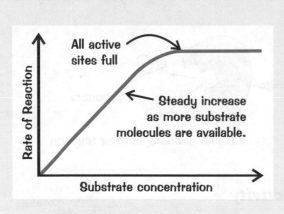

1) A <u>higher substrate concentration</u> means there are <u>more</u> substrate molecules present.

2) The higher the <u>substrate concentration</u>, the <u>faster the reaction</u>.

3) This is because it's more likely that the enzyme will <u>meet up</u> and <u>react</u> with a substrate molecule.

4) This is only true <u>up to a point</u> though.

5) After that, there are <u>so many</u> substrate molecules that all the <u>active sites</u> on the enzymes are <u>full</u>.

6) At this point, adding more substrate molecules makes <u>no difference</u>.

Enzyme Concentration Also Affects the Rate of Reaction

1) A <u>higher enzyme concentration</u> means there are <u>more</u> enzyme molecules present.

2) The more <u>enzyme molecules</u> there are, the <u>more likely</u> it is that a substrate molecule and an enzyme molecule will <u>meet up</u> and <u>react</u>.

3) So the higher the <u>enzyme concentration</u>, the <u>faster the reaction</u>.

4) But, if the amount of <u>substrate</u> is <u>limited</u>, there comes a point when there are more than enough enzyme molecules for all the <u>substrate</u>.

5) At this point, adding more enzyme has <u>no further effect</u>.

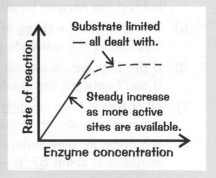

If only enzymes could speed up revision...

Make sure you use the special terms like 'active site' and 'denatured' — the examiners will love it.

Q1   Explain why an enzyme may not work if the pH is too high.   [2 marks]

Investigating Enzyme Activity

You'll soon know how to investigate the effect of a <u>variable</u> on the rate of <u>enzyme activity</u>... I bet you're thrilled.

You Can Investigate How Temperature Affects Enzyme Activity

1) The experiments below show two different ways of investigating how <u>temperature</u> affects <u>enzyme activity</u>.

2) You could <u>adapt</u> these experiments to investigate other variables instead (e.g. <u>pH</u>, <u>substrate concentration</u> or <u>enzyme concentration</u>).

You can use buffer solutions to alter the pH of the enzyme and substrate mixtures.

You Can Measure How Fast a Product Appears...

PRACTICAL

1) The enzyme <u>catalase</u> breaks down <u>hydrogen peroxide</u> into <u>water</u> and <u>oxygen</u>.

2) You can collect the <u>oxygen</u> and measure <u>how much</u> is produced in a <u>set time</u>.

3) Use a <u>pipette</u> to add a set amount of <u>hydrogen peroxide</u> to a <u>boiling tube</u>.

4) Put the tube in a <u>water bath</u> at 10 °C.

5) <u>Set up</u> the rest of the apparatus as shown.

6) Add a source of <u>catalase</u> to the <u>hydrogen peroxide</u>. Quickly <u>attach the bung</u>.

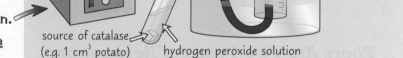

water bath at constant temperature — upside down measuring cylinder

delivery tube

amount of oxygen produced per minute is measured

source of catalase (e.g. 1 cm³ potato) — hydrogen peroxide solution

7) Record how much <u>oxygen</u> is produced in the <u>first minute</u>. <u>Repeat three times</u> and calculate the <u>mean</u>.

8) <u>Repeat</u> at 20 °C, 30 °C and 40 °C.

9) <u>Control any variables</u> (e.g. pH, the potato used, the size of potato pieces, etc.) to make it a <u>fair test</u>.

10) Calculate the <u>mean rate of reaction</u> at each temperature. Do this by <u>dividing</u> the mean <u>volume of oxygen</u> produced (in cm³) by the <u>time taken</u> (i.e. 60 s). The units will be <u>cm³/second</u>.

...Or How Fast a Substrate Disappears

PRACTICAL

1) The enzyme <u>amylase</u> helps to break down <u>starch</u> to <u>maltose</u>.

2) It's easy to <u>detect starch</u> using <u>iodine solution</u> — if starch is present, the iodine solution will change from <u>browny-orange</u> to <u>blue-black</u>.

3) <u>Set up</u> the apparatus as shown.

4) Put a drop of iodine solution into <u>each well</u> on the spotting tile.

5) Every ten seconds, <u>drop</u> a sample of the <u>mixture</u> into a well using a <u>pipette</u>. Record the time when the iodine solution <u>remains</u> browny-orange (i.e. when there's no more starch).

6) <u>Repeat</u> with the water bath at <u>different temperatures</u>. Remember to <u>control</u> all of the <u>variables</u> each time.

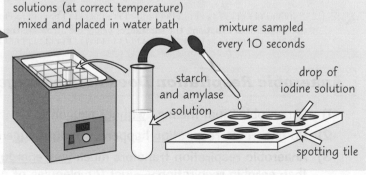

solutions (at correct temperature) mixed and placed in water bath

mixture sampled every 10 seconds

starch and amylase solution

drop of iodine solution

spotting tile

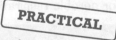
You could improve the accuracy of this experiment by using a colorimeter (see p.221).

Mad scientists — they're experi-mental...

The key thing with experiments is to only change the thing you're testing — and absolutely nothing else. Sorted.

Q1 An enzyme-controlled reaction was carried out at 25 °C. After 60 seconds, 33 cm³ of product had been released. Calculate the rate of reaction in cm³/second. [1 mark]

Respiration

You need <u>energy</u> to keep your body going. Energy comes from <u>food</u>, and it's <u>transferred</u> by <u>respiration</u>.

Respiration is NOT "Breathing In and Out"

1) <u>Respiration</u> is the process of <u>transferring energy</u> from <u>glucose</u> (a sugar).
2) It goes on in <u>every cell</u> in <u>all</u> living organisms, <u>all the time</u> — it's a <u>universal</u> chemical process.
3) The energy transferred by respiration <u>can't be used directly</u> by cells — so it's used to make a substance called <u>ATP</u>.
4) ATP <u>stores</u> the energy needed for many <u>cell processes</u>.
5) Respiration is an <u>exothermic reaction</u> — it <u>releases energy</u>. Some of this energy is released as <u>heat</u>.
6) Organisms <u>don't always</u> use glucose for respiration. They can break down other <u>biological molecules</u>, e.g. other <u>carbohydrates</u>, <u>proteins</u> and <u>lipids</u> (see p.20).
7) The molecule <u>broken down</u> in respiration is called the <u>substrate</u>.

There Are Two Types of Respiration:

Aerobic Respiration Needs Plenty of Oxygen

In eukaryotic cells, respiration takes place in the mitochondria.

1) "<u>Aerobic</u>" just means "<u>with oxygen</u>".
2) So, <u>aerobic respiration</u> is respiration with oxygen.
3) Aerobic respiration produces <u>lots</u> of <u>ATP</u> — <u>32</u> molecules per molecule of glucose.
4) This is the type of respiration that you're using <u>most of the time</u>.
5) Here is the <u>equation</u> for aerobic respiration:

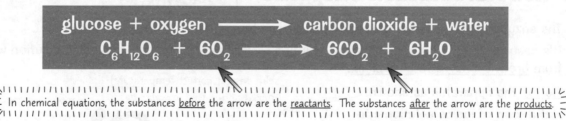

$$\text{glucose} + \text{oxygen} \longrightarrow \text{carbon dioxide} + \text{water}$$
$$C_6H_{12}O_6 + 6O_2 \longrightarrow 6CO_2 + 6H_2O$$

In chemical equations, the substances <u>before</u> the arrow are the <u>reactants</u>. The substances <u>after</u> the arrow are the <u>products</u>.

Anaerobic Respiration Doesn't Use Oxygen At All

1) "<u>An</u>aerobic" just means "<u>without</u> oxygen".
2) So <u>anaerobic respiration</u> happens without oxygen.
3) Anaerobic respiration transfers much <u>less energy per glucose molecule</u> than aerobic respiration — just <u>2</u> molecules of <u>ATP</u> are produced.
4) The process of anaerobic respiration is slightly <u>different</u> in <u>different organisms</u>. See the next page for how it works in <u>animals</u>, <u>plants</u> and <u>fungi</u>.

Respiration transfers energy — but this page has worn me out...

Thank goodness for respiration — transferring the energy stored in my tea and biscuits to my brain cells. Great.

Q1   Why can respiration be described as an exothermic reaction?   [1 mark]

More on Respiration

Now more on the second type of respiration — <u>anaerobic respiration</u>.

Animals Produce Lactic Acid During Anaerobic Respiration

1) When you <u>exercise really hard</u>, your muscles can't get enough <u>oxygen</u> to respire aerobically. They have to start <u>respiring anaerobically as well</u>.

2) In animals (like us), anaerobic respiration produces <u>lactic acid</u>.

3) This is the <u>word equation</u>:

$$glucose \longrightarrow lactic\ acid$$

Plants and Fungi Produce Ethanol and Carbon Dioxide

1) Sometimes <u>plants</u> may need to respire anaerobically. E.g. in <u>waterlogged soil</u> there is <u>little or no oxygen</u>, so plant <u>root cells</u> respire anaerobically.

2) Some <u>fungi</u> (such as <u>yeast</u>) can respire <u>anaerobically</u> too.

3) Anaerobic respiration in plants and fungi produces <u>ethanol</u> (alcohol) and <u>carbon dioxide</u> instead of lactic acid.

4) This is the <u>word equation</u>:

$$glucose \longrightarrow ethanol + carbon\ dioxide$$

You Need to Compare Aerobic and Anaerobic Respiration

This handy table shows the <u>differences</u> and <u>similarities</u> between <u>aerobic</u> and <u>anaerobic</u> respiration:

	Aerobic	Anaerobic
Conditions	Oxygen present	Not enough oxygen present
Substrate	Glucose (or other biological molecules)	
Products	Carbon dioxide and water	In animals — lactic acid In plants and some fungi (e.g. yeast) — ethanol and carbon dioxide
Energy transferred per molecule of glucose	Lots — 32 ATP made	Much less — 2 ATP made

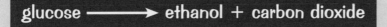

My friend Anne O'Robic is rather odd — I only see her at the gym...

Make sure you know those word equations and can compare the processes of aerobic and anaerobic respiration.

Q1 Name the product(s) of anaerobic respiration in plants. [2 marks]

Q2 Why is it better for organisms to respire aerobically rather than anaerobically? [1 mark]

Biological Molecules

Biological molecules are molecules found in living organisms — things like carbohydrates, proteins and lipids. They're generally big molecules made up from smaller basic units.

Biological Molecules Can be Broken Down to Fuel Respiration

1) Big biological molecules such as carbohydrates, proteins and lipids can be broken down into smaller molecules.

2) This allows energy to be transferred from them during respiration (see p.18).

3) You need to know how the structures of these big biological molecules are formed from their basic units:

Carbohydrates are Made Up of Simple Sugars

1) The smallest units of carbohydrates are simple sugars, e.g. glucose molecules.

2) These are monomers (see page 14).

3) These monomers can be joined together in long chains to synthesise (make) large, complex carbohydrates, e.g. starch.

4) These long chains are polymers (see p.14).

5) Enzymes can break the polymers back down into sugars.

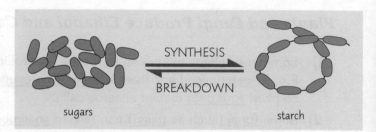

sugars   SYNTHESIS / BREAKDOWN   starch

Proteins are Made Up of Amino Acids

1) Proteins are made up of long chains of amino acids.

2) Enzymes can break proteins back down into amino acids.

Proteins are polymers and amino acids are monomers.

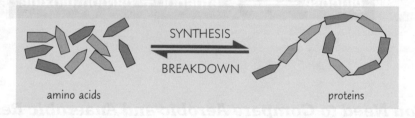

amino acids   SYNTHESIS / BREAKDOWN   proteins

Lipids are Made Up of Fatty Acids and Glycerol

1) Lipids (fats and oils) are made from glycerol and three fatty acids.

2) They are NOT POLYMERS. This is because they don't form a long chain of repeating units.

3) Enzymes can break lipids back down into glycerol and fatty acids.

When lipids are broken down, the fatty acids will make the solution they are in more acidic (it will have a lower pH).

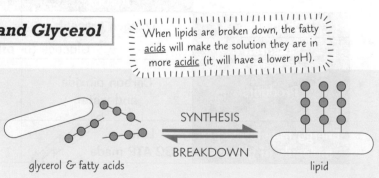

glycerol & fatty acids   SYNTHESIS / BREAKDOWN   lipid

What do you call an acid that's eaten all the pies...
...a fatty acid

This page isn't too bad really, once you've got the whole monomer/polymer thing sorted. But you still need to make sure you learn it properly. So look, cover and scribble 'til you can do the whole lot standing on your head.

Q1   Name the monomers that result from the breakdown of: a) carbohydrates, b) proteins.   [2 marks]

Photosynthesis

You don't know photosynthesis until you know its equation. It's in a nice green box so you can't miss it.

Plants and Algae Make Their Own Food by Photosynthesis

1) During photosynthesis, energy from the Sun is used to make glucose.

2) Some of the glucose is used to make larger molecules that the plants or algae need to grow. These molecules make up the organism's biomass. Biomass means 'the mass of living material'.

3) When an animal eats a plant, the energy in the plant's biomass is passed on to the animal. When this animal is eaten by other animals, energy gets passed up the food chain.

4) So, plants and algae are really important — they are the main food producers for life on Earth.

You Need to Know How Photosynthesis Happens

1) Photosynthesis happens inside chloroplasts (see p.11). Chloroplasts contain chlorophyll which absorbs light.

2) This is the equation for photosynthesis:

$$\text{carbon dioxide} + \text{water} \xrightarrow[\text{chlorophyll}]{\text{LIGHT}} \text{glucose} + \text{oxygen}$$
$$6CO_2 + 6H_2O \longrightarrow C_6H_{12}O_6 + 6O_2$$

3) Photosynthesis is an endothermic reaction — this means that energy is taken in during the reaction.

4) Photosynthesis happens in two main stages:

- First, energy transferred by light is used to split water into oxygen gas and hydrogen ions.
- Then carbon dioxide gas combines with the hydrogen ions to make glucose.

Some Things can Limit the Rate of Photosynthesis

These three things can all affect the rate of photosynthesis:

① Light intensity — photosynthesis gets faster as light intensity (the strength of light) increases.

② Carbon dioxide concentration — photosynthesis gets faster as carbon dioxide concentration increases.

③ Temperature — photosynthesis gets faster as temperature increases, but only up to a certain temperature. If it gets too hot, photosynthesis slows down and can stop altogether.

Enzymes are needed for photosynthesis. Temperature affects the rate of photosynthesis because it affects enzyme activity (see page 15).

I'm working on sunshine — woah oh...

Once you've got that very important equation learnt, make sure you learn those three factors that can affect the rate of photosynthesis. The next page is all about how you can investigate them — fun times are on their way.

Q1   Explain how photosynthesis helps to make up a plant's biomass.   [2 marks]

Investigating Photosynthesis

So now you know what photosynthesis is, I bet you're dying to know how to investigate it. Well here goes...

Oxygen Production Shows the Rate of Photosynthesis

PRACTICAL

Pondweed can be used to investigate the rate of photosynthesis. Here's how:

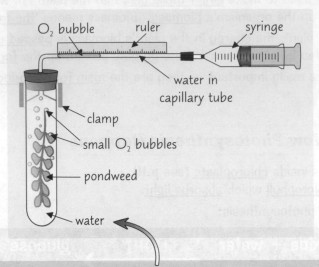

1) The experiment is set up as shown in the diagram.

2) The pondweed is left to photosynthesise for a set amount of time.

3) The oxygen produced in photosynthesis collects in the capillary tube.

4) At the end of the experiment, the syringe is used to draw the gas bubble in the tube up alongside a ruler.

5) The length of the gas bubble is then measured — this indicates the volume of oxygen that was produced.

6) The volume of oxygen collected can be used to calculate the rate of oxygen production.

$$\text{Rate of } O_2 \text{ production} = \frac{\text{volume of } O_2 \text{ produced}}{\text{time taken}}$$

The amount of oxygen collected is not the total amount produced by photosynthesis — some of it is used up in respiration.

7) The experiment is then repeated to test a range of values for the factor being investigated. For example, if you're investigating temperature you should use a range of different temperatures.

8) Variables other than the one being investigated should be kept the same. For example, if you're investigating temperature you should keep the light intensity and the carbon dioxide concentration the same. You should also keep other variables the same such as the time the pondweed is left for.

You can adapt the method above to investigate different factors that affect the rate of photosynthesis. For example:

- To investigate light intensity you could move a lamp closer to or further away from your plant.

- To investigate carbon dioxide concentration you could dissolve different amounts of sodium hydrogen-carbonate in the water. (Sodium hydrogen-carbonate gives off carbon dioxide.)

- To investigate temperature you could put the boiling tube into water baths set to different temperatures.

Don't blame it on the sunshine, don't blame it on the CO_2...

You could also measure how much oxygen's produced by counting the bubbles — fun, but it's not as accurate.

Q1 Raj is investigating the effect of carbon dioxide concentration on the rate of photosynthesis. Give two variables that he must control during his experiment.

[2 marks]

The Cell Cycle and Mitosis

Your cells have to be able to <u>divide</u> for your body to <u>grow</u>. And that means your <u>DNA</u> has to be <u>copied</u>...

New Cells are Needed for Growth and Repair

1) The cells of your body <u>divide</u> to <u>produce more cells</u>.
   This means that your body can <u>grow</u> and <u>replace</u> damaged cells.

2) Cells <u>grow</u> and <u>divide</u> over and over again — this is called the <u>cell cycle</u>. There are <u>two main parts</u>:

Cell division doesn't just happen in humans — animals and plants do it too.

First the cell grows and replicates its contents...

1) The time when the cell <u>grows</u> and <u>replicates</u> (copies) its contents is divided up into <u>three</u> stages.

2) These are called $\underline{G_1}$, $\underline{S}$ and $\underline{G_2}$:

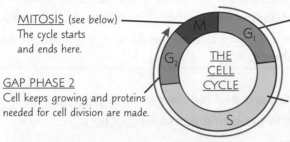

MITOSIS (see below)
The cycle starts
and ends here.

GAP PHASE 1
Cell grows and new cell structures
and proteins are made.

GAP PHASE 2
Cell keeps growing and proteins
needed for cell division are made.

SYNTHESIS (S phase)
Cell replicates its DNA. When it splits during
mitosis the two new cells will contain identical DNA.

...then it splits into two by Mitosis

Mitosis is when a cell reproduces itself <u>by splitting</u> to form <u>two identical offspring</u>.

The cell has <u>two copies</u> of its DNA all spread out in <u>long strings</u>.

Before the cell <u>divides</u>, the DNA forms <u>X-shaped</u>
chromosomes. Each 'arm' of a chromosome is
an <u>exact copy</u> of the other.

Chromosomes are long lengths of coiled DNA — see page 48.

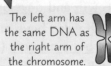

The left arm has
the same DNA as
the right arm of
the chromosome.

The chromosomes then <u>line up</u> at the centre of the
cell. <u>Cell fibres</u> pull them apart. The <u>two arms</u> of
each chromosome go to <u>opposite ends</u> of the cell.

<u>Membranes</u> form around each of the sets of chromosomes.
These become the <u>nuclei</u> of the two new cells.

Nuclei is just the word for more than one nucleus.

Lastly, the <u>cytoplasm</u> divides.

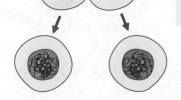

You now have <u>two new cells</u> containing exactly the same DNA
— they're <u>genetically identical</u> to <u>each other</u> and to the <u>parent cell</u>.

A cell's favourite computer game — divide and conquer...

This can seem tricky at first. But don't worry — just go through it slowly, one step at a time and it'll soon sink in.

Q1   Explain why a cell's DNA is replicated during the cell cycle.   [1 mark]

Q2   What is mitosis?   [1 mark]

Cell Differentiation and Stem Cells

Multicellular organisms have lots of cells — most of these cells are specialised to do a particular job...

Most Cells are Specialised for a Specific Job

1) Differentiation is when a cell changes to become specialised for its job.
2) Having specialised cells is important — it allows organisms to work more efficiently.
3) Most cells are specialised to carry out a particular job. For example:

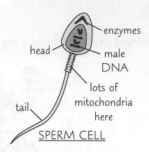

head

enzymes

male DNA

lots of mitochondria here

tail

SPERM CELL

SPERM

The function of sperm is to get the male DNA to the female DNA during reproduction (see page 50). They have features to help them to do this:
- They have long tails and streamlined heads to help them swim.
- They contain lots of mitochondria to provide them with energy.
- They have enzymes in their heads to digest through the egg cell membrane.

4) In multicellular organisms, specialised cells are grouped together to form tissues.
5) Tissues are groups of cells working together to perform a particular function.
6) Different tissues work together to form organs.
7) Different organs make up an organ system.

Stem Cells can Differentiate into Different Types of Cells

1) Stem cells are undifferentiated (not specialised).
2) They can divide by mitosis to become new cells, which then differentiate.
3) Embryonic stem cells are found in early human embryos. They can turn into any kind of cell at all.
4) This means stem cells are important for the growth and development of organisms.
5) Adults also have stem cells, but they're only found in certain places, like bone marrow (a tissue inside bones).
6) Adult stem cells can only produce certain types of specialised cell.
7) In animals, adult stem cells are used to replace damaged cells, e.g. to make new skin cells.

undifferentiated stem cell

differentiated white blood cell

Meristems Contain Plant Stem Cells

1) Plants have tissues called meristems.
2) Meristems are found in the areas of a plant that are growing, e.g. the tips of the roots and shoots.
3) Meristems produce stem cells that are able to divide and form any cell type in the plant. They can do this for as long as the plant lives.

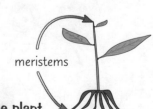

meristems

Cheery cells, those merry-stems...

Turns out stem cells are pretty nifty. Now, let's see if you're specialised to answer this question...

Q1   What is differentiation?   [1 mark]

Diffusion and Active Transport

Substances can move in and out of cells by <u>diffusion</u> and <u>active transport</u> (and osmosis too — see next page).

Diffusion — Don't be Put Off by the Fancy Word

<u>Diffusion</u> is the <u>movement</u> of particles from places where there are <u>lots</u> of them to places where there are <u>fewer</u> of them. Here's the fancy <u>definition</u>:

> **DIFFUSION** is the <u>net (overall) movement</u> of <u>particles</u> from an area of <u>higher concentration</u> to an area of <u>lower concentration</u>.

If something moves from an area of higher concentration to an area of lower concentration it is said to have moved down its concentration gradient.

Cell Membranes are Pretty Clever

1) Cell membranes let stuff <u>in and out</u> of the cell.

2) Substances can move in and out of cells by <u>diffusion</u>, <u>active transport</u> and <u>osmosis</u> (see next page).

3) Only very <u>small</u> molecules can <u>diffuse</u> through cell membranes though (e.g. <u>glucose</u>, <u>amino acids</u>, <u>water</u> and <u>oxygen</u>). <u>Big</u> molecules like <u>starch</u> and <u>proteins</u> can't fit through the membrane.

4) Particles move through the cell membrane from where there's a <u>higher concentration</u> (more of them) to where there's a <u>lower concentration</u> (not such a lot of them).

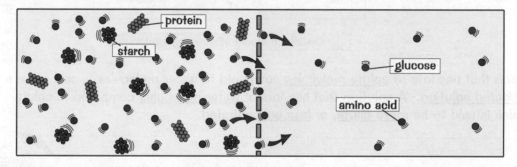

Active Transport is the Opposite of Diffusion

> **ACTIVE TRANSPORT** is the <u>movement of particles</u> across a membrane from an area of <u>lower concentration</u> to an area of <u>higher concentration</u>. It uses <u>energy</u>.

1) Active transport moves particles in the <u>opposite direction</u> to <u>diffusion</u>.

2) This means active transport moves particles <u>against</u> a <u>concentration gradient</u>.

3) This requires <u>energy</u> (unlike diffusion). The energy is released by <u>respiration</u> (see p.18).

4) Here's an example of active transport at work in the <u>digestive system</u>:

> 1) <u>Nutrients</u> from our <u>food</u> have to get from our <u>gut</u> into our <u>blood</u>.
>
> 2) When there's a <u>higher concentration</u> of nutrients in the gut they <u>diffuse</u> into the blood.
>
> 3) <u>BUT</u> — sometimes there's a <u>lower concentration</u> of nutrients in the gut than in the blood.
>
> 4) Active transport allows nutrients to be taken into the blood, even though the <u>concentration gradient</u> is the wrong way. This is important to stop us starving.

Revision by diffusion — you wish...

Hopefully there'll have been an overall movement of information from this page into your brain...

Q1   What is: a) diffusion   b) active transport?   [3 marks]

Osmosis

If you've got your head round <u>diffusion</u>, osmosis will be a <u>breeze</u>. If not, have a read of the previous page...

Osmosis Involves Water Molecules

<u>OSMOSIS</u> is the movement of <u>water molecules</u> across a <u>partially permeable membrane</u> from an area of <u>higher water concentration</u> to an area of <u>lower water concentration</u>.

1) A <u>partially permeable</u> membrane is a membrane with very <u>small holes</u> in it.

2) <u>Small molecules</u> can pass through the holes, but <u>bigger</u> molecules <u>can't</u>.

3) Water molecules pass <u>both ways</u> through a membrane during osmosis.

4) But the <u>overall movement</u> of <u>water molecules</u> is from where there are <u>lots</u> of them to where there are <u>fewer</u> of them.

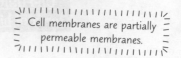
Cell membranes are partially permeable membranes.

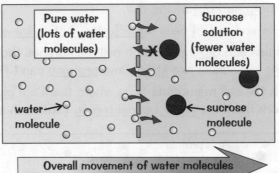

The sucrose is a solute — a molecule dissolved in the water.

Overall movement of water molecules

5) A solution that has lots of <u>solute molecules</u> compared to water molecules is said to be a <u>concentrated solution</u>. A solution that has lots of <u>water molecules</u> compared to solute molecules is said to be <u>more dilute</u>, or <u>less concentrated</u>.

I'm telling you, I've got great potential...

Water Potential Tells You How Concentrated a Solution is

1) You can talk about osmosis in terms of <u>water potential</u>.

2) <u>Water potential</u> is how <u>likely</u> it is that <u>water molecules</u> will diffuse <u>out of</u> or <u>into</u> a solution.

3) If a solution has a <u>high</u> water potential, then it has a <u>high concentration</u> of water molecules. If it has a <u>low</u> water potential, then it has a <u>low concentration</u> of water molecules.

4) So, you can say that <u>osmosis</u> is the <u>diffusion</u> of <u>water molecules</u> across a <u>partially permeable membrane</u> down a <u>water potential gradient</u>. (In other words, it moves from an area of <u>higher water potential</u> to an area of <u>lower water potential</u>).

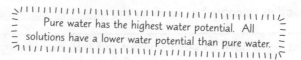

Pure water has the highest water potential. All solutions have a lower water potential than pure water.

Try saying osmosis backwards — it's not that fun, or educational...

If you put a piece of potato in a solution with a lower water potential than in the potato's cells, it'll shrink. Woah. This happens because water moves out of the potato, from an area of higher water concentration (the potato cells) to an area of lower water concentration (the solution that it's placed in).

Q1   Define osmosis.   [1 mark]

Q2   A piece of carrot is placed in a solution of lower water potential than its cells. Describe the overall movement of water. Explain your answer.   [2 marks]

Exchange of Materials

All organisms need to do a little bit of <u>give</u> and <u>take</u> to survive...

Organisms Exchange Substances with their Environment

Organisms need to <u>take in</u> substances from the environment. They also need to <u>get rid</u> of <u>waste products</u>. For example, they...

TAKE IN:
- <u>oxygen</u>
- <u>water</u>
- <u>food</u>
- <u>mineral ions</u>

GET RID OF:
- <u>carbon dioxide</u> (a waste product of aerobic respiration)
- <u>urea</u> (a waste product of protein breakdown in animals)

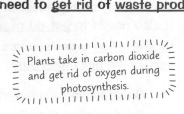

Plants take in carbon dioxide and get rid of oxygen during photosynthesis.

There's more on diffusion, osmosis and active transport on pages 25-26.

Substances are <u>exchanged</u> by <u>diffusion</u>, <u>osmosis</u> and <u>active transport</u>.
The <u>rate</u> that they are exchanged at is affected by <u>surface area to volume ratio</u>.

You Can Calculate an Organism's Surface Area to Volume Ratio

1) A <u>ratio</u> shows <u>how big</u> one value is <u>compared</u> to another.

2) So, a <u>surface area to volume ratio</u> shows how big a shape's <u>surface</u> is compared to its <u>volume</u>.

3) Here's one way of calculating an <u>organism's</u> surface area to volume ratio:

- A 2 cm × 4 cm × 4 cm <u>block</u> can be used to <u>estimate</u> the surface area to volume ratio of this <u>hippo</u>.
- The <u>area</u> of a square or rectangle is found by the equation: LENGTH × WIDTH.
  - The <u>top and bottom surfaces</u> of the block have a <u>length of 4 cm</u> and a <u>width of 4 cm</u>.
  - There are <u>four sides</u> to the block. They each have a <u>length of 4 cm</u> and a <u>height of 2 cm</u>.
  - So the hippo's <u>total surface area</u> is:
    (4 × 4) × 2 (top and bottom surfaces)
    + (4 × 2) × 4 (four sides)
    = <u>64 cm²</u>.

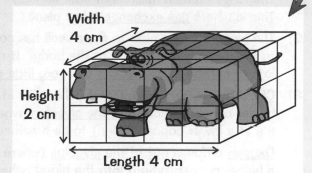

Width 4 cm

Height 2 cm

Length 4 cm

- The <u>volume</u> of a block is found by the equation: LENGTH × WIDTH × HEIGHT.
  So the hippo's <u>volume</u> is 4 × 4 × 2 = <u>32 cm³</u>.

The surface area to volume ratio (<u>SA : V</u>) of the hippo can be written as <u>64 : 32</u>.
To get the ratio so that volume is equal to <u>one</u>, <u>divide both sides</u> of the ratio by the <u>volume</u>.
So the SA : V of the hippo is <u>2 : 1</u>.

4) The <u>larger</u> the organism, the <u>smaller</u> its surface area is compared to its volume.

> **Example:** SA : V of hippo = 2 : 1   SA : V of mouse = 6 : 1
> The <u>mouse</u> has a larger surface area compared to its volume.

Simplifying ratios so that the volume is equal to one, means that you can easily compare the surface area to volume ratios of different organisms.

5) The <u>smaller</u> its <u>surface area</u> compared to its <u>volume</u>, the <u>harder</u> it is for an organism to <u>exchange substances</u> with its environment. There's more about this on the next page.

If you're bored, work out the surface area : volume of a loved one...

Time to exchange any useless facts stored in your brain with the information on this page. Then try this question...

Q1   Calculate the surface area : volume ratio of a cube with sides measuring 5 cm.   [1 mark]

Exchange Surfaces

Multicellular organisms need special <u>exchange surfaces</u> — and here's <u>why</u>...

Exchanging Substances is Trickier in Multicellular Organisms

1) Remember, an organism needs to <u>supply</u> its <u>cells</u> with the substances it needs to live. It also needs to <u>get rid of waste products</u>.

2) <u>Single-celled</u> organisms are only one cell big. Substances can <u>diffuse straight into</u> and <u>out of</u> the cell <u>across</u> the <u>cell membrane</u>. Diffusion is <u>quite quick</u> because:

   • Substances only have to <u>travel</u> a <u>short distance</u>.

   • Single-celled organisms have a <u>large</u> surface area to volume ratio. This means they can exchange <u>enough substances</u> across their cell membrane to supply the volume of the cell.

3) In <u>multicellular organisms</u> it is more <u>difficult</u> to <u>exchange substances</u>. Diffusion across the outer membrane is <u>too slow</u> because:

   • Some cells are <u>deep inside</u> the organism — it's a <u>long way</u> from them to the <u>outside environment</u>.

   • <u>Larger organisms</u> have a <u>low</u> surface area to volume ratio. It's difficult to exchange enough substances to <u>supply</u> a <u>large volume of organism</u> through a <u>small outer surface</u>.

4) So, multicellular organisms need <u>specialised exchange surfaces</u>.

5) They also need <u>transport systems</u> to <u>carry materials</u> to the body cells and to <u>remove waste products</u>.

In animals, the transport system is the circulatory system (see the next page). In plants, it's the xylem and phloem vessels (see page 32).

The Alveoli are an Example of a Specialised Exchange Surface

1) The lungs contain millions of little air sacs called <u>alveoli</u>. This is where <u>gas exchange</u> takes place.

2) The <u>blood</u> passing next to the alveoli has come back to the <u>lungs</u> from the rest of the body. It contains <u>lots of carbon dioxide (CO_2)</u> and <u>very little oxygen (O_2)</u>.

3) <u>CO_2</u> diffuses <u>out</u> of the <u>blood</u> (where it's at a higher concentration) <u>into the alveolus</u> (where it's at a lower concentration) to be breathed out.

4) <u>Oxygen</u> diffuses <u>out</u> of the <u>alveolus</u> (where it's at a higher concentration) <u>into the blood</u> (where it's at a lower concentration).

5) The alveoli are specialised to allow lots of <u>oxygen</u> and <u>carbon dioxide</u> to diffuse. They have:

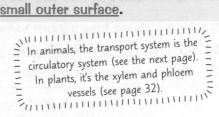

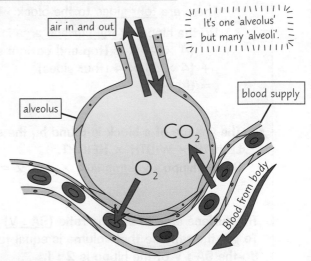

It's one 'alveolus' but many 'alveoli'.

air in and out

alveolus

blood supply

CO_2

O_2

Blood from body

   • A <u>big</u> surface area. This means a <u>lot</u> of oxygen and carbon dioxide can move <u>at once</u>.

   • Very <u>thin walls</u>. This means that oxygen and carbon dioxide only have a <u>short distance</u> to travel.

   • A <u>good blood supply</u>. This means that oxygen and carbon dioxide can get into and out of the <u>blood</u> quickly.

A root hair cell is another example of a specialised exchange surface — see page 32.

Al Veoli — the Italian gas man...

Living organisms are really well adapted for getting the substances they need to their cells.

Q1   Explain why multicellular organisms need specialised exchange surfaces.   [4 marks]

The Circulatory System

As you saw on the previous page, <u>multicellular organisms</u> need <u>transport systems</u> to move substances around. In <u>humans</u>, it's the job of the <u>circulatory system</u>.

Humans Have a Double Circulatory System

1) The circulatory system is made up of the <u>heart</u>, <u>blood vessels</u> and <u>blood</u>.
2) Humans have a <u>double circulatory system</u> — <u>two circuits</u> joined together.
3) In the first circuit, the <u>heart</u> pumps <u>deoxygenated</u> blood (blood without oxygen) to the <u>lungs</u>. The blood picks up <u>oxygen</u> in the lungs.
4) <u>Oxygenated</u> blood (blood with oxygen) then <u>returns</u> to the heart.
5) In the second circuit, the <u>heart</u> pumps <u>oxygenated</u> blood around all the <u>other organs</u> of the <u>body</u>. This delivers oxygen to the <u>body cells</u>.
6) <u>Deoxygenated blood</u> then returns to the heart.
7) Having a double circulatory system means <u>more oxygen</u> can be delivered to the <u>cells</u>. This is important for mammals as they use up a lot of <u>oxygen</u> in <u>respiration</u> to keep their <u>body temperature</u> steady.

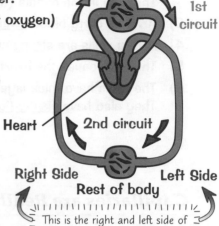

Blue = deoxygenated blood.
Red = oxygenated blood.

The Heart Pumps Blood Around The Body

1) The <u>heart</u> is a pumping <u>organ</u> that keeps blood flowing around the body. It's made of <u>cardiac muscle</u>.
2) The heart has four chambers — two <u>atria</u> and two <u>ventricles</u>. When the chambers <u>contract</u> it squeezes blood through the heart.
3) This is how the <u>heart</u> uses its chambers to <u>pump blood</u> around:

Atria is plural. Atrium is when there is just one.

This is the right and left side of the person whose heart it is.

Right Side   **Left Side**

① • The <u>right atrium</u> gets <u>deoxygenated blood</u> from the <u>body</u>.
  • This comes through the <u>vena cava</u>.

② • The deoxygenated blood goes to the <u>right ventricle</u>.
  • The right ventricle pumps it to the <u>lungs</u> through the <u>pulmonary artery</u>.

③ • The <u>left atrium</u> gets <u>oxygenated blood</u> from the <u>lungs</u>.
  • This comes through the <u>pulmonary vein</u>.

④ • The oxygenated blood then goes to the <u>left ventricle</u>.
  • The left ventricle pumps it out through the <u>aorta</u> and round the <u>whole body</u>.

4) The heart has <u>valves</u> to make sure that blood flows in the right direction. When the ventricles <u>contract</u>, the valves to the <u>atria close</u> and the valves to the <u>blood vessels open</u>. This prevents the blood from flowing <u>backwards</u> (<u>backflow</u>).

Okay — let's get to the heart of the matter...

Make sure you learn the names of the different parts of the heart and all the blood vessels that are attached to it.

Q1   Which chamber of the heart pumps deoxygenated blood to the lungs?   [1 mark]

The Blood Vessels

If you want to know more about the circulatory system you're in luck. Because here's a whole extra page.

Arteries Carry Blood Under Pressure

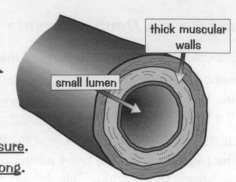

1) This is an artery.
2) The walls are thick.
   The hole in the middle (the lumen) is small.
3) Arteries carry blood away from the heart.
4) Artery walls are strong and elastic.
5) This is because the heart pumps blood out at high pressure.
6) The walls have thick layers of muscle to make them strong.
   They also have elastic fibres to allow them to stretch.

thick muscular walls

small lumen

Capillaries are Really Small

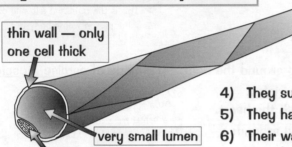

thin wall — only one cell thick

very small lumen

nucleus of cell

1) Arteries branch into capillaries.
2) Capillaries are really tiny — too small to see.
3) They can squeeze into the gaps between cells and carry blood really close to every cell in the body.
4) They supply food and oxygen, and take away waste like CO_2.
5) They have permeable walls, so substances can diffuse in and out.
6) Their walls are usually only one cell thick, so substances can diffuse in and out quickly (because they only have a small distance to cross).

Veins Take Blood Back to the Heart

1) Capillaries join up to form veins.
2) The walls of veins are thinner than artery walls.
3) This is because veins carry blood at low pressure.
4) Veins have a bigger lumen than arteries.
5) This helps the blood to flow, even though the pressure is low.
6) Veins also have valves.
7) These help to stop the blood flowing backwards.

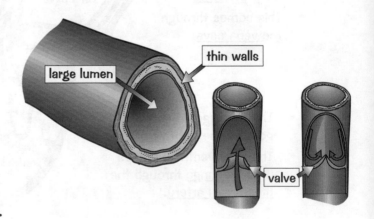

large lumen

thin walls

valve

Learn this page — don't struggle in vein...

Here's an interesting fact for you — your body contains about 60 000 miles of blood vessels. That's about six times the distance from London to Sydney in Australia. It's hard to imagine all of that inside you.

Q1   Why are capillary walls usually only one cell thick?   [1 mark]

Q2   Describe how veins are adapted to carry blood back to the heart.   [2 marks]

The Blood

Now that you know about <u>blood vessels</u>, it's onto the <u>blood</u> itself...

Blood Acts as a Transport System

Blood consists of <u>plasma</u>, <u>platelets</u>, <u>red blood cells</u> and <u>white blood cells</u>.
For now, all you need to know about is the <u>plasma</u> and the <u>red blood cells</u>...

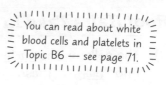
You can read about white blood cells and platelets in Topic B6 — see page 71.

Plasma is the Liquid Bit of Blood

1) <u>Plasma</u> is a pale yellow liquid.

2) It <u>carries just about everything</u> that needs transporting around your body:

- <u>Red blood cells</u> (see below), <u>white blood cells</u>, and <u>platelets</u>.
- <u>Water</u>.
- Digested <u>food products</u> like <u>glucose</u> and <u>amino acids</u> from the gut to all the body cells.
- Waste products like <u>carbon dioxide</u> and <u>urea</u> (see p.27).
- <u>Hormones</u> — these act like chemical messengers (see p.37).
- <u>Antibodies</u> — these are part of the body's immune response (see p.71).

Red Blood Cells Have the Job of Carrying Oxygen

1) Red blood cells carry <u>oxygen</u> from the <u>lungs</u> to <u>all</u> the cells in the body.

2) The <u>structure</u> of a red blood cell is adapted to its <u>function</u>:

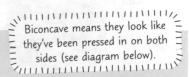
Biconcave means they look like they've been pressed in on both sides (see diagram below).

- Red blood cells have a <u>biconcave disc</u> shape.
  Their shape gives them a <u>large surface area</u> for <u>absorbing oxygen</u>.
- They contain a red substance called <u>haemoglobin</u>.
  It allows red blood cells to <u>carry oxygen</u>.
- Red blood cells <u>don't</u> have a <u>nucleus</u> —
  this leaves more space for carrying oxygen.
- They are <u>small</u> and very <u>flexible</u>.
  This means that they can easily pass through the <u>tiny capillaries</u>.

Blood's other function is to let you know you're bleeding...

Every single drop of blood contains millions of red blood cells — all of them perfectly designed for carrying plenty of oxygen to where it's needed. Right now, that's your brain, so you can get on with learning this page.

Q1   Explain three ways in which red blood cells are adapted to carry oxygen.   [3 marks]

Transport in Plants

Plants have <u>root hair cells</u> for taking in <u>minerals</u> and <u>water</u>. They also need to move stuff around <u>inside them</u>. Flowering plants have <u>two types</u> of <u>transport tube</u> to do this — <u>xylem</u> and <u>phloem</u>.

Root Hairs Take In Minerals and Water

1) The cells on the <u>surface</u> of <u>plant roots</u> grow into "<u>hairs</u>". These <u>stick out</u> into the soil.

2) Each branch of a root has <u>millions</u> of these hairs.

3) This gives the plant a <u>large surface area</u> for absorbing <u>water</u> and <u>mineral ions</u> from the soil.

4) Mineral ions are absorbed by <u>active transport</u> (see p.25).

5) Water is absorbed by <u>osmosis</u> (see p.26).

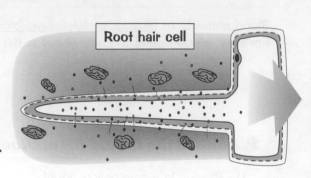

Root hair cell

Phloem Tubes Transport Food

1) Phloem tubes are made of <u>living cells</u>.

2) There are <u>end walls</u> between the cells — these are called <u>sieve plates</u>.

3) These end walls have small <u>holes</u> to allow stuff to <u>flow through</u>.

4) Plants make <u>food substances</u> in their <u>leaves</u>.

5) Phloem tubes transport these <u>food substances</u> (mainly <u>sugars</u>) around the plant.

6) This process is called <u>translocation</u>.

7) The cells that make up phloem tubes have <u>no nucleus</u>. This means that they <u>can't survive</u> on their own. So each of these cells has a <u>companion cell</u> to carry out the <u>functions</u> that it needs to survive.

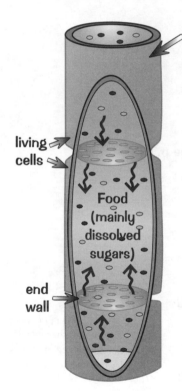

living cells

Food (mainly dissolved sugars)

end wall

Xylem Tubes Take Water UP

1) Xylem tubes are made of <u>dead cells</u>.

2) There is a <u>hole</u> down the middle of the dead cells.

3) There are <u>no</u> end walls between the cells.

4) The cells contain a material called <u>lignin</u>. This makes them <u>stronger</u>.

5) Xylem tubes carry <u>water</u> and <u>mineral ions</u> from the <u>roots</u> to the <u>stem</u> and <u>leaves</u>.

6) The movement of water <u>from</u> the <u>roots</u>, <u>through</u> the <u>xylem</u> and <u>out</u> of the <u>leaves</u> is called the <u>transpiration stream</u> (see next page).

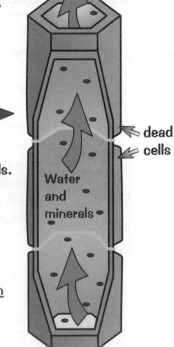

dead cells

Water and minerals

Don't let revision stress you out — just go with the phloem...

Phloem tubes transport substances in any direction around a plant. Xylem tubes only transport things upwards.

Q1   Describe the structure of phloem tubes.   [3 marks]

Transpiration and Stomata

Make sure you understand all about <u>root hairs</u> and <u>xylem tubes</u> from the previous page. The <u>transpiration stream</u> joins up the roots, xylem and leaves. Read on for more...

Transpiration is the Loss of Water from the Plant

1) Transpiration is caused by the <u>evaporation</u> and <u>diffusion</u> of water from a plant's surface (mainly the leaves).

2) Here's how it happens:

Evaporation is when water turns from a liquid into a gas. See page 25 for more on diffusion.

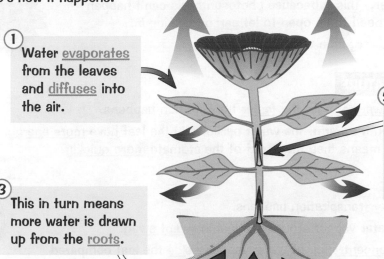

① Water <u>evaporates</u> from the leaves and <u>diffuses</u> into the air.

② • This creates a slight <u>shortage</u> of water in the leaf.
• More water is drawn up from the rest of the plant through the <u>xylem tubes</u> to replace it.

③ This in turn means more water is drawn up from the <u>roots</u>.

3) So there's a constant <u>stream of water</u> through the plant. This is called the <u>transpiration stream</u>.

4) The transpiration stream carries <u>mineral ions</u> that are dissolved in the water along with it.

Stomata are Involved in Transpiration

1) Stomata are <u>tiny pores</u> (holes) on the surface of a plant.

2) They're mostly found on the <u>lower surface</u> of <u>leaves</u>.

3) Stomata can <u>open</u> and <u>close</u>.

4) When they are open, <u>carbon dioxide</u> and <u>oxygen</u> can <u>diffuse</u> in and out of a leaf. <u>Water vapour</u> can also diffuse <u>out</u> of the leaf during <u>transpiration</u>.

Remember, plants need to take in carbon dioxide for photosynthesis.

5) This is how stomata open and close:

1) Stomata are surrounded by <u>guard cells</u>.

2) These <u>change shape</u> to control the size of the stoma:

When the guard cells are <u>swollen</u>, the stomata are OPEN.

It's one stoma, but two or more stomata.

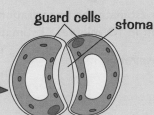

guard cells   stoma

When the guard cells are <u>limp</u>, the stomata are CLOSED.

I say stomaaaarta, you say stomaaaayta...

Remember, stomata are the little holes between guard cells, not the guard cells themselves. When the stomata are open, water vapour can escape from the leaf. This gets the whole transpiration stream moving.

Q1   Name the cells that control the size of stomata.   [1 mark]

Investigating Transpiration

This page is about the factors that affect transpiration <u>rate</u> (the <u>speed</u> of transpiration). During transpiration, water is taken up by a plant — so a faster rate of <u>transpiration</u> means a faster rate of <u>water uptake</u>.

Transpiration Rate is Affected by These Factors:

LIGHT INTENSITY

1) The <u>brighter</u> the light, the <u>faster</u> transpiration happens.
2) <u>Stomata close</u> as it gets darker. This is because photosynthesis can't happen in the dark, so stomata don't need to be open to let <u>carbon dioxide</u> in.
3) When the stomata are <u>closed</u>, very little water can <u>escape</u>.

TEMPERATURE

1) The <u>warmer</u> it is, the <u>faster</u> transpiration happens.
2) When it's warm, the water particles in the leaf have <u>more energy</u>. This means they move out of the stomata <u>more quickly</u>.

AIR FLOW

1) The <u>more windy</u> it is, the <u>faster</u> transpiration happens.
2) <u>Fast</u> moving air means that water vapour around the leaf is <u>swept away</u>.
3) This means there's a <u>higher concentration</u> of water vapour <u>inside</u> the leaf compared to <u>outside</u>. So water vapour moves <u>out</u> of the leaf quickly by <u>diffusion</u> (see p.25).

You Can Estimate Transpiration Rate

1) A <u>potometer</u> is a special piece of equipment.
2) You can use a <u>potometer</u> to <u>estimate transpiration rate</u>.
3) Here's what you do:

- Set up the equipment as in the diagram.
- Record the <u>starting position</u> of the <u>air bubble</u>.
- Start a <u>stopwatch</u>.
- As the plant takes up water, the air bubble gets <u>sucked</u> along the tube.
- Record <u>how far</u> the air bubble moves in a <u>set time</u>.
- Then you can <u>estimate</u> the <u>transpiration rate</u>.

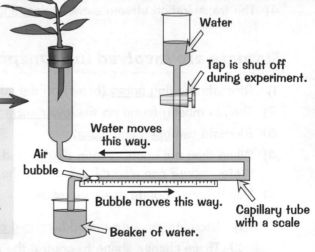

Water

Tap is shut off during experiment.

Water moves this way.

Air bubble

Bubble moves this way.

Capillary tube with a scale

Beaker of water.

EXAMPLE: A potometer was used to estimate the transpiration rate of a plant cutting. The bubble moved 25 mm in 10 minutes. Estimate the transpiration rate.

To estimate the <u>transpiration rate</u>, divide the <u>distance</u> the bubble moved by the <u>time taken</u>.

$$\text{Transpiration rate} = \frac{\text{distance bubble moved}}{\text{time taken}} = \frac{25 \text{ mm}}{10 \text{ min}}$$
$$= 2.5 \text{ mm min}^{-1}$$

4) You can use a potometer to estimate how <u>light intensity</u>, <u>temperature</u> or <u>air flow</u> affect transpiration rate. Just remember to <u>only change one variable at a time</u> and keep the rest <u>the same</u>.

So, blowing on a plant makes it thirsty...?

Sunny, warm and windy — the perfect conditions for transpiration and for hanging out your washing.

Q1   Explain how low light intensity affects the rate of transpiration through a plant.   [3 marks]

Revision Questions for Topics B1 and B2

Well, that's Topics B1 and B2 covered — time to see how much stayed in...
- Try these questions and tick off each one when you get it right.
- When you've done all the questions under a heading and are completely happy with it, tick it off.

Cells, Microscopy and DNA (p.11-14) ☑

1) List four features that animal and plant cells have in common. ☑
2) Name the two different types of lens found on a light microscope. ☑
3) What is a polymer? ☑

Enzymes (p.15-17) ☑

4) Draw a diagram to show how the 'lock and key' hypothesis of enzymes works. ☑
5) Give two factors that can affect the rate of an enzyme-controlled reaction. ☑
6) Give two variables that need controlling when investigating
   the effect of pH on an enzyme-controlled reaction. ☑

Respiration and Biological Molecules (p.18-20) ☑

7) Name the type of respiration that needs oxygen. ☑
8) Which type of respiration transfers more energy per glucose molecule? ☑
9) Name the basic units that lipids are made from. ☑

Photosynthesis (p.21-22) ☑

10) In what part of a cell does photosynthesis take place? ☑
11) Give three factors that can affect the rate of photosynthesis. ☑
12) Describe how you could investigate the effect of CO_2 concentration on the rate of photosynthesis. ☑

The Cell Cycle, Cell Differentiation and Stem Cells (p.23-24) ☑

13) Explain why the cells produced during mitosis are genetically identical. ☑
14) Give an example of a cell that is specialised to carry out a particular function. ☑
15) Where are stem cells found in plants? ☑

Diffusion, Active Transport and Osmosis (p.25-26) ☑

16) Give three substances that move across cell membranes by diffusion. ☑
17) Explain how active transport is different from diffusion. ☑
18) What is meant by the term 'water potential'? ☑

Exchanging and Transporting Substances (p.27-28) ☑

19) Name two waste products that animals need to get rid of. ☑
20) True or false? Large organisms have a high surface area to volume ratio. ☑

The Circulatory System, Blood Vessels and Blood (p.29-31) ☑

21) Which vessel carries blood away from the ventricle of the heart? ☑
22) Which type of blood vessel carries blood at high pressure? ☑
23) What is the role of plasma? ☑

Plant Transport Systems and Transpiration (p.32-34) ☑

24) What is carried by xylem tubes? ☑
25) Give three factors that affect the rate of transpiration. ☑

The Nervous System

The <u>nervous system</u> lets you <u>react</u> to what goes on around you.

The Central Nervous System (CNS) Coordinates a Response

1) The nervous system is made up of <u>neurones</u> (nerve cells), which go to <u>all parts</u> of the body.

2) The body has lots of <u>sensory receptors</u>. These can detect a <u>change in your environment</u> (a <u>stimulus</u>). Different receptors detect <u>different stimuli</u>. For example, receptors in your <u>eyes</u> detect <u>light</u>.

3) When a <u>stimulus</u> is detected by <u>receptors</u>, the information is sent as <u>nervous (electrical) impulses</u>.

4) These impulses are sent along <u>sensory neurones</u> to the <u>CNS</u> (the <u>brain</u> and <u>spinal cord</u>).

5) The CNS <u>coordinates</u> the response (it <u>decides what to do</u> about the stimulus and tells something to do it).

6) The CNS sends impulses along a <u>motor neurone</u> to an <u>effector</u> (<u>muscle</u> or <u>gland</u>).

7) The effector then <u>responds</u> — e.g. a <u>muscle</u> may <u>contract</u> or a <u>gland</u> may <u>secrete a hormone</u>.

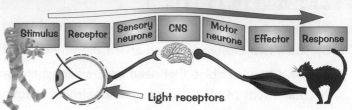

Stimulus | Receptor | Sensory neurone | CNS | Motor neurone | Effector | Response

Light receptors

Neurones Transmit Information as Electrical Impulses

1) <u>Electrical impulses</u> are passed along the <u>axon</u> of a neurone.

2) Neurones have <u>branched endings</u> (<u>dendrites</u>) so they can <u>connect</u> with lots of other neurones.

3) Some axons are surrounded by a <u>fatty (myelin) sheath</u>. This <u>speeds up</u> the electrical impulse.

A typical neurone

dentrites

myelin sheath

axon

Direction of impulse

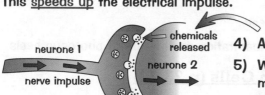

neurone 1

nerve impulse

chemicals released

neurone 2

4) A <u>synapse</u> is where two neurones <u>join together</u>.

5) When an impulse reaches a synapse, chemicals move across the <u>gap</u>. These chemicals then set off a <u>new impulse</u> in the <u>next</u> neurone.

Reflex Actions Stop You Injuring Yourself

1) <u>Reflex actions</u> are <u>automatic</u> (done without thinking). This makes them <u>quicker</u> than normal responses.

2) Reflexes help to <u>stop</u> you getting <u>hurt</u>, e.g. you <u>quickly</u> move your hand if you touch something <u>hot</u>.

3) The passage of information in a reflex (from receptor to effector) is called a <u>reflex arc</u>.

4) The neurones in reflex arcs go through the <u>spinal cord</u> or through an <u>unconscious part of the brain</u> (part of the brain not involved in thinking).

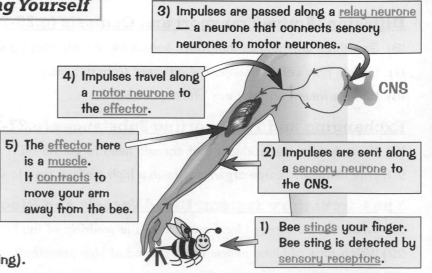

3) Impulses are passed along a <u>relay neurone</u> — a neurone that connects sensory neurones to motor neurones.

4) Impulses travel along a <u>motor neurone</u> to the <u>effector</u>.

CNS

5) The <u>effector</u> here is a <u>muscle</u>. It <u>contracts</u> to move your arm away from the bee.

2) Impulses are sent along a <u>sensory neurone</u> to the CNS.

1) Bee <u>stings</u> your finger. Bee sting is detected by <u>sensory receptors</u>.

Don't let the thought of exams play on your nerves...

Make sure you understand how the different parts of the nervous system work together to coordinate a response.

Q1   Name the two main parts of the central nervous system.   [2 marks]

Hormones

The other way to <u>send information</u> around the body (apart from along neurones) is by using <u>hormones</u>.

Hormones Are Chemical Messengers Sent in the Blood

1) <u>Hormones</u> are <u>chemicals</u> released by glands.
2) These glands are called <u>endocrine glands</u>. They make up your <u>endocrine system</u>.
3) Hormones are released directly into the <u>blood</u>.
4) They are then carried in the <u>blood</u> to other parts of the body.
5) They travel all over the body but they only affect <u>particular cells</u> in particular places.
6) The cells they affect are called <u>target cells</u> — they have the right <u>receptors</u> to respond to that hormone.
7) An organ that contains target cells is called a <u>target organ</u>.

These are the Endocrine Glands and Hormones You Need to Know About:

THE PITUITARY GLAND

1) This releases lots of different <u>hormones</u>.
2) These hormones act on <u>other glands</u>, making them <u>release hormones</u>.
3) <u>FSH</u> (<u>follicle-stimulating hormone</u>) is a hormone released from the pituitary gland.
4) It's involved in the <u>menstrual cycle</u>.

There's more about the hormones involved in the menstrual cycle on the next page.

THE PANCREAS

1) This produces <u>insulin</u>.
2) Insulin controls the <u>blood glucose level</u> (see page 40).

OVARIES — females only

1) These produce <u>oestrogen</u> and <u>progesterone</u>.
2) <u>Oestrogen</u> is the <u>main female sex hormone</u>. It's involved in the <u>menstrual cycle</u>. It also promotes female <u>sexual characteristics</u>, e.g. breast development.
3) <u>Progesterone</u> helps to support <u>pregnancy</u>. It's also involved in the <u>menstrual cycle</u>.

FSH, oestrogen, progesterone and testosterone are all known as 'sex hormones'.

TESTES — males only

1) These produce <u>testosterone</u> — the <u>main male sex hormone</u>.
2) It stimulates <u>sperm production</u>.
3) It's also important for the development of the male <u>reproductive system</u>.

Testes — not quite as bad as examies...

Hormones are really important. They control many different organs and cells in the body. For example, they help to control reproduction (see the next page) and they help to keep our blood sugar level steady (see page 40).

Q1   Explain how the endocrine system allows communication within the body.   [4 marks]

The Menstrual Cycle

The menstrual cycle is the <u>monthly</u> release of an <u>egg</u> from a woman's <u>ovaries</u>.
It's also the <u>build-up</u> and <u>breakdown</u> of the protective lining in the <u>uterus</u> (womb).

The Menstrual Cycle Has Four Stages

<u>Stage 1</u> — Day 1 is when <u>menstruation</u> (bleeding) <u>starts</u>. The lining of the uterus breaks down and is released.

<u>Stage 2</u> — The <u>uterus lining</u> is <u>built up</u> from day 4 to day 14.

<u>Stage 3</u> — An <u>egg develops</u> and is <u>released</u> from the ovary at about day 14. This is <u>ovulation</u>.

<u>Stage 4</u> — The <u>lining</u> is then <u>maintained</u> (kept thick) until day 28.

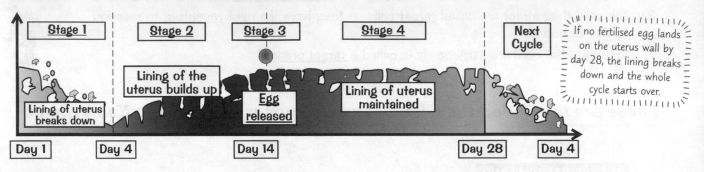

If no fertilised egg lands on the uterus wall by day 28, the lining breaks down and the whole cycle starts over.

The Menstrual Cycle is Controlled by Three Hormones

1. FSH

1) Causes an <u>egg to mature</u> in one of the ovaries.
2) <u>Stimulates</u> the <u>ovaries</u> to produce <u>oestrogen</u>.

2. Oestrogen

1) Causes the uterus lining to <u>thicken</u> and <u>grow</u>.
2) <u>Inhibits</u> (prevents) the production of <u>FSH</u>. This happens so that only <u>one egg</u> is released in each cycle.

3. Progesterone

1) <u>Maintains</u> the uterus lining.
   When the progesterone level <u>falls</u> and there's a <u>low oestrogen level</u>, the lining <u>breaks down</u>.
2) <u>Inhibits</u> the production of <u>FSH</u>.
3) A <u>low</u> progesterone level allows <u>FSH</u> to <u>increase</u>... and then the whole cycle starts again.

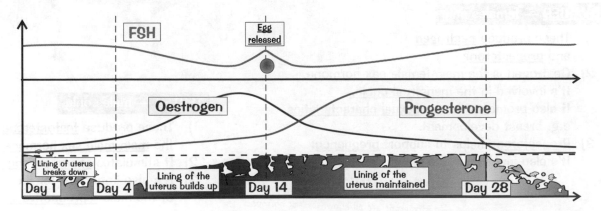

What do you call a fish with no eye — FSH...

OK, this stuff is pretty tricky. Try scribbling down everything on the page until you can get it all without peeking.

Q1   Which hormone causes an egg to mature in the menstrual cycle?   [1 mark]

Topic B3 — Organism Level Systems

Contraception

Pregnancy can happen if sperm reaches an egg. Contraception tries to stop this happening.

Contraceptives are Things That Prevent Pregnancy

Hormones can be Used to Prevent Pregnancy

1) The hormones that control the menstrual cycle (see previous page) can be used in contraceptives. E.g:

  - If oestrogen levels are kept high for a long time, egg development stops.
  - So oestrogen can be used to stop an egg being released.

  - Progesterone makes the mucus in the cervix very thick.
  - This stops sperm swimming through the cervix and reaching the egg.

  The cervix is the opening to the uterus.

2) Some hormonal contraceptives contain both oestrogen and progesterone — e.g. the combined pill and the contraceptive patch (which is worn on the skin).

3) The mini-pill and the contraceptive injection only contain progesterone.

  The combined pill and the mini-pill are both oral contraceptives — that means that they're taken through the mouth.

Non-Hormonal Methods Can Also Prevent Pregnancy

1) Barrier methods are non-hormonal contraceptives (they don't involve hormones). They put a barrier between the sperm and egg so they don't meet. For example:

  - Condoms — male condoms are worn over the penis during sexual intercourse. Female condoms are worn inside the vagina.
  - Diaphragms — these are flexible, dome-shaped devices that cover the cervix. They are inserted before sex.

  Diaphragms must be used with a spermicide — a chemical that kills sperm.

I've got this barrier thing sorted...

2) An intrauterine device (IUD) is another non-hormonal method. It is a T-shaped device that contains copper. It is inserted into the uterus to kill sperm. It can also stop fertilised eggs from attaching to the uterus lining.

Hormonal and Non-Hormonal Contraceptive Methods Have Pros and Cons

1) When they're used correctly, hormonal methods are usually better at preventing pregnancy than non-hormonal methods.

2) Also, when using hormonal methods, a couple don't have to think about contraception each time they have sex (as they would if they relied on barrier methods).

3) However, hormonal methods can have unpleasant side-effects, like headaches, acne and mood changes.

4) They have to be used correctly — e.g. if a woman doesn't take her pills at the right time they won't work.

5) Hormonal methods don't protect against sexually transmitted infections (STIs) — condoms are the only form of contraception that do this.

Be prepared...

...for the exam. You could be given information about different contraceptives and be asked to evaluate them.

Q1   Give one reason why a woman may prefer to use a diaphragm rather than an oral contraceptive.   [1 mark]

Controlling Blood Sugar Level

You need to keep your blood sugar level nice and steady. Time to put that biscuit down and get reading...

Insulin Controls Blood Sugar Level

1) Conditions in your internal environment (inside your body) need to be kept steady.

2) This allows your metabolic reactions to happen at the correct rate.
Metabolic reactions are all the reactions needed to keep you alive.

3) To keep conditions steady, your body needs to respond to changes that happen outside it (external changes) and changes that happen inside it (internal changes).

4) One condition that's kept steady is the level of glucose (sugar) in the blood:

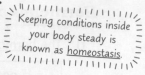

Keeping conditions inside your body steady is known as homeostasis.

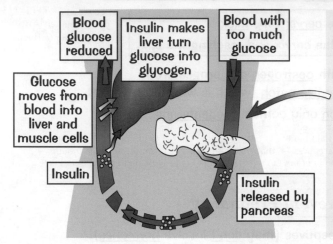

Blood glucose reduced

Insulin makes liver turn glucose into glycogen

Blood with too much glucose

Glucose moves from blood into liver and muscle cells

Insulin

Insulin released by pancreas

- Eating carbohydrates puts glucose into the blood.
- The normal reactions of cells remove glucose from the blood. When you exercise, a lot more glucose is removed from the blood.
- Changes in blood glucose are monitored and controlled by the pancreas.
- If the blood glucose level gets too high, the pancreas releases the hormone insulin.
- Insulin converts glucose into glycogen.
- Glycogen is stored in the liver and muscle cells.
- So insulin removes glucose from the blood.

Having Diabetes Means You Can't Control Your Blood Sugar Level

Diabetes is a condition that affects your ability to control your blood sugar level. There are two types:

TYPE 1

1) Type 1 diabetes is where the pancreas produces little or no insulin.

2) This means that a person's blood glucose level can rise to a level that can kill them.

3) People with type 1 diabetes need insulin therapy. This usually means injecting insulin.

4) People with type 1 diabetes also need to think about:
- Not eating too much sugary food (which causes the blood glucose level to rise quickly).
- Taking regular exercise — this helps to remove excess glucose from the blood.

TYPE 2

1) Type 2 diabetes is where a person's cells don't respond properly to the insulin they produce.

2) Being overweight can increase your chance of developing type 2 diabetes.
This is because obesity is a risk factor for the disease (see page 76).

3) Type 2 diabetes can be controlled by eating a healthy diet, exercising regularly and losing weight if needed. Some drugs can improve the way that the body's cells respond to insulin.

And people used to think the pancreas was just a cushion...

This stuff can seem a bit confusing at first, but if you learn the diagram, it'll all start to get a lot easier.

Q1   Describe how the production of insulin differs between type 1 and type 2 diabetes.   [2 marks]

Ecosystems and Competition

It might look pretty wild out there, but everything is actually quite <u>organised</u>.

Here are Some Words You Need to Learn Before You Start

1) <u>Individual</u> — A <u>single</u> organism.

2) <u>Species</u> — A <u>group</u> of <u>similar organisms</u> that can <u>reproduce</u> to give offspring that can also reproduce.

3) <u>Habitat</u> — The <u>place</u> where an organism <u>lives</u>, e.g. a rocky shore or a field.

4) <u>Population</u> — All the organisms of <u>one species</u> in a <u>habitat</u>.

5) <u>Community</u> — All the organisms of <u>different species</u> living in a <u>habitat</u>.

6) <u>Ecosystem</u> — A community of <u>organisms</u>, along with all the <u>non-living</u> conditions (see next page) in the area where they live.

Ecosystems are Organised into Different Levels

1) These are the <u>levels</u> of organisation in an ecosystem:

Individual ⟶ Population ⟶ Community ⟶ Ecosystem

2) The <u>smallest</u> level is an <u>individual organism</u>.

3) Individual organisms make up a <u>population</u>. Several populations make up a <u>community</u>.

4) The <u>biggest</u> level is the <u>ecosystem</u>.

Organisms Compete for Resources to Survive

1) Organisms need <u>resources</u> (things from their <u>environment</u>) in order to <u>survive</u> and <u>reproduce</u>.

- <u>Plants</u> need <u>light</u>, <u>space</u>, <u>water</u> and <u>minerals (nutrients)</u> from the soil.
- <u>Animals</u> need <u>space</u>, <u>food</u>, <u>water</u> and <u>mates</u>.

2) Organisms <u>compete with other species</u> (and members of their own species) for the <u>same resources</u>.

- For example, <u>red and grey squirrels</u> live in the <u>same habitat</u> and eat the <u>same food</u>.
- The <u>grey</u> squirrels are <u>better at competing</u> for these resources than the red squirrels.
- This means there's <u>not enough food</u> for the <u>reds</u>. So the <u>population</u> of red squirrels is <u>decreasing</u>.

It's all one big competition...

Make sure you know the difference between a population, a community and an ecosystem. It'll help a lot with the rest of the topic (and the exam). Then get your head around the things that organisms compete for.

Q1   Name the smallest level of organisation within an ecosystem.   [1 mark]

Q2   Give two things that animals might compete for.   [2 marks]

Abiotic and Biotic Factors

Let me stop you right there. If you haven't learnt all the words at the top of page 41, go back and do it now.

Communities are Affected by Abiotic and Biotic Factors

1) Abiotic factors are non-living factors, e.g. temperature.
2) Biotic factors are related to living things, e.g. predation (predators eating prey).
3) Both abiotic and biotic factors affect population size — they can make a population bigger or smaller.
4) They also affect the distribution of populations (where organisms live).

Abiotic Factors Include...

LIGHT INTENSITY

1) As trees grow they make the ground below more shaded.
2) This might stop grass growing underneath the trees because grass needs lots of light.
3) But mosses and fungi might grow there instead — they grow well in shade.

MOISTURE LEVEL

1) Daisies grow best in soils that are slightly wet.
2) If the soil becomes too wet or too dry, the population of daisies will decrease in size.

The moisture level just means the amount of water.

TEMPERATURE

1) If a cold country gets warmer, organisms that prefer warmer temperatures might move there.
2) But organisms that prefer the cold might be forced out.

pH OF THE SOIL

1) Different species of plant prefer either acidic or alkaline soil.
2) If the pH of the soil changes too much from what the plant prefers, the population will decrease.

Biotic Factors Include...

Availability of Food
1) If there's lots of food for a population, the population might increase.
2) This is because there will be enough food for all of them, so they are more likely to survive and reproduce.

Number of Predators
1) If the number of predators goes down, then the number of prey will go up.
2) This is because fewer of the prey will be eaten by the predators.
3) If the number of predators goes up, then the number of prey will go down.
4) This is because more of the prey will be eaten by the predators.

See the next page for more on predator-prey relationships.

Revision — an abiotic factor causing stress in my community...

Organisms like everything to be just right — temperature, light, food... I'd never get away with being that fussy.

Q1   Give two abiotic factors that could affect the community in an ecosystem.   [2 marks]

Topic B4 — Community Level Systems

Interactions Between Organisms

The <u>organisms</u> in an ecosystem are always <u>interacting</u> — well, if you can call <u>eating one another</u> interacting...

Populations of Prey and Predators Go in Cycles

1) The <u>population</u> of any species is usually <u>limited</u> by the amount of <u>food</u> there is.

2) If the population of the <u>prey</u> increases, then so will the population of the <u>predators</u> (because the <u>predators</u> have <u>more food</u> to eat).

3) But, as the population of predators <u>increases</u>, the number of prey will <u>decrease</u> (because lots more of the <u>prey</u> get <u>eaten</u>).

4) For example:

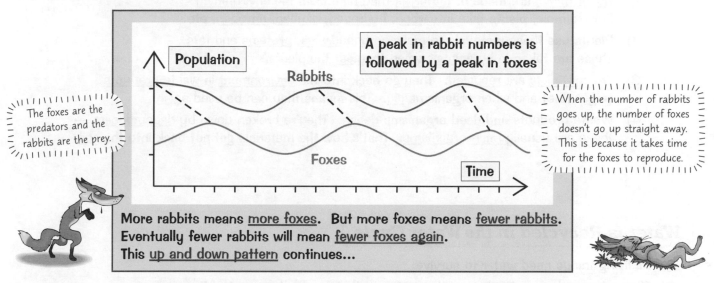

The foxes are the predators and the rabbits are the prey.

Population

Rabbits

A peak in rabbit numbers is followed by a peak in foxes

When the number of rabbits goes up, the number of foxes doesn't go up straight away. This is because it takes time for the foxes to reproduce.

Foxes

Time

More rabbits means <u>more foxes</u>. But more foxes means <u>fewer rabbits</u>. Eventually fewer rabbits will mean <u>fewer foxes again</u>. This <u>up and down pattern</u> continues...

5) Predator-prey cycles (like the one above) show that populations are <u>interdependent</u>. Being <u>interdependent</u> means that organisms <u>depend</u> on each other for <u>survival</u>.

There are Other Types of Interdependence...

① PARASITIC RELATIONSHIPS (PARASITISM)

1) <u>PARASITES</u> live off a host. They <u>take</u> what they need to survive, <u>without</u> giving anything <u>back</u>.

2) This often <u>harms</u> the host.

3) For example, <u>fleas</u> are <u>parasites</u>. <u>Dogs</u> (the hosts) <u>gain nothing</u> from having fleas.

② MUTUALISTIC RELATIONSHIPS (MUTUALISM)

1) <u>MUTUALISM</u> is a relationship where <u>both</u> organisms <u>benefit</u>.

2) For example, lots of plants are <u>pollinated</u> by insects. This allows the plant to <u>reproduce</u>. In return, the insects get a sip of sweet, <u>sugary nectar</u>.

There's another example of a mutualistic relationship on page 46.

My sister's a parasite — she takes my shoes, my dresses...

In summary, everything affects everything else. But, it's probably best if you learn the proper terms for the exams.

Q1   A cow's stomach is an ideal environment for some types of bacteria.
Without these bacteria, cows are unable to digest grass fully.
What type of interdependence is this an example of? Explain your answer.   [2 marks]

Recycling and the Water Cycle

All the <u>nutrients</u> in our environment are constantly being <u>recycled</u> — there's a nice balance between what <u>goes in</u> and what <u>goes out</u> again. The same goes for <u>water</u> — it goes round and round in the <u>water cycle</u>.

Materials are Constantly Recycled in an Ecosystem

1) Materials are recycled through the <u>biotic</u> (living) parts of an ecosystem — these include <u>animals</u>, <u>plants</u> and <u>microorganisms</u> (really, really tiny organisms, e.g. bacteria).

2) Materials are also recycled through the <u>abiotic</u> (non-living) parts of the ecosystem — for example, the <u>air</u> and <u>soil</u>.

There's more on biotic and abiotic factors on page 42.

1) <u>Living things</u> are made of <u>materials</u> they take from the <u>environment</u>. For example, plants take in <u>carbon</u>, <u>hydrogen</u>, <u>oxygen</u>, <u>nitrogen</u>, etc.

2) Plants use these materials to make <u>carbohydrates</u>, <u>proteins</u> and <u>fats</u>. These are taken in by <u>animals</u> when they <u>eat</u> the plants.

3) The <u>materials</u> are <u>recycled</u>. They go back into the <u>environment</u> in <u>waste products</u> (e.g. urine) and when organisms <u>die</u>. This means they can be used <u>again</u>.

4) Waste products and dead organisms <u>decay</u>. They're broken down by <u>decomposers</u> — these are usually <u>microorganisms</u>. That's how the materials get put back into the <u>soil</u>.

Water is Recycled in the Water Cycle

1) All living things need <u>water</u> to survive.

2) The <u>water cycle</u> constantly <u>recycles</u> water so that we <u>don't run out</u> of it.

3) The flow of water also means that <u>nutrients</u> can be taken to <u>different ecosystems</u>.

4) This is the <u>water cycle</u>:

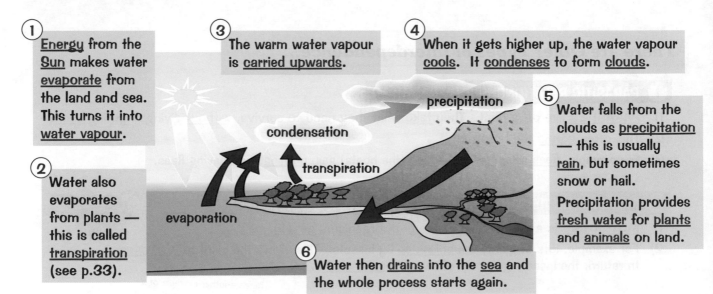

(1) <u>Energy</u> from the <u>Sun</u> makes water <u>evaporate</u> from the land and sea. This turns it into <u>water vapour</u>.

(2) Water also evaporates from plants — this is called <u>transpiration</u> (see p.33).

(3) The warm water vapour is <u>carried upwards</u>.

(4) When it gets higher up, the water vapour <u>cools</u>. It <u>condenses</u> to form <u>clouds</u>.

(5) Water falls from the clouds as <u>precipitation</u> — this is usually <u>rain</u>, but sometimes snow or hail.

Precipitation provides <u>fresh water</u> for <u>plants</u> and <u>animals</u> on land.

(6) Water then <u>drains</u> into the <u>sea</u> and the whole process starts again.

precipitation

condensation

transpiration

evaporation

Come on out, it's only a little water cycle, it won't hurt you...

Next time you get soaked on your way to school and moan about the rain, think back to this page. Rain is a really important part of the water cycle, and it's the water cycle that keeps us all alive.

Q1   Explain how water from the sea can eventually fall as rain.   [4 marks]

The Carbon Cycle

Carbon flows through the Earth's ecosystems in the carbon cycle.
Carbon is recycled — it's used by organisms but then ends up back in the atmosphere again.

The Carbon Cycle Shows How Carbon is Recycled

1) Carbon is an important material that living things are made from.
2) But there's only a fixed amount of carbon in the world.
3) This means it needs to be constantly recycled:

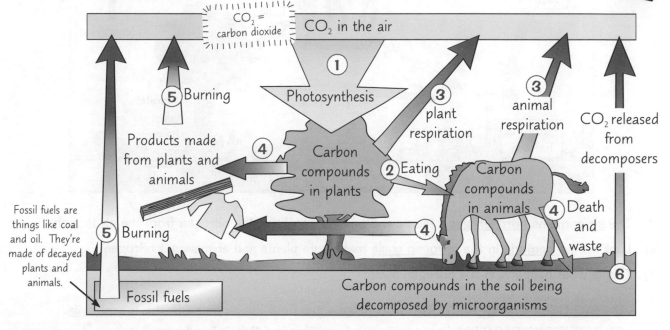

CO_2 = carbon dioxide

CO_2 in the air

① Photosynthesis

⑤ Burning

Products made from plants and animals

④

Carbon compounds in plants

② Eating

③ plant respiration

③ animal respiration

CO_2 released from decomposers

Carbon compounds in animals

④ Death and waste

Fossil fuels are things like coal and oil. They're made of decayed plants and animals.

⑤ Burning

Fossil fuels

Carbon compounds in the soil being decomposed by microorganisms

⑥

① Plants take in CO_2 from the air during photosynthesis.
They use the carbon in CO_2 to make carbon compounds, e.g. carbohydrates, fats and proteins.

② Eating passes the carbon compounds in plants along to animals that eat them.

③ Both plant and animal respiration releases CO_2 back into the air.

④ Plants and animals eventually die, or are killed and turned into useful products.

⑤ Burning plant and animal products (and fossil fuels) releases CO_2 back into the air.

⑥ Decomposers (microorganisms such as bacteria and fungi) break down animal waste
and dead organisms. As they break down the material, decomposers release CO_2 back
into the air through respiration.

Decomposition (decay) of materials helps to maintain habitats for the organisms that live there.
It means that nutrients are returned to the soil. It also means that waste material (e.g. dead leaves)
doesn't just pile up.

Carbon cycle — isn't that what Bradley Wiggins rides...

The biotic parts of the ecosystem in the diagram above are the horse, tree and microorganisms in the soil.
The abiotic parts include the air and soil. Go back to p.42 if you need a reminder about biotic and abiotic factors.

Q1   Describe the role of microorganisms in the carbon cycle.   [3 marks]

The Nitrogen Cycle

Just like water and carbon, <u>nitrogen</u> is constantly being <u>recycled</u>. It's amazing really — the nitrogen in your body might once have been in the <u>air</u>. And before that in a <u>plant</u>. Or even in some <u>horse wee</u>. Nice.

Nitrogen is Recycled in the Nitrogen Cycle

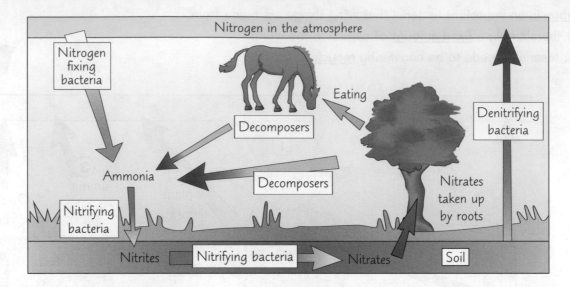

Nitrogen in the atmosphere

Nitrogen fixing bacteria

Eating

Decomposers

Denitrifying bacteria

Ammonia

Decomposers

Nitrates taken up by roots

Nitrifying bacteria

Nitrites   Nitrifying bacteria   Nitrates   Soil

1) The <u>air</u> contains <u>nitrogen gas</u>. Plants and animals <u>can't</u> use the nitrogen from the air though.

2) Luckily, the <u>bacteria</u> in the <u>nitrogen cycle</u> make sure plants and animals get nitrogen.

3) This is what happens in the nitrogen cycle:

> 1) <u>NITROGEN-FIXING BACTERIA</u> take <u>nitrogen gas</u> from the air and turn it into <u>ammonia</u>.
>
> 2) <u>NITRIFYING BACTERIA</u> turn ammonia into <u>nitrites</u> and then into <u>nitrates</u>. Nitrates can be taken up by <u>plants</u>.
>
> 3) Plants use the nitrogen in nitrates to make <u>proteins</u>.
>
> 4) <u>Animals</u> take in nitrogen when they <u>eat plants</u> (and each other).
>
> 5) Bacteria (and fungi) working as <u>DECOMPOSERS</u> break down <u>dead plants</u> and <u>animals</u> (and animal waste). This releases more <u>ammonia</u>.
>
> 6) <u>DENITRIFYING BACTERIA</u> turn nitrates back into <u>nitrogen gas</u>. This <u>doesn't help</u> organisms at all.

Some Bacteria Have a Mutualistic Relationship

1) Some <u>nitrogen-fixing bacteria</u> live in the <u>soil</u>.

2) Others live on the <u>roots</u> of <u>pea</u> and <u>bean</u> plants. These plants are good at putting nitrogen compounds <u>back into the soil</u>.

3) The plants have a <u>mutualistic relationship</u> with the bacteria. The bacteria get <u>food</u> from the plant, and the plant gets <u>nitrogen compounds</u> from the bacteria.

4) So the relationship helps <u>both</u> of them.

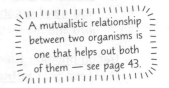

A mutualistic relationship between two organisms is one that helps out both of them — see page 43.

It's the cyyyycle, the cyycle of liiiiife...

Bacteria do all the hard work in the nitrogen cycle. But you need to do a bit of hard work here too. Don't leave this page until you feel happy about what's going on in the diagram above. Then you can put the kettle on.

Q1   Describe how the nitrogen in dead leaves is turned into nitrates in the soil.   [2 marks]

Revision Questions for Topics B3 and B4

Right, now it's time to find out how much you really know about the last two topics...

- Try these questions and tick off each one when you get it right.
- When you've done all the questions under a heading and are completely happy with it, tick it off.

The Nervous System (p.36) ☑

1) Describe the role of sensory neurones. ☑
2) Give an example of an effector. ☑
3) Draw a diagram of a typical neurone and label all the parts. ☑
4) What is the purpose of a reflex action? ☑
5) Describe the pathway of a reflex arc from stimulus to response. ☑

Hormones, The Menstrual Cycle and Contraception (p.37-39) ☑

6) What is the endocrine system? ☑
7) State where each of these hormones is produced:
   a) testosterone,   b) oestrogen,   c) progesterone,   d) FSH. ☑
8) Describe the role of oestrogen in the menstrual cycle. ☑
9) Explain how the combined pill prevents pregnancy when taken as a contraceptive. ☑
10) Give one pro and one con of a hormonal method of contraception. ☑

Controlling Blood Sugar Level (p.40) ☑

11) Why is it important to maintain steady conditions in the body? ☑
12) Which organ monitors and controls the blood glucose level? ☑
13) Describe the role of insulin in controlling a person's blood sugar level. ☑
14) Explain how type 1 and type 2 diabetes can be treated. ☑

Ecosystems and Interactions Between Organisms (p.41-43) ☑

15) What is meant by the term 'population' in the organisation of ecosystems? ☑
16) Give two things that plants could compete for in ecosystems. ☑
17) Give two biotic factors that could affect communities in ecosystems. ☑
18) Explain why the populations of predators and prey often change in cycles. ☑
19) What is a parasitic relationship? ☑

The Water Cycle and Nutrient Cycles (p.44-46) ☑

20) List the four main processes in the water cycle. ☑
21) Name the process that removes carbon from the air in the carbon cycle. ☑
22) Name two processes that put carbon back into the air in the carbon cycle. ☑
23) What is the role of nitrogen-fixing bacteria in the nitrogen cycle? ☑
24) Which microorganisms turn nitrates into nitrogen gas? ☑

Genes and Variation

You may remember the <u>structure of DNA</u> from page 14. Well, now you get to learn why DNA is so <u>important</u>...

Chromosomes Are Really Long Molecules of DNA

1) The <u>genome</u> is the <u>entire genetic material</u> of an organism.

2) The <u>genetic material</u> is stored in the nucleus of a cell. It's arranged into <u>chromosomes</u>.

3) <u>Chromosomes</u> are <u>long</u>, <u>coiled up</u> molecules of <u>DNA</u>.

4) A <u>gene</u> is a <u>short section</u> of a chromosome.

5) Each gene codes for a <u>particular protein</u>.

6) The <u>order of bases</u> (see page 14) in the gene decides <u>what</u> protein is made.

7) Different proteins <u>control</u> the development of different <u>characteristics</u>, e.g. dimples.

8) Genes can exist in <u>different versions</u>. Each version gives a different form of a <u>characteristic</u>, like blue or brown eyes.

9) The different versions of the same gene are called <u>alleles</u> or <u>variants</u> (see next page).

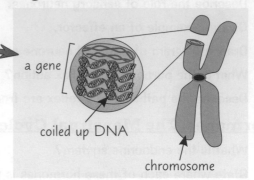

a gene

coiled up DNA

chromosome

Organisms of the Same Species Have Differences

1) Different species look... well... different — my dog definitely doesn't look like a daisy.

2) But even organisms of the <u>same species</u> usually look slightly <u>different</u>.

3) For example, all dogs are the <u>same species</u>, but different breeds of dog look different from each other (e.g. a <u>Dalmatian</u> looks quite different to a <u>Pug</u>).

4) These differences are called the <u>variation</u> within a species.

Variation Can be Genetic or Environmental

GENETIC VARIATION

1) Genotype is all of the <u>genes</u> and <u>alleles</u> that an organism has.

2) Variation can be <u>genetic</u> — this means it's caused by differences in <u>genotype</u>.

3) An organism's genotype affects its <u>phenotype</u> — the <u>characteristics</u> that it <u>shows</u>.

4) An organism's genes are <u>inherited</u> (passed down) from its parents (see page 50).

ENVIRONMENTAL VARIATION

1) <u>Variation</u> is also caused by the <u>environment</u> (the conditions in which organisms live).

2) For example, a plant grown on a sunny windowsill could grow <u>healthy</u> and <u>green</u>. The same plant grown in darkness would grow <u>tall</u> and <u>spindly</u> with <u>yellow leaves</u> — these are <u>environmental variations</u>.

BOTH

1) <u>Most</u> variation in phenotype is caused by a <u>mixture</u> of <u>genes</u> and the <u>environment</u>.

2) For example, the <u>maximum height</u> that an animal or plant <u>could</u> grow to depends on its <u>genes</u>. But whether it <u>actually</u> grows that tall depends on its <u>environment</u> (e.g. how much food it gets).

Environmental variation — pretty much sums up British weather...

It's dead important that you understand this page — it'll help everything else in this topic make much more sense.

Q1　　What is meant by an organism's 'genotype'?　　　　　　　　　　　　　　　　　[1 mark]

More on Variation and Genetic Variants

You saw on the previous page that organisms show variation. This can be due to differences in their <u>DNA</u>. These differences can happen because of <u>mutations</u> (see below).

Variation can be Discontinuous or Continuous

Discontinuous Variation

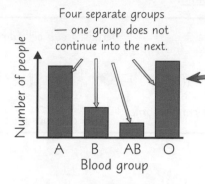

Four separate groups — one group does not continue into the next.

1) <u>Discontinuous variation</u> is when there are <u>two or more separate groups</u> — each individual belongs to <u>only one</u> of these groups.

<u>Blood group</u> is an example of discontinuous variation. Humans can <u>only</u> be <u>blood group</u> A, B, AB or O. They <u>can't</u> be anything <u>in between</u>.

2) Characteristics that show discontinuous variation are usually:
- only caused by <u>one gene</u>,
- <u>not</u> caused by the <u>environment</u>.

Continuous Variation

1) <u>Continuous variation</u> is when the individuals in a population <u>vary within a range</u> — there are <u>no separate groups</u>.

- The <u>height of people</u> is an example of continuous variation. You <u>don't</u> just get 'tall' people or 'short' people. There is a <u>whole range</u> of heights that people can be.
- The <u>mass</u> of organisms is another example. Organisms can be any mass <u>within a range</u>.

2) Characteristics that show continuous variation are likely to be:
- caused by <u>more than one gene</u> or,
- caused by <u>both genes</u> and the <u>environment</u>.

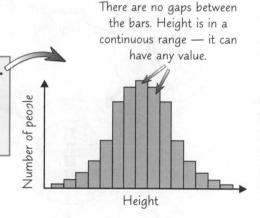

There are no gaps between the bars. Height is in a continuous range — it can have any value.

Mutations are Changes to the Genome

1) <u>Mutations</u> are changes to the <u>order of bases</u> in DNA. (See the previous page for more on DNA bases.)
2) When mutations happen within a <u>gene</u> they create a <u>genetic variant</u> (a <u>different version</u> of the gene).
3) <u>Most</u> mutations don't have <u>any effect</u> on the <u>phenotype</u> (characteristics) of an organism.
4) But <u>some</u> mutations do alter an individual's phenotype <u>slightly</u>. E.g. a mutation might give an animal <u>grey fur</u> instead of <u>brown fur</u>.
5) Very <u>rarely</u>, a single mutation will have a <u>big effect</u> on phenotype.

Alleles (see previous page) are genetic variants.

I was hoping for the 'grow wings' mutation — I'm still waiting...

Make sure you understand the differences between continuous and discontinuous variation. Mutations can cause variation by altering an organism's phenotype. But remember, most mutations don't have any effect on phenotype.

Q1   What is meant by a mutation? [1 mark]

Topic B5 — Genes, Inheritance and Selection

Sexual Reproduction and Meiosis

Ever wondered how <u>sperm</u> and <u>egg cells</u> are made? Well today's your lucky day.

Sexual Reproduction Involves Gametes

1) <u>Gametes</u> are 'sex cells'. In <u>animals</u>, they're <u>sperm</u> and <u>egg</u> cells.

2) Gametes only contain <u>half the number</u> of <u>chromosomes</u> of normal cells — they are <u>haploid</u>. <u>Normal cells</u> (with the full number of chromosomes) are called <u>diploid</u>.

3) During <u>sexual reproduction</u>, an egg and a sperm cell <u>combine</u>.

4) This forms a <u>fertilised egg cell</u>. The fertilised egg cell gets a <u>full set</u> of chromosomes (it's diploid).

5) The fertilised egg cell develops into an <u>embryo</u>. The embryo then grows into a <u>new organism</u> (an <u>offspring</u>).

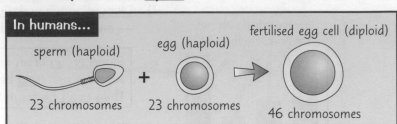

In humans...
sperm (haploid) + egg (haploid) → fertilised egg cell (diploid)
23 chromosomes + 23 chromosomes → 46 chromosomes

Gametes are Produced by Meiosis

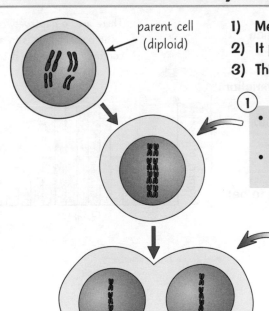

parent cell (diploid)

1) Meiosis is a type of <u>cell division</u>.
2) It produces <u>four gametes</u> from each parent cell.
3) This is how it happens:

①
• The DNA in the parent cell is <u>copied</u>. It makes <u>X-shaped chromosomes</u>.
• <u>Half</u> of the chromosomes have come from the organism's <u>father</u> and half have come from the organism's <u>mother</u>.

②
• The cell <u>divides</u>.
• Each new cell gets <u>half</u> of the chromosomes.

③
• Each cell divides <u>again</u>.
• The <u>X-shaped chromosomes</u> are <u>pulled apart</u>.
• You end up with <u>four</u> new <u>cells</u>. These are the <u>gametes</u>.
• Each gamete is <u>haploid</u>. This means that when two gametes combine in sexual reproduction, the fertilised egg cell will get the <u>right number</u> of chromosomes.
• Each gamete is also <u>genetically different</u>. This is important as it means there will be <u>genetic variation</u> (a mix of different variants) in the offspring.

A variant (allele) is a different version of a gene.

gametes (haploid)

Now that I have your undivided attention...

So, gametes are sex cells. They're haploid — they have only half the number of chromosomes of normal body cells.

Q1 A haploid gamete has 12 chromosomes. Two of these gametes combine to make a fertilised egg cell. How many chromosomes will there be in the fertilised egg cell? [1 mark]

Genetic Diagrams

Genetic diagrams help to predict how characteristics will be passed on from parents to offspring (children).

Different Genes Control Different Characteristics

1) Some characteristics are controlled by a single gene.
2) However, most characteristics are controlled by several genes.

Alleles are Different Versions of the Same Gene

1) Chromosomes come in pairs — there are two copies of each one.
2) You have two alleles of every gene in your body — one on each chromosome in a pair.
3) If the two alleles are the same, then the organism is homozygous.
4) If the two alleles are different, then the organism is heterozygous.
5) Some alleles are dominant (these are shown with a capital letter on genetic diagrams, e.g. 'C').
   Some alleles are recessive (these are shown by a small letter on genetic diagrams, e.g. 'c').
6) For an organism to show a recessive characteristic, both its alleles must be recessive (e.g. cc).
   But to show a dominant characteristic, only one allele needs to be dominant (e.g. either CC or Cc).
7) Remember, an organism's genotype is the genes and alleles it has.
   Its phenotype is the characteristics that it displays.

Genetic Diagrams show the Possible Alleles in the Offspring

1) The way that a single gene is passed from parents to offspring is called single gene inheritance.
2) You can use genetic diagrams to show single gene inheritance.
3) Genetic diagrams help to predict the phenotype of the offspring from the genotype of the parents. E.g.

1) An allele that causes hamsters to have superpowers is recessive ("b").
2) Normal hamsters don't have superpowers due to a dominant allele ("B").
3) Two homozygous hamsters (BB and bb) are crossed (bred together).
   A genetic diagram shows what could happen:

A hamster with the genotype BB or Bb will be normal. A hamster with the genotype bb will have superpowers.

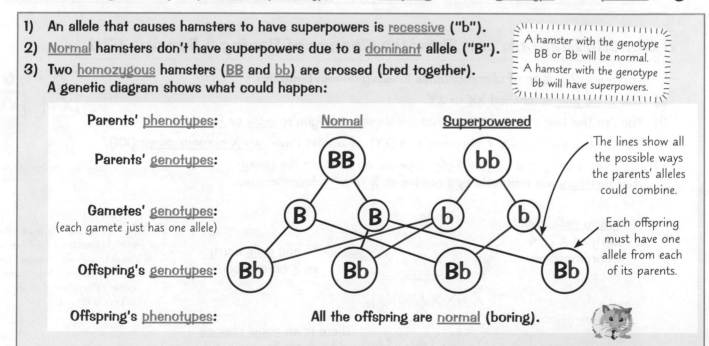

The lines show all the possible ways the parents' alleles could combine.

Each offspring must have one allele from each of its parents.

Your meanotype determines how nice you are to your sibling...

This stuff can look quite confusing. But the more you go over it, the more it makes sense.

Q1   People with albinism lack pigment in their skin and hair, and can appear pale-skinned and white-haired.
     The gene for albinism (a) is recessive. Give the genotype of a person with albinism.   [1 mark]

More Genetic Diagrams & Sex Determination

If you liked the genetic diagram on the previous page, then you're in luck — there are more on this page.

Each Outcome of a Genetic Cross Can be Written as a Probability

1) The genetic cross on the previous page was quite simple — all the offspring had the same phenotype.

2) Sometimes the results of genetic crosses can be a bit more interesting. For example:

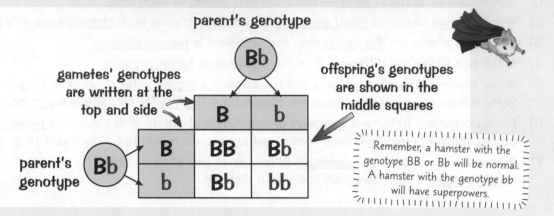

1) The genetic diagram below is called a Punnett square.
   It looks different to the one on the previous page but it works in the same way.

2) It shows a cross between two heterozygous hamsters (Bb and Bb):

parent's genotype

gametes' genotypes are written at the top and side

offspring's genotypes are shown in the middle squares

parent's genotype

Remember, a hamster with the genotype BB or Bb will be normal. A hamster with the genotype bb will have superpowers.

3) You can write the probability of the outcomes in different ways. E.g. you could say that:
   - There's a 3 in 4 (75%) chance that offspring will be normal.
   - There's a 1 in 4 (25%) chance that offspring will have superpowers.
   - There's a 3 normal : 1 superpowers ratio (3:1).
   - Out of 100 hamsters, the proportion of them you'd expect to be superpowered would be 25.

A Genetic Diagram can Show the Chance of Having a Boy or a Girl

1) There are 23 pairs of chromosomes in every human body cell.

2) The 23rd pair is labelled XX or XY.

3) They're the two chromosomes that decide whether you're male or female.

4) Males have an X and a Y chromosome (XY). Females have two X chromosomes (XX).

5) Whether a baby is a boy or a girl depends on whether the sperm that fertilises the mother's egg carries an X or a Y chromosome.

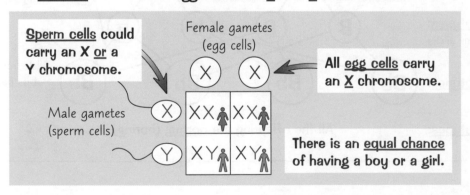

Sperm cells could carry an X or a Y chromosome.

Female gametes (egg cells)

All egg cells carry an X chromosome.

Male gametes (sperm cells)

There is an equal chance of having a boy or a girl.

The genetic diagram to show how X and Y chromosomes are inherited is similar to a genetic diagram for alleles. It just shows chromosomes rather than different alleles.

Have you got the Y-factor...

Genetic diagrams only tell you probabilities. They don't say what will definitely happen.

Q1   What are the 23rd pair of chromosomes labelled as in a female?   [1 mark]

Classification

People really seem to like <u>putting things</u> into <u>groups</u> — biologists certainly do anyway...

Classification is Organising Living Organisms into Groups

1) Looking at the <u>similarities</u> and <u>differences</u> between organisms allows us to <u>classify</u> them into groups.

2) In the past, organisms were <u>classified</u> using the <u>characteristics</u> you can see (like number of legs). This system of putting organisms into groups is known as an <u>artificial classification system</u>.

3) As people began to understand more about evolution, <u>natural classification systems</u> became more common.

4) Natural classification systems use information about how <u>closely related</u> organisms are.

5) To find out how closely related organisms are, scientists sometimes have to look in detail at the <u>structures</u> that organisms have.

> For example, even though <u>bats</u> and <u>humans</u> have many differences, the <u>bone structure</u> of a <u>bat wing</u> is similar to that of a <u>human hand</u>. So in a natural classification system, bats and humans are grouped together.

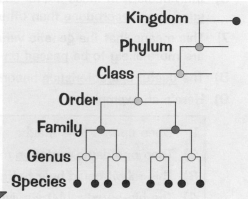

6) In natural classification systems, living things are divided into five <u>kingdoms</u> (e.g. the plant kingdom, the animal kingdom).

7) The kingdoms are then <u>split</u> into smaller and smaller groups.

8) These groups are <u>phylum</u>, <u>class</u>, <u>order</u>, <u>family</u>, <u>genus</u>, <u>species</u>.

9) The <u>species</u> groups only contain <u>one type</u> of organism (e.g. humans, dogs).

Developments in Biology Lead to Improvements in Classification

1) As <u>technology improves</u>, scientists are able to learn more and more about how organisms are <u>related</u> to each other.

2) Many years ago, the invention of the <u>microscope</u> helped scientists to classify organisms. It meant that they could examine <u>small structures</u> within organisms, e.g. <u>cells</u>.

3) These days, other <u>new technologies</u> are helping scientists to classify organisms better.

4) For example, there's a new area in science called <u>molecular phylogenetics</u>.

5) <u>New technologies</u> in molecular phylogenetics mean that scientists can look at the <u>sequence</u> of <u>DNA bases</u> in organisms. This is called <u>DNA sequencing</u>.

There's more on DNA on page 14.

6) The <u>more similar</u> the DNA base sequence between organisms, the more <u>closely related</u> they are.

> For example, the DNA sequence for <u>humans</u> and <u>chimpanzees</u> is about <u>94%</u> the same. This suggests that humans and chimpanzees are <u>closely related</u>.

My brother's been reclassified — he's back with the apes...

As new techniques let us study organisms' DNA, our classification systems get better and better.

Q1 Describe the main difference between an artificial and a natural classification system.   [2 marks]

Evolution and Natural Selection

Evolution is the <u>slow and continuous change</u> of organisms from one generation to the next.
<u>Natural selection</u> is used to explain how <u>evolution</u> happens.

Natural Selection Increases the Most Useful Characteristics

1) Populations of species usually show a lot of <u>genetic variation</u>.

2) This means that there's a big <u>mix</u> of genetic <u>variants</u> (alleles) in the population.

3) Genetic variants are caused by <u>mutations</u> in DNA (see page 49).

4) In order to <u>survive</u>, individuals must <u>compete</u> for <u>resources</u>, such as food and shelter.

5) Some genetic <u>variants</u> give individuals characteristics that make them <u>better suited</u> to a particular environment (e.g. long legs so they can run away from predators faster).

6) Individuals with these useful characteristics are <u>more likely</u> to <u>survive</u> and <u>reproduce</u> than other individuals in the population.

Remember, the characteristics an organism has can also be called its 'phenotype'.

7) This means that the genetic variants for the useful characteristics are more likely to be <u>passed on</u> to the <u>next generation</u>.

8) The <u>useful characteristics</u> become more <u>common</u> in the population over time.

9) Here's an example:

> 1) Once upon a time maybe all rabbits had <u>small ears</u>.
>
> 2) Then one day a <u>mutation</u> meant that one rabbit was born with <u>big ears</u>.
>
> 3) This rabbit could <u>hear better</u> — it was always the first to <u>hide</u> at the sound of a predator.
>
> 4) The big-eared rabbit <u>survived</u> and pretty soon it had lots of <u>baby rabbits</u> with <u>big ears</u>.
>
> 5) The <u>big-eared rabbits</u> were <u>more likely to survive</u> than small-eared rabbits.
>
> 6) The <u>big-eared rabbits</u> continued to <u>have babies</u> with big ears and <u>small-eared rabbits</u> became <u>less and less common</u>.
>
> 7) Eventually, the <u>whole population</u> had <u>big ears</u>.

Evolution is a Change in Inherited Characteristics

1) Natural selection leads to the <u>evolution</u> of species.

2) Here's how evolution is <u>defined</u>:

> Evolution is the change in the inherited characteristics of a population over time, through the process of natural selection.

3) This means that as species evolve, the <u>characteristics</u> in the population <u>gradually change</u>.

4) Evolution can mean that a species' <u>phenotype</u> changes so much that a completely <u>new species</u> is formed.

5) Some species evolve <u>faster</u> than others. This is partly due to how <u>quickly</u> they <u>reproduce</u> — the <u>faster</u> a species <u>produces offspring</u>, the <u>faster</u> they can <u>evolve</u>.

'Natural selection' — sounds like vegan chocolates...

Natural selection is a really important process in biology — make sure you've got your head around what happens and how it leads to evolution. There's more about evolution coming up on the next page.

Q1   Musk oxen have thick fur, which helps them to survive in the cold climate in which they live.
Explain how the musk oxen may have developed this adaptation over many years.   [4 marks]

Evidence for Evolution

If you're sitting there thinking evolution is a load of <u>old nonsense</u>, here's a bit of <u>evidence</u> to help sway you...

Fossils Provide Evidence for Evolution

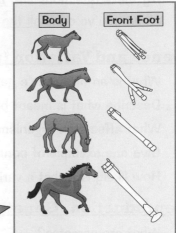

1) A fossil is <u>any trace</u> of an animal or plant that lived <u>long</u> ago. They are most commonly found in <u>rocks</u>.

2) They can tell us a lot about what the organisms <u>looked like</u> and <u>how long ago</u> they lived.

3) By arranging fossils in date order, <u>gradual changes</u> in organisms can be seen.

4) This provides <u>evidence</u> for <u>evolution</u>. It shows how species have <u>changed</u> and <u>developed</u> over many years. For example, if you look at the <u>fossilised bones</u> of a <u>horse</u>, you can put together a family tree to suggest how the modern horse might have <u>evolved</u>.

Antibiotic-Resistant Bacteria Also Provide Evidence for Evolution

<u>Antibiotics</u> are drugs that kill <u>bacteria</u>. Bacteria can become <u>resistant</u> to antibiotics — this means that they're <u>not killed</u> by them. They become resistant by <u>natural selection</u>:

1) <u>Most</u> bacteria in a population <u>won't be resistant</u> to an antibiotic. However, <u>some</u> bacteria will have <u>genetic variants</u> which make them <u>resistant</u> to an antibiotic.

2) A person who is being <u>treated with antibiotics</u> might have <u>resistant bacteria</u> inside them.

3) The resistant bacteria are more likely to <u>survive</u> and <u>reproduce</u> than the non-resistant bacteria.

4) This leads to the genetic variants for antibiotic resistance being <u>passed on</u> to lots of <u>offspring</u>.

5) So, antibiotic resistance <u>spreads</u> and becomes <u>more common</u> in a population of bacteria <u>over time</u>.

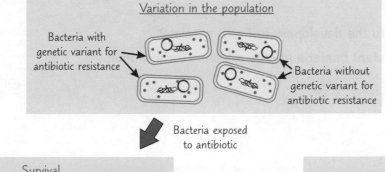

Variation in the population

Bacteria with genetic variant for antibiotic resistance

Bacteria without genetic variant for antibiotic resistance

Bacteria exposed to antibiotic

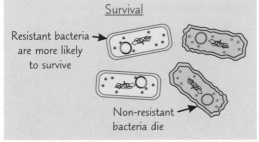

Survival

Resistant bacteria are more likely to survive

Non-resistant bacteria die

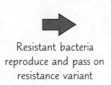

Resistant bacteria reproduce and pass on resistance variant

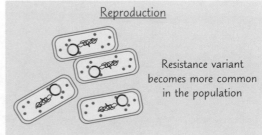

Reproduction

Resistance variant becomes more common in the population

6) Antibiotic-resistant bacteria provide <u>evidence for evolution</u>. There is a <u>change</u> in the <u>inherited characteristics</u> of a population <u>over time</u>. It happens by <u>natural selection</u>.

Fossils — they rock...

Life on Earth is still evolving — the evidence is right under our feet and under our microscopes.

Q1   Describe how fossils provide evidence for evolution.   [2 marks]

Topic B5 — Genes, Inheritance and Selection

Revision Questions for Topic B5

Right, that wraps up Topic B5 — time to find out how much of it you've got stored away in your head.

- Try these questions and tick off each one when you get it right.
- When you've done all the questions under a heading and are completely happy with it, tick it off.

Genes and Variation (p.48-49) ☑

1) What is an organism's genome?

2) Describe what is meant by the term 'phenotype'.

3) What affects an organism's phenotype, apart from its genotype?

4) Give one example of continuous variation.

5) How likely is it that a variant will have a really big effect on an organism's phenotype?

Reproduction, Genetic Diagrams and Sex Determination (p.50-52) ☑

6) What are gametes?

7) What does it mean if a cell is 'haploid'?

8) What does it mean to be homozygous for a characteristic?

9) The allele for pink flowers (P) is dominant. Give two possible genotypes for a plant with pink flowers.

10) Draw a genetic diagram showing that there's an equal chance of a baby being a boy or a girl.

Classification (p.53) ☑

11) What is the smallest group that organisms are divided into in a natural classification system?

12) Describe how the invention of the microscope helped with the classification of organisms.

13) Describe how DNA sequencing is used in classification.

Evolution (p.54-55) ☑

14) How is evolution defined?

15) How might evolution lead to the development of new species?

16) Explain how antibiotic-resistant bacteria provide evidence for evolution.

Investigating Distribution and Abundance

There are lots of <u>different methods</u> you can use to <u>investigate organisms</u> in their <u>habitat</u>. Hurrah.

Organisms Live in Different Places

1) The <u>abundance</u> of an organism is <u>how many</u> individuals you find in an area (i.e. <u>population size</u>).

2) The <u>distribution</u> of an organism is <u>where</u> an organism is <u>found</u> in a habitat, e.g. in a part of a field.

3) You need to know how to <u>investigate</u> the distribution and abundance of organisms in a <u>habitat</u>.

4) You do this by taking <u>samples</u>, rather than investigating the whole habitat.
(Often counting organisms in the whole habitat would take <u>too long</u>.)

INVESTIGATING ABUNDANCE

- Count all the <u>individuals</u> of your organism in <u>several sample areas</u>.

- Use your findings to estimate the <u>population size</u> in the total area you're studying (see page 59).

Each sample area should be the same size.

INVESTIGATING DISTRIBUTION

- Count all the <u>individuals</u> of your organism in <u>one sample area</u>.

- Repeat this in a second <u>sample area</u>.

- <u>Compare</u> your findings.

You can also use transects to measure distribution (see page 61).

Pooters Are For Collecting Ground Insects*

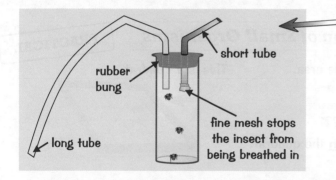

rubber bung

short tube

fine mesh stops the insect from being breathed in

long tube

1) This is a <u>pooter</u>.

2) You put the end of the <u>long tube</u> over an <u>insect</u> you want to collect.

3) When you <u>suck</u> on the <u>shorter tube</u> the insect gets <u>sucked into the jar</u>.

4) In <u>each of your sample areas</u>, suck up as many insects as you can in a <u>set time</u>.

5) <u>Count</u> the insects you collect in <u>each area</u>.

Pitfall Traps Are Another Way to Investigate Ground Insects

1) This is a <u>pitfall trap</u>.

2) <u>Insects</u> that come along <u>fall</u> into the container and <u>can't get out</u> again.

3) Set up a trap in <u>each of your sample areas</u>.

4) Leave the traps <u>overnight</u>.

5) The next day, <u>count</u> how many insects have fallen into <u>each trap</u>.

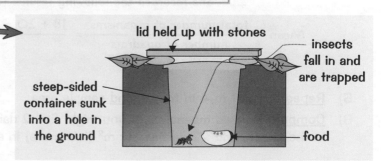

lid held up with stones

insects fall in and are trapped

steep-sided container sunk into a hole in the ground

food

Health and safety advises placing tiny cones around pitfall traps...

For these experiments, you should repeat the measurements several times and then take the average result.

Q1   A student wants to find out which ground insects are present in two different areas of a woodland over a 24-hour period. Describe a method the student could use to sample the areas.   [3 marks]

*That's insects on the ground, not some kind of powdered wasp and ant mixture.

More on Investigating Distribution and Abundance

Here's a bit more on studying the distribution and abundance of organisms...

Sweep Nets Are For Collecting Small Animals From Long Grass

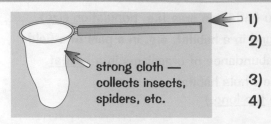

strong cloth —
collects insects,
spiders, etc.

1) This is a sweep net.
2) In each sample area, stand still and sweep the net once from left to right through the grass.
3) Then quickly sweep the net up and tip the animals into a container.
4) Count the organisms you collect in each area.

Pond Nets Are For Collecting Small Animals From Ponds and Rivers

1) This is a pond net.
2) In each sample area, sweep the net along the bottom of the pond or river.
3) Empty the net into a white tray with a bit of water in.
4) Count the organisms you collect in each area.

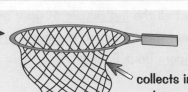

collects insects,
water snails, etc.

Use a Quadrat to Study The Distribution of Small Organisms

PRACTICAL

1) Place a quadrat on the ground in your first sample area. Quadrats need to be placed at random so that you get a sample which shows the general features of the whole area. For more about random sampling take a look at page 221.
2) Count all the organisms you're interested in within the quadrat.
3) Repeat steps 1 and 2 lots of times.
4) Work out the mean number of organisms per quadrat.

This is a quadrat.

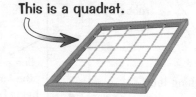

EXAMPLE: Anna counted the number of daisies in 7 quadrats. She recorded the following results: 18, 20, 22, 23, 23, 23, 25

$$\text{Mean} = \frac{\text{total number of organisms}}{\text{number of quadrats}} = \frac{18 + 20 + 22 + 23 + 23 + 23 + 25}{7} = \frac{154}{7} = 22 \text{ daisies per quadrat}$$

5) Repeat steps 1 to 4 in the second sample area.
6) Compare the two means. E.g. you might find 2 daisies per m² in the shade, and 22 daisies per m² (lots more) in an open field.

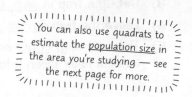

You can also use quadrats to estimate the population size in the area you're studying — see the next page for more.

Drat, drat and double drat — my favourite use of quadrats...

Quadrats are great for investigating organisms that don't move, such as plants. Be careful with the living things in any habitat you're studying, e.g. don't trample all over plants and make sure you release any animals you collect.

Q1   Describe how you could investigate the number of insects living in a sample area of a pond.   [3 marks]

Population Size

PRACTICAL

Population size is how many of a particular organism there are in a certain area, e.g. how many daisies there are in a field. Here are two different ways of estimating population size...

Estimate Population Sizes by Scaling Up from a Small Sample Area

1) Once you have counted the number of organisms in several quadrats (see previous page) you can work out the population size of the organisms in a habitat.

2) Divide the area of the habitat by the quadrat size. Then multiply this figure by the mean number of organisms per quadrat.

EXAMPLE:

Students used quadrats, each with an area of 0.5 m², to randomly sample daisies in a field. They found a mean of 10 daisies per quadrat. The field's area was 800 m². Estimate the population of daisies in the field.

1) Divide the area of the habitat by the quadrat size.   800 ÷ 0.5 = 1600

2) Multiply this by the mean number of organisms per quadrat.   1600 × 10 = 16 000 daisies in the field

You Can Also Estimate Animal Population Sizes Using Capture-Recapture

1) Capture a sample of the population.
2) Mark the animals in a harmless way.
3) Release all the animals back into the environment.
4) Recapture another sample of the population.
5) Count how many of this sample are marked.
6) Then estimate population size with this equation:

$$\text{Population Size} = \frac{\text{number in first sample} \times \text{number in second sample}}{\text{number in second sample previously marked}}$$

EXAMPLE:

A pitfall trap was set up in an area of woodland. 30 woodlice were caught in an hour. They were marked on their shell and then released back into the environment. The next day, 35 woodlice were caught in an hour — only 5 of these were marked. Estimate the population size.

All you need to do is put the numbers into the population size equation (shown above).

Population size = (30 × 35) ÷ 5 = **210 woodlice**

number in the first sample   number in the second sample   number in the second sample previously marked

The population size of my chocolate mice has fallen...

When using the capture-recapture method you have to assume some things. For example, that marking the animals hasn't affected their chance of survival (e.g. made it more likely that they'll get eaten).

Q1   Capture-recapture was used to estimate the population of crabs on a beach. In the first sample 22 were caught. A second sample had 26 crabs, 4 of which were marked. Estimate the population size. [2 marks]

Using Keys and Factors Affecting Distribution

On this page we cover keys — things that help you to figure out what you're actually looking at when you're doing fieldwork. And then there's some more stuff to learn about the distribution of organisms.

Keys are Used to Identify Creatures

1) A key is a set of questions that you can use to figure out what an unknown organism is.

2) Each question asks you something about your organism. You are given different options for the answers.

3) You go through the questions until you're just left with one possible species your organism could be.

Part of a key is shown below. It can be used to identify types of organisms that might be found on a woodland floor.

Some keys use statements, rather than questions.

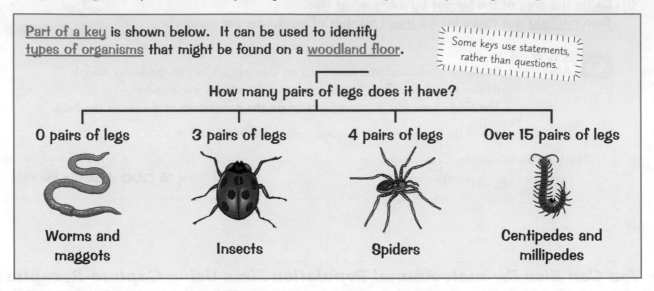

How many pairs of legs does it have?

0 pairs of legs	3 pairs of legs	4 pairs of legs	Over 15 pairs of legs
Worms and maggots	Insects	Spiders	Centipedes and millipedes

The Distribution of Organisms is Affected by Biotic and Abiotic Factors

1) Biotic factors are factors in an environment that are related to living things, e.g. predation.

2) Abiotic factors are non-living factors, e.g. light intensity.

3) Both biotic and abiotic factors can affect the distribution of organisms. For example:

See page 42 for more on biotic and abiotic factors.

- **BIOTIC** — a new species might move into an area. The new species might be better at competing for food than species already living there — so the old species might move somewhere else.
- **ABIOTIC** — daisies might be more common in an open area of a field compared to under trees. This could be because there's more light in the open area.

4) You can measure abiotic factors that you think might be affecting distribution.

For example, you could measure:
- light intensity — using a light sensor
- temperature — using a thermometer
- soil pH — using a pH monitor
- soil moisture — using a moisture meter

Identification keys — not much use when you're locked out...

Keys help you identify organisms you've found when sampling. This is pretty important when you want to talk about the different organisms that you've seen — it's not much use saying you found six slimy things in a pond...

Q1   Give two abiotic factors that might be measured on a sandy shore.   [2 marks]

Topic B6 — Global Challenges

Using Transects

Transects are another way of investigating the distribution and abundance of organisms...

Transects are Used to Investigate Distribution

1) The distribution of organisms often changes gradually across an area. You can investigate this using a line called a transect.

2) For example, a transect could be used to investigate how the distribution of a plant species changes from a hedge towards the middle of a field.

3) When you sample along the length of a transect using a quadrat (see p.58) this is called a belt transect.

4) To do a belt transect follow the steps below:

- Mark out a line in the area you want to study using a tape measure.
- Place a quadrat at the start of the line. Count and record the organisms you find in the quadrat.
- Then, take samples by moving your quadrat along the line.
  You can put each quadrat down straight after the one before (this might take ages though).
  Or you can leave gaps between each quadrat, e.g. just put a quadrat down every 2 m.

5) You might also want to investigate whether abiotic factors affect the distribution and abundance of organisms in the habitat. You could do this by taking measurements of abiotic factors (see p.42) at points along the transect.

You Can Estimate Percentage Cover Instead of Counting Individuals

1) It might be difficult to count all the individual organisms in the quadrat (e.g. if they're grass plants).

2) In this case you can calculate the percentage cover.

3) This means estimating the percentage area of the quadrat covered by a particular type of organism, e.g. by counting the number of little squares covered by the organisms.

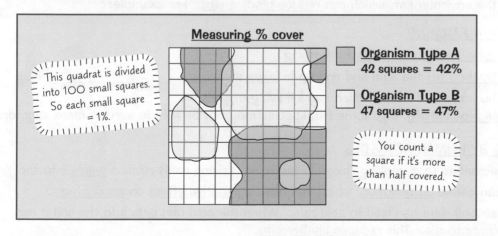

Measuring % cover

This quadrat is divided into 100 small squares. So each small square = 1%.

Organism Type A
42 squares = 42%

Organism Type B
47 squares = 47%

You count a square if it's more than half covered.

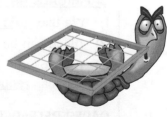

Quadrats are not suitable for investigating all types of organism.

My bedroom floor has a high percentage cover of dirty socks...

Transects involve using quadrats in a very organised way. It's exciting, I know, so here's a question to tackle...

Q1 Explain how you would set up a belt transect to record the distribution of species across a field. [5 marks]

Human Impacts on Ecosystems

Time for something less happy. We <u>humans</u> can have some <u>really negative impacts</u> (effects) on ecosystems...

Human Activities Have an Impact on Ecosystems

1) <u>Biodiversity</u> is the <u>variety of living organisms</u> in an <u>ecosystem</u>.
2) If the number of species in an area <u>decreases</u>, biodiversity will also <u>decrease</u>.
3) If the number of species in an area <u>increases</u>, so will <u>biodiversity</u>.
4) <u>Humans</u> often affect biodiversity.
5) We can affect <u>local biodiversity</u> (the number of species in the local area).
   We can also affect <u>global biodiversity</u> (the number of species on the entire planet).
6) Sometimes we have a <u>positive</u> effect on biodiversity (see next page).
7) But we often have a <u>negative</u> effect. Here are some examples:

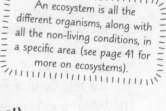

An ecosystem is all the different organisms, along with all the non-living conditions, in a specific area (see page 41 for more on ecosystems).

Land Use by Humans Can Have a Negative Effect on Ecosystems

1) Humans use land for things like <u>building</u>, <u>farming</u>, <u>dumping waste</u> and <u>quarrying</u>.
2) These activities often <u>damage ecosystems</u> and <u>reduce biodiversity</u>.
3) For example:

Destroying Woodland

1) Large areas of <u>woodland</u> are often cleared so that the land can be used for <u>farming</u>.
2) This reduces the number of <u>tree species</u>, so <u>reduces biodiversity</u>.
3) It also <u>destroys the habitats</u> of other organisms, e.g. birds that live in the trees.
4) This means that species might <u>die</u> or have to <u>move somewhere else</u>, which <u>reduces biodiversity</u>.

Pollution

Human activities can lead to lots of <u>waste products</u> being produced.
These can <u>pollute</u> the environment, which can <u>reduce biodiversity</u>. For example:

<u>CHEMICALS USED IN FARMING</u>

1) We use <u>toxic (poisonous) chemicals</u> for farming.
2) These can be <u>washed off</u> the land and end up in <u>lakes</u> and <u>rivers</u>.
3) This <u>pollutes</u> the lakes and rivers, which can kill living organisms.
   This can <u>reduce biodiversity</u>, e.g. some fish species may not be able to survive there anymore.

<u>GASES RELEASED BY HUMAN ACTIVITIES</u>

1) Many human activities (e.g. making things in factories, driving cars) release <u>gases</u> into the <u>air</u>.
2) These gases can cause <u>air pollution</u>, which can have a <u>negative effect</u> on <u>ecosystems</u>.
3) For example, air pollution can lead to <u>acid rain</u>. When the acid rain gets into the soil it can cause some <u>plants</u> to <u>die</u>. This <u>reduces biodiversity</u>.

I'm sorry but I'd prefer it if biodiversity was low inside my house...

I don't know about you but I feel a bit guilty. Human activities can be very bad news for the planet.

Q1   Describe how the construction of houses on a meadow could reduce local biodiversity.   [2 marks]

Topic B6 — Global Challenges

More Human Impacts on Ecosystems

Some _more human impacts on ecosystems_ are on the menu for this page. First up, another _negative_ impact. But don't worry, things will start looking up after that...

Hunting has a Negative Effect on Ecosystems

1) Some animal species are _hunted_, which _reduces_ their numbers. E.g.

   > Species of rhino are _hunted_ for their horns. This has led to them becoming _endangered_.

2) If too many individuals are killed, it might result in the _extinction_ of the species. E.g.

   > Over-fishing can _reduce fish levels_ so much that it might cause a species to _die out completely_.

3) The removal of a particular species from an area reduces the _biodiversity_ of that area. It can also have _knock-on effects_ on _food chains_. This could cause a _further decrease_ in biodiversity.

Conservation (Protection) of Species has a Positive Impact on Ecosystems

Conservation schemes help to _protect_ species or their habitats. This can help to _protect biodiversity_. Examples of conservation methods include:

Protecting habitats

An example of this is _controlling water levels_ to prevent bogs and marshes from getting too dry. This allows organisms to _stay living in their natural habitat_.

Preventing the introduction of harmful species

Some schemes aim to stop _harmful species_ from coming into the habitat. For example, there are schemes to control the number of _grey squirrels_ in some areas. This is because grey squirrels can cause the population size of _red squirrels_ to _fall_ (see page 41).

Creating protected areas for organisms

Protected areas include places like _national parks_ and _nature reserves_. _Development_ of the land is _limited_ in these areas (e.g. not as much of the land can be used for _building_ or _farming_). This protects both organisms and habitats.

Protecting organisms in safe areas away from their natural habitat

Safe areas include _zoos_. In these areas, organisms can be protected from harmful activities such as _hunting_ and _habitat destruction_. Safe areas can also be used to _increase numbers_ of organisms before they are released into the wild.

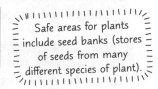
Safe areas for plants include seed banks (stores of seeds from many different species of plant).

My room is a protected area from the 'Horrible Sister' species...

Make sure you get your head around how humans can have a negative or positive effect on ecosystems. Negative actions can reduce biodiversity, but positive actions can keep biodiversity steady (or even increase it).

Q1   A frog species is nearly extinct in the wild as a result of its habitat being damaged.
      Explain how a protected area could help to prevent the frog species from becoming extinct.   [2 marks]

Maintaining Biodiversity

Trying to preserve biodiversity can be <u>tricky</u>, but there are <u>benefits</u> for doing it...

Maintaining Biodiversity Benefits Wildlife and Humans

Conservation schemes (see previous page) often help <u>humans</u>:

1) <u>Protecting the human food supply</u> — over-fishing has <u>greatly reduced fish numbers</u> in oceans. Conservation schemes make sure that people will have <u>fish to eat</u> in the <u>future</u>.

2) <u>Providing future medicines</u> — many of the medicines we use today come from <u>plants</u>. Undiscovered plant species may contain <u>new chemicals</u> that we can use in medicines. If these plants become <u>extinct</u>, we could miss out on new medicines.

3) <u>Providing materials and fuels</u> — plant and animal species are needed to make <u>materials</u> (e.g. wood, paper and oils) and some <u>fuels</u>. If these species become extinct these materials may become <u>more difficult</u> to produce.

Ecotourism is Another Benefit of Maintaining Biodiversity

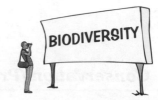

1) <u>Ecotourism</u> is when people go to visit <u>natural areas</u>, often where <u>conservation schemes</u> are taking place. The tourism <u>doesn't</u> cause a lot of <u>harm</u> to the ecosystems being visited.

> The <u>Eden Project</u> in Cornwall is a sort of 'eco theme park'. It contains huge plastic domes that represent different ecosystems (e.g. a rainforest). It also educates visitors about conservation.

2) Ecotourism helps <u>bring money</u> into areas where conservation work is taking place — e.g. when <u>tourists buy stuff</u> in local shops, it means the <u>local area</u> gets <u>more money</u>.

3) Tourists spending money at <u>ecotourism attractions</u> (like the Eden Project's gift shop) also helps to <u>pay for</u> conservation work.

Maintaining Biodiversity can be Challenging

Maintaining biodiversity can be <u>difficult</u>. Here are a few examples of why:

Agreements about conservation schemes can be difficult to arrange

1) Some conservation schemes need several different countries to <u>work together</u>. Sometimes this can be difficult as some countries <u>don't want</u> to sign up to an agreement. E.g. lots of countries have signed up to <u>stop killing whales</u>, but there are still some countries that <u>haven't</u> (e.g. Norway and Iceland).

2) Sometimes <u>local people don't agree</u> with conservation schemes. E.g. people living in a <u>fishing village</u> might not support a scheme that <u>reduces fishing</u> (as they won't get as much <u>money</u>).

Conservation schemes can be difficult to monitor

E.g. some conservation schemes <u>limit</u> the <u>amount of fish</u> that can be caught at sea. But trying to <u>keep track</u> of how many fish have been caught can be <u>tricky</u>. So it's hard to work out if the scheme is <u>working</u> and if people are <u>sticking to it</u>.

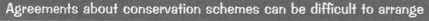

Locking your fridge also protects the human food supply...

Hmmm, I guess maintaining biodiversity can be a bit tricky. But if it keeps food on the table I'm keen...

Q1   Explain why maintaining biodiversity could be important for providing medicines in the future.   [2 marks]

Selective Breeding

'Selective breeding' sounds like it could be a tricky topic, but it's actually dead simple.

Selective Breeding is Very Simple

1) <u>Selective breeding</u> is when <u>humans choose</u> which plants or animals are going to <u>breed</u>.
2) Organisms are <u>selectively bred</u> to develop features that are <u>useful</u> or <u>attractive</u>. For example:

- Animals that produce more <u>meat</u> or <u>milk</u>.
- Crops with <u>disease resistance</u>.
- Dogs with a <u>good, gentle personality</u>.
- Plants that produce <u>bigger fruit</u>.

This is the basic process involved in <u>selective breeding</u>:

1) From your <u>existing stock</u> select the ones which have the <u>feature</u> you're after.
2) <u>Breed them</u> with each other.
3) Select the <u>best</u> of the <u>offspring</u>, and <u>breed them together</u>.
4) Continue this process over <u>several generations</u>. Eventually, <u>all</u> offspring will have the feature you want.

This is how we ended up with <u>edible crops</u> from <u>wild plants</u> and <u>domesticated animals</u> like cows and dogs.

Here's an Example:

A farmer might want his cattle to produce <u>more meat</u>:

- <u>Genetic variation</u> means some cattle will have <u>better characteristics</u> for producing meat than others, e.g. a <u>larger size</u>.
- The farmer could select the <u>largest</u> cows and bulls and <u>breed them</u> together.
- He could then select the <u>largest offspring</u> and breed them together.
- After <u>several generations</u>, he would get cows with a <u>very high meat yield</u>.

Selective Breeding Has Disadvantages

There's more on alleles on page 48.

1) The main <u>problem</u> with selective breeding is that it <u>reduces</u> the number of <u>different alleles</u> in a population.
2) This is because the "<u>best</u>" animals or plants are always used for breeding, and they are all <u>closely related</u>.
3) This means there's more chance of selectively bred organisms having <u>health problems</u> caused by their <u>genes</u>.
4) There can also be serious problems if a <u>new disease</u> appears.
5) This is because it's less likely that organisms in the population will have <u>resistance alleles</u> for the disease.
6) So, if <u>one</u> individual is affected by the disease, <u>the rest</u> are <u>also</u> likely to be affected.

I use the same genes all the time too — they flatter my hips...

Different breeds of dog came from selective breeding. For example, somebody thought 'I really like this small, yappy wolf — I'll breed it with this other one'. After thousands of generations, we got poodles.

Q1 Give one use of selective breeding in agriculture. [1 mark]

Genetic Engineering

As well as <u>selective breeding</u>, humans can also use <u>genetic engineering</u> to control an organism's features.

Genetic Engineering Involves Changing an Organism's Genome

1) <u>Genetic engineering</u> is used to give organisms <u>new</u> and <u>useful characteristics</u>.

2) It involves <u>cutting a gene</u> out of one organism's genome and <u>putting it into</u> another organism's genome.

3) Organisms that have had a new gene <u>inserted</u> are called <u>genetically modified</u> (GM) organisms.

Remember, an organism's genome is all of its genetic material. See page 48 for more.

Genetic Engineering is Useful in Agriculture and Medicine

For example, in <u>agriculture</u>:

1) <u>Crops</u> can be genetically engineered to be <u>resistant to herbicides</u> (chemicals that kill plants).

2) This means that farmers can <u>spray</u> their crops to <u>kill weeds</u>, <u>without</u> affecting the crop itself.

3) This can <u>increase crop yield</u> (the amount of food produced).

In <u>medicine</u>:

1) <u>Bacteria</u> can be genetically engineered to produce <u>human insulin</u>.

2) The bacteria can be grown in <u>large numbers</u>.

3) They can then be used to produce insulin for people with <u>diabetes</u> (see p.40).

But There are Some Concerns About Genetic Engineering

There are <u>concerns</u> about using genetic engineering in <u>animals</u>:

1) It can be hard to <u>predict</u> how changing an animal's genome will affect the animal.

2) Many genetically modified embryos <u>don't survive</u>.

3) Some genetically modified <u>animals</u> also suffer from <u>health problems</u> later in life.

There are also <u>concerns</u> about growing <u>genetically modified crops</u>:

1) <u>Genes</u> used in genetic engineering may get out into the <u>environment</u>. E.g. a herbicide resistance gene may be picked up by <u>weeds</u>, creating a new '<u>superweed</u>' that can't be killed.

2) Some people are worried that GM crops might have a <u>negative effect</u> on <u>food chains</u> or <u>human health</u>.

I say it's great.

If only there was a gene to make revision easier...

Genetically modified (GM) organisms could be very useful. But we don't yet know what all the outcomes of using them might be — so make sure you know the arguments for and against them.

Q1   Explain one benefit of being able to genetically engineer herbicide-resistant crops.   [2 marks]

Health and Disease

Some grim reading coming up — it's time to find out about <u>diseases</u> and the <u>nasties</u> that can <u>cause</u> them...

Health Can be Affected by Disease

1) A <u>healthy</u> organism is one that is <u>working</u> just as it <u>should</u> be — both <u>physically</u> and <u>mentally</u>.

2) A <u>disease</u> is a condition that <u>stops</u> an organism working as well as it should.

3) Both <u>plants</u> and <u>animals</u> can get diseases.

Diseases Can be Communicable or Non-Communicable

Communicable Diseases

1) A <u>communicable</u> disease is a disease that can <u>spread</u> between organisms.

2) They are caused by <u>pathogens</u> infecting the organism.

3) A <u>pathogen</u> is a type of <u>microorganism</u> (microbe) that causes <u>disease</u>.

4) Types of pathogen include <u>bacteria</u>, <u>viruses</u>, <u>protists</u> and <u>fungi</u> (see the next page).

Communicable diseases are also known as infectious diseases.

Non-communicable Diseases

1) <u>Non-communicable</u> diseases <u>cannot</u> be passed from one organism to another, e.g. cancers and diabetes.

2) They generally last for a <u>long time</u> and <u>progress slowly</u>.

3) They are often linked to <u>unhealthy lifestyles</u> (see page 76-77).

One Disease Can Lead to Another

Sometimes having <u>one disease</u> can make it <u>more likely</u> that you will get <u>another disease</u>.
Here are two <u>examples</u> that you need to know about:

1) The <u>immune system</u> is the body's way of <u>protecting itself</u> against disease — see p.71.

2) <u>HIV</u> is a virus that stops the <u>immune system</u> from <u>working properly</u>.

3) The <u>bacteria</u> that cause a disease called <u>tuberculosis</u> are normally <u>killed</u> by the immune system.

4) But, if the tuberculosis bacteria infect someone with <u>HIV</u>, the bacteria are <u>not killed</u> by the immune system.

5) This means people with <u>HIV</u> are <u>more likely</u> to suffer with <u>tuberculosis</u>. It's also <u>more difficult</u> for them to <u>recover</u> from tuberculosis.

There's more about HIV on page 69.

1) <u>HPV</u> is a <u>virus</u> that can infect the <u>reproductive system</u>.

2) Some <u>HPV infections</u> can cause <u>cell changes</u>. This can cause certain types of <u>cancer</u> to develop.

3) It's thought that <u>nearly all</u> cervical cancer cases result from HPV infections.

Cervical cancer is cancer of the cervix. The cervix is the opening to a woman's uterus (womb).

I have a communicable disease — it's telling me to go to bed...

Communicable diseases can be <u>passed</u> between people because they involve <u>pathogens</u>.

Q1   What is a non-communicable disease? [1 mark]

How Disease Spreads

Well, here are loads of ways you can catch diseases. As if I wasn't feeling paranoid enough already...

Communicable Diseases are Caused by Pathogens

Pathogens are microbes that cause communicable diseases (see previous page). There are four types:

1) BACTERIA — these are very small cells (much, much smaller than your body cells). They make you feel ill by producing toxins (poisons) that damage your cells and tissues.

2) VIRUSES — these are not cells. They're really tiny — even smaller than bacteria. They copy themselves inside the infected organism's cells. These cells then burst, releasing the viruses.

3) PROTISTS — protists that cause disease are often parasites (see p.43). They're usually single-celled.

4) FUNGI — some fungi have thread-like structures. These can grow and pierce human skin and the surface of plants, causing diseases. They can also produce spores. These can spread to other plants and animals.

Once inside an organism, pathogens can multiply really quickly.
As this happens, the infected organism will start to show symptoms of the disease.

Communicable Diseases are Spread in Different Ways

Pathogens infect both animals and plants. They can spread in different ways. For example:

1) Water

Some pathogens can be picked up by drinking or bathing in dirty water. For example:

> Cholera is a bacterial infection that causes diarrhoea and dehydration.
> It's spread by drinking water containing the diarrhoea of other sufferers.

2) Food

Some pathogens are picked up by eating contaminated (infected) food. For example:

1) Salmonella bacteria are found in some foods, e.g. raw meat.
2) If these foods are kept too long or not cooked properly, the bacteria can cause food poisoning.

3) Contact

Some pathogens can be picked up by touching contaminated surfaces. For example:

1) Tobacco mosaic disease affects many types of plants, e.g. tomatoes.
2) It's caused by a virus called tobacco mosaic virus (TMV).
3) This virus makes the leaves of plants patchy and discoloured.

> Discoloured just means that they lose their normal colour.

4) The discolouration means the plant can't photosynthesise as well, so the virus affects their growth.
5) It's spread when infected leaves rub against healthy leaves.

Ahh...Ahh... Ahhhhh Chooooooooo — urghh, this page is catching...

Pathogens are usually really small — you often need a microscope to see them. They're found all over the place. There's more about the different ways that diseases can spread coming up on the next page.

Q1   How is tobacco mosaic disease spread between plants?   [1 mark]

More on How Disease Spreads

Brace yourself. Time for some more <u>ways</u> that communicable diseases can <u>spread</u>. First up, body fluids...

1) Body Fluids

Some pathogens (e.g. HIV) are spread by <u>body fluids</u> such as:

*   <u>breast milk</u> (by breast feeding)
*   <u>blood</u> (e.g. by <u>sharing needles</u> to inject drugs)
*   <u>semen</u> (through sex)

1)   <u>HIV</u> is a <u>virus</u> spread by <u>exchanging body fluids</u>.
2)   At first it causes <u>flu-like symptoms</u>.
3)   The virus then attacks the <u>immune system</u> (see page 71).
4)   If the immune system isn't working properly, it <u>can't cope</u> with <u>other infections</u> (see p.67) or <u>cancers</u>.
5)   At this stage, the virus is known as <u>late stage HIV</u>, or <u>AIDS</u>.

Diseases which can be spread though sex are called sexually transmitted infections.

2) Animal Vectors

Animals that <u>spread disease</u> are called <u>vectors</u>.

1)   <u>Malaria</u> is a disease caused by a <u>protist</u>.
2)   Part of the protist's <u>life cycle</u> takes place inside a <u>mosquito</u>.
3)   Mosquitoes act as <u>vectors</u> — they <u>pick up</u> the malarial protist when they <u>feed</u> on an <u>infected animal</u>.
4)   Every time the mosquito feeds on another animal, it <u>infects the new animal</u> with the protist.
5)   Malaria causes <u>fever</u>. It can also cause <u>death</u>.

3) Soil

Some <u>pathogens</u> can live in the <u>soil</u>. This means plants in the <u>contaminated</u> soil may be <u>infected</u>.

1)   Bacteria called *Agrobacterium tumefaciens* cause <u>crown gall disease</u>.
2)   These bacteria can live in <u>some soils</u> and on the <u>roots</u> of some plants.
3)   If the bacteria enter a plant, they can cause <u>growths</u> (lumps) on the plant. These are called <u>galls</u>.
4)   The galls can <u>damage</u> the plant <u>tissue</u>. This can <u>slow</u> the flow of <u>water</u> through the plant.
5)   This causes the plant to become <u>weaker</u> and it may eventually <u>die</u>.

4) Air

1)   Some pathogens are carried in the <u>air</u>. For example:

*   *Erysiphe graminis* is a <u>fungus</u> that causes <u>barley powdery mildew</u>.
*   It makes <u>white</u>, <u>fluffy patches</u> appear on the <u>leaves</u> of <u>barley plants</u>.
*   This means the plant can't <u>photosynthesise</u> as well. This can reduce <u>growth</u>.
*   It's spread by <u>fungal spores</u> that are <u>blown</u> between plants by the <u>wind</u>.

2)   Pathogens can be carried in the <u>air</u> in <u>droplets</u> produced when you <u>cough</u> or <u>sneeze</u>. Other people can then <u>breathe them in</u>.

So there you have it — loads of different ways to get ill...

Animals, body fluids, air — there's no escape... Luckily for you, you've got some built-in defence systems to help you out. Have a look at page 71 to find out more...

Q1   What plant disease does the bacteria *Agrobacterium tumefaciens* cause?   [1 mark]

Reducing and Preventing the Spread of Disease

Aha, a page about what we can do to <u>avoid</u> catching communicable diseases. Things are definitely <u>looking up</u>.

The Spread of Disease Can Be Reduced or Prevented in Humans...

There are things that we can do to <u>reduce</u>, and even <u>prevent</u>, the spread of disease. For example:

1) <u>Being hygienic</u> (<u>clean</u>) — Doing things like <u>washing your hands</u> before making food or after you've sneezed can stop you infecting another person.

2) <u>Destroying vectors</u> — By <u>getting rid of</u> the organisms that spread disease (vectors), you can <u>stop</u> the disease from being <u>passed on</u>. When <u>insects</u> are the vectors, they can be killed using chemicals called <u>insecticides</u>. Their <u>habitats</u> (where they live) can be destroyed so that they can no longer breed.

3) <u>Isolating people with disease</u> — This <u>stops</u> them from <u>passing it on</u>.

4) <u>Vaccination</u> — Vaccinating people and animals against communicable diseases means that they <u>can't</u> develop the disease. If they don't have the disease, they can't <u>pass it on</u> to someone else.

There's more about how vaccination works on page 72.

... And in Plants

Here are some ways that the spread of disease in plants can be <u>controlled</u>:

1) <u>Controlling the movement of plants</u> — this makes sure that <u>infected</u> plants don't come into <u>contact</u> with <u>healthy</u> plants. E.g. garden centres are not allowed to sell plants which have crown gall disease (see previous page).

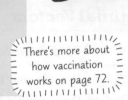

2) <u>Destroying infected plants</u> — this stops them being <u>sources</u> of infection.

3) <u>Chemical control</u> — for example, <u>fungicides</u> can be used to kill <u>fungal</u> pathogens.

Identifying a Disease Quickly can Help to Reduce its Spread

1) If you can <u>detect</u> and <u>treat</u> a disease quickly, you can <u>limit its spread</u>.

2) This can <u>reduce</u> the chance of the disease being passed on to others.

3) There are a number of ways that diseases can be <u>identified</u>. For example:

- Detecting a pathogen's <u>antigens</u>. (<u>Antigens</u> are <u>molecules</u> found on the <u>surface</u> of a cell — see the next page.)

- Testing to see if the <u>DNA</u> of a pathogen is present.

- <u>Looking</u> for the signs of the disease.

For example, a <u>plant pathologist</u> might be able to tell that a plant has <u>tobacco mosaic disease</u> (see p.68) by looking at its leaves to see if they are <u>discoloured</u>.

A plant pathologist is a scientist who studies plant diseases.

The spread of disease — mouldy margarine...

You may be sick of diseases already (geddit?) but don't turn this page until you've got the facts fixed in your brain.

Q1   Malaria is spread by mosquitoes which carry protists. The protists enter the bloodstream of animals when the mosquito feeds on them. Explain one way in which the spread of malaria could be reduced.   [2 marks]

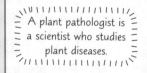

The Human Immune System

Right, back to <u>humans</u>. Your body has some pretty neat features when it comes to <u>fighting disease</u>.

Your Body Has a Pretty Good Defence System

The human body has got features that <u>stop</u> a lot of nasties getting <u>inside</u> it.
These are <u>non-specific</u> defences — they aren't produced in response to a <u>particular</u> pathogen.

The SKIN — It <u>stops pathogens</u> getting <u>inside</u> you. It also <u>releases substances</u> that <u>kill pathogens</u>.

HAIRS in your nose — They <u>trap</u> particles that could contain pathogens.

MUCUS (snot) — The whole <u>respiratory tract</u> (<u>airways</u> and <u>lungs</u>) releases <u>mucus</u> to trap pathogens.

CILIA (hair-like structures) — The <u>respiratory tract</u> is lined with <u>cilia</u>. They <u>push the mucus</u> up to the throat where it can be <u>swallowed</u>.

STOMACH ACID — The stomach makes <u>hydrochloric acid</u>. This <u>kills pathogens</u>.

The EYES — The <u>eyes</u> produce a chemical called <u>lysozyme</u>. This <u>kills bacteria</u> on the <u>surface</u> of the eye.

PLATELETS — When you damage a blood vessel, <u>platelets</u> (<u>tiny bits</u> of cells) in the blood clump together. This '<u>plugs</u>' the damaged area. This is known as <u>blood clotting</u>. It <u>stops you losing</u> too much <u>blood</u>. It also stops <u>microorganisms</u> from entering the wound.

Your Immune System Can Attack Pathogens

1) If pathogens do make it into your body, your <u>immune system</u> kicks in to destroy them.

2) The most important part of your immune system is the <u>white blood cells</u>.

3) When they come across an <u>invading</u> pathogen they <u>attack</u> in three ways:

1) CONSUMING THEM

Some white blood cells contain lots of <u>enzymes</u> and can <u>change shape</u>.
They can <u>engulf</u> (surround) pathogens and <u>digest</u> them. This is called <u>phagocytosis</u>.

pathogen

white blood cell

2) PRODUCING ANTIBODIES

1) Every pathogen has unique molecules on its surface. These molecules are called <u>antigens</u>.

2) When your white blood cells come across an <u>antigen</u> they don't know, they will start to produce <u>proteins</u> called <u>antibodies</u>.

3) Antibodies <u>lock onto</u> the new pathogens. The antibodies are <u>specific</u> to that type of antigen — they won't lock on to any others.

antigens
new pathogen
white blood cell
antibodies produced
new pathogens attacked by new antibodies

4) Antibodies are then produced <u>quickly</u> and carried around the body to <u>lock on</u> to all similar pathogens.

5) The antibodies make sure the pathogens can be <u>found</u> and <u>engulfed</u> by other white blood cells.

6) Some white blood cells (called <u>memory cells</u>) stay around in the blood after the pathogen has been fought off. If the person is infected with the same pathogen again, the memory cells cause antibodies to be made <u>quickly</u>. These help to kill the pathogen. This means the person is <u>naturally immune</u> to that pathogen and won't get ill.

3) PRODUCING ANTITOXINS These stop <u>toxins</u> produced by the <u>invading bacteria</u> from causing harm.

Fight disease — give your nose a blow with boxing gloves...

The <u>body</u> makes <u>antibodies</u> against the <u>antigens</u> on <u>pathogens</u>. There, don't say I never help you.

Q1   Describe the role of platelets in the defence of the body against pathogens.   [2 marks]

Vaccinations and Medicines

Vaccinations mean we don't always have to treat a disease — we can stop the disease in the first place.

Vaccinations Stop You Getting Infections

1) Vaccination involves injecting <u>dead, inactive or weakened</u> pathogens into the body.

2) These pathogens are <u>harmless</u>. But they have <u>antigens</u> on their surface.

3) The antigens cause your white blood cells to produce <u>antibodies</u> to attack the pathogens.

4) Some of these white blood cells will remain in the blood as <u>memory cells</u> (see previous page).

5) If you're infected with the <u>same</u> pathogen later, your memory cells cause lots of <u>antibodies</u> to be <u>produced quickly</u>.

6) These antibodies help <u>kill the pathogen</u> so you <u>don't become ill</u>.

7) For example, you can be vaccinated against the <u>measles</u> virus:

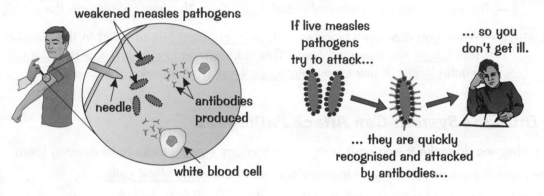

weakened measles pathogens

needle

antibodies produced

white blood cell

If live measles pathogens try to attack...

... they are quickly recognised and attacked by antibodies...

... so you don't get ill.

Medicines are Used to Treat Disease

1) ANTIBIOTICS

1) <u>Antibiotics</u> are chemicals that kill <u>bacteria</u>. They do this without killing your own body cells.

2) Lots of antibiotics are produced <u>naturally</u> by <u>fungi</u> and other <u>microbes</u>.

3) They're useful for treating <u>bacterial</u> infections.

4) Antibiotics <u>DON'T KILL VIRUSES</u>.

5) Some bacteria are <u>resistant</u> to (not killed by) certain antibiotics (see p.55).

6) The number of <u>resistant bacteria</u> has increased. This is because some antibiotics are <u>not being used properly</u>. E.g. some doctors are <u>prescribing</u> them when they're not really needed.

2) ANTIVIRALS

<u>Antivirals</u> are drugs that are used to treat <u>viral infections</u>.

3) ANTISEPTICS

1) <u>Antiseptics</u> are chemicals that <u>destroy microorganisms</u> or <u>stop them growing</u>.

2) Antiseptics are used <u>outside</u> the body to help to <u>clean wounds</u> and <u>surfaces</u>. They're used to <u>prevent infection</u> rather than treat it.

Prevention is better than cure...

Kapow, down with you, nasty pathogens — we will kill you all. Ahem, sorry. You'd best learn this lot.

Q1   What do vaccinations cause white blood cells to produce?   [1 mark]

Topic B6 — Global Challenges

Investigating Antimicrobials   PRACTICAL

Antibiotics and antiseptics are both examples of <u>antimicrobials</u> — they <u>destroy microbes</u>.
You can <u>grow</u> your own <u>microbes</u> to see how <u>effective</u> different <u>antimicrobials</u> are...

You Can do a Practical to Investigate Antimicrobials

You can test the action of <u>antimicrobials</u> (e.g. <u>antibiotics</u>) by <u>growing microorganisms</u>:

'Sterile' means totally clean.

1) Pour hot, sterilised <u>agar jelly</u> into a sterile <u>Petri dish</u> (a shallow round dish).
The jelly is a <u>culture medium</u> — it contains loads of things that microorganisms need to <u>grow</u>.

2) When the jelly has set, use an <u>inoculating loop</u> (a wire loop) to <u>move</u> microorganisms to it.

3) Then take <u>three discs</u> of filter paper. Soak one disc in an <u>antibiotic</u> (disc A) and another in a <u>different antibiotic</u> (disc B). The third disc (disc C) is a <u>control</u> disc (see below) — soak it in <u>sterile water</u>.

4) Place the discs on the jelly using <u>sterile forceps</u> (big tweezers).

5) Lightly tape the <u>lid</u> onto the dish (to stop other microbes getting in).

6) The antibiotic will <u>diffuse</u> (soak) into the agar jelly.

You need to control all other variables, such as temperature, disc size, etc.

7) Leave the dish for <u>48 hours</u> at <u>25 °C</u>. The bacteria will <u>multiply</u> and cover the jelly.

8) Anywhere the bacteria can't grow is called a '<u>clear zone</u>'. The <u>better</u> the antibiotic is at killing the bacteria, the <u>larger</u> the <u>clear zone</u> around the disc will be — see next page.

9) Using a <u>control disc</u> means that you can be sure that any <u>difference</u> in the size of the clear zone around the <u>control</u> disc and around the <u>antibiotic</u> discs is due to the <u>effect</u> of the antibiotic <u>alone</u>.

No clear zone around an antibiotic disc could mean that the bacteria are resistant to it — see page 55.

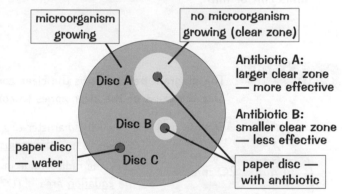

microorganism growing

no microorganism growing (clear zone)

Antibiotic A: larger clear zone — more effective

Antibiotic B: smaller clear zone — less effective

Disc A

Disc B

Disc C

paper disc — water

paper disc — with antibiotic

In the <u>lab at school</u>, cultures of microorganisms are kept at about <u>25 °C</u>.
<u>Harmful pathogens</u> aren't likely to grow at this temperature.
In <u>industry</u>, higher <u>temperatures</u> are used so microbes can grow <u>faster</u>.

You Need to Make Sure the Culture Doesn't Get Contaminated

If <u>unwanted</u> microorganisms <u>contaminate</u> (get into) your dish it will <u>affect your results</u>.
It could also result in the growth of <u>pathogens</u>. To <u>avoid</u> this, you should:

1) Regularly <u>disinfect</u> work surfaces.

2) <u>Sterilise equipment</u> before and after use, e.g. <u>inoculating loops</u> should be <u>sterilised</u> by <u>passing them through a hot flame</u>.

3) Work near a <u>Bunsen flame</u>. Hot air rises, so <u>microbes</u> in the <u>air</u> should be <u>drawn away</u> from the <u>culture</u>.

4) The <u>microorganisms</u> to put on your agar come in a glass container. Briefly <u>flame</u> the <u>neck</u> of the glass container just <u>after</u> it's <u>opened</u> and just <u>before</u> it's <u>closed</u>. This causes air to <u>move out</u> of the container, preventing unwanted <u>microbes</u> from <u>falling in</u>.

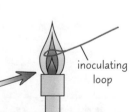

inoculating loop

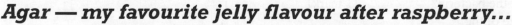

Agar — my favourite jelly flavour after raspberry...

You really don't want to grow microbes that make you ill — that's partly why it's important to keep things sterile.

Q1 Explain why it is important to use a control when investigating the effectiveness of different antibiotics on the growth of bacteria.
[2 marks]

Comparing Antimicrobials

Once you've done all that boring <u>practical</u> stuff, you get to do the really fun stuff — a lovely bit of <u>maths</u>.
Woo. Here's how you can <u>compare</u> your <u>clear zones</u>...

Calculate the Sizes of the Clear Zones to Compare Results

1) You can <u>compare</u> the <u>effectiveness</u> of different antibiotics (or antiseptics)
on bacteria by looking at the <u>sizes</u> of the <u>clear zones</u>.

2) The <u>larger</u> the clear zone around a disc,
the <u>more effective</u> the antibiotic is against the bacteria.

3) First you need to measure the clear zone's <u>diameter</u>.
The diameter is just the distance <u>across the middle</u>.

4) Once you know the diameter, you can use
<u>this equation</u> to calculate the <u>area</u> of a clear zone:

*Don't open the
Petri dish to measure
the clear zones —
they should be visible
through the bottom
of the dish.*

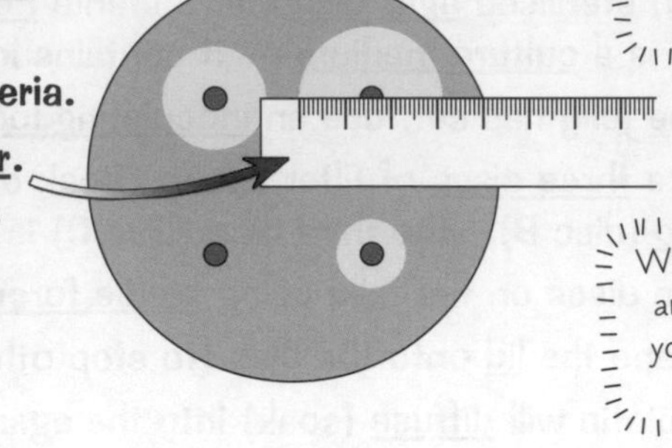

*When you calculate the
area of the clear zone
you should include the
area of the disc.*

This is the equation
for the area of a circle.
You're likely to use the
units cm^2 or mm^2.

$$\text{Area} = \pi r^2$$

r is the radius of the clear zone
— it's equal to half the diameter.

π is just a number. You should have a button for
it on your calculator. If not, just use the value 3.14.

EXAMPLE:

The diagram below shows the clear zones produced by antibiotics A and B.
Use the areas of the clear zones to compare the effectiveness of the antibiotics.

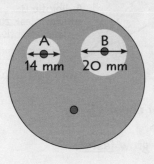

1) Divide the diameter of zone A
by <u>two</u> to find the <u>radius</u>.

Radius of A = 14 ÷ 2 = 7 mm

2) Stick the radius value into
the <u>equation</u> area = πr^2.

Area of A = $\pi \times 7^2$ = 154 mm^2

3) <u>Repeat</u> steps 1 and 2 for zone B.

Radius of B = 20 ÷ 2 = 10 mm

4) <u>Compare</u> the <u>sizes</u> of the <u>areas</u>.
314 mm^2 is just over twice 154 mm^2,
so you could say that:

Area of B = $\pi \times 10^2$ = 314 mm^2

**The clear zone of antibiotic B is roughly twice
the size of the clear zone of antibiotic A, so
antibiotic B is more effective than antibiotic A.**

My brother's football socks create a clear zone...

Make sure you know how to calculate the area of a clear zone. Then give this question a go to see if you've got it.

Q1 A researcher was investigating the effect of three
different antiseptics on the growth of bacteria.
The diagram on the right shows the results.

a) Which antiseptic was most
effective against the bacteria? [1 mark]

b) Calculate the size of the
clear zone for Antiseptic C.
Give your answer in mm^2. [2 marks]

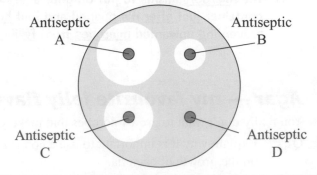

Antiseptic A

Antiseptic B

Antiseptic C

Antiseptic D

Developing New Medicines

New medicines are constantly being developed. This little page tells you all about how that happens.

New Drugs are Tested in the Laboratory in Pre-Clinical Trials...

1) Any new drugs to treat disease need to be really well tested before they can be used.
2) This is to make sure they're safe and that they work.
3) New drugs first go through pre-clinical trials:

1) Computer Models

Computer models are often used first of all. These predict a human's response to a drug.

2) Human cells and tissues

The drugs are then developed further by testing them on human cells and tissues.

3) Animals

Drugs are then developed and tested using animals. Some people think it's cruel to test on animals. Other people think this is the safest way to make sure a drug isn't dangerous before it's given to humans.

... Then Tested on Humans in Clinical Trials

If the drug passes the tests on animals, then it's tested on human volunteers in a clinical trial.

1) First, the drug is tested on healthy volunteers. This is to make sure that it doesn't have any harmful side effects when the body is working normally.
2) If these results are good, the drugs can be tested on people with the illness.
3) To test how well the drug works, patients are put into two groups...

Group 1 is given the new drug.

Group 2 is given a placebo (a substance that looks like the drug being tested but doesn't do anything).

4) The doctor compares the two groups of patients to see if the drug makes a real difference.
5) Clinical trials are blind — the patient doesn't know whether they're getting the drug or the placebo.
6) In fact, they're often double-blind — neither the patient nor the doctor knows who's taken the drug and who's taken the placebo until all the results have been gathered.
7) This is so the doctors studying the patients and the results aren't influenced by their knowledge.
8) Human drug trials usually last a very long time. Sometimes it takes a while for a drug to have the effect it was designed for, e.g. treating cancer. It's also important to find out if a drug has any side effects. These may only appear after a long time.

Double Blindman's Buff — now that's got to be fun...

So it's computers, then cells and tissues, then animals and then humans. Phew. I suppose it's better to be safe than sorry. Make sure you know what goes on in pre-clinical and clinical testing before you look at the next page.

Q1   What is the difference between a blind clinical trial and a double-blind clinical trial?   [1 mark]

Non-Communicable Diseases

You may remember <u>non-communicable diseases</u> from page 67. Well, here's a bit more about them...

Lots of Factors Interact to Cause Non-Communicable Diseases

1) All diseases have <u>risk factors</u> — things that <u>increase</u> a person's <u>chance</u> of getting that disease.
   Risk factors can be:
   - to do with <u>lifestyle</u> (e.g. how much exercise a person does)
   - things in the <u>environment</u> (e.g. air pollution)
   - <u>genetic</u> (e.g. inheriting certain mutated alleles — see p.49)

2) Many <u>non-communicable</u> diseases are caused by different risk factors <u>interacting</u> with each other, rather than one factor alone. E.g.

   > Sometimes you can <u>inherit genes</u> that make you <u>more likely</u> to get <u>cancer</u>. The genes alone don't mean you <u>will</u> get cancer but the chance is <u>increased</u> if you have other risk factors too.

   > Normally, when cells have <u>divided enough times</u> to make enough new cells, they <u>stop</u>. But, sometimes changes in cells can make them <u>grow out of control</u>. They <u>keep on dividing</u> by <u>mitosis</u> to make more and more cells. This forms a <u>tumour</u>. Cancer is a tumour that <u>invades</u> surrounding tissue.

3) Diseases that can be caused by <u>risk factors interacting</u> include:
   - <u>cardiovascular disease (CVD)</u> (diseases of the heart or blood vessels, see p.78)
   - some <u>nutrition-related diseases</u> (e.g. type 2 diabetes, see p.40)
   - some <u>lung diseases</u>
   - some <u>liver diseases</u>
   - many types of <u>cancer</u>

4) Risk factors are found by scientists looking for <u>correlations</u> (relationships) in data.
5) But <u>correlation doesn't always equal cause</u> (see p.9).
6) Sometimes a risk factor is linked to <u>another factor</u>.
   It's this other factor that actually causes the disease.

   > E.g. a <u>lack of exercise</u> and a <u>high fat diet</u> are linked to a higher chance of <u>CVD</u>, but they can't cause it <u>directly</u> (see below).

7) There <u>are</u> some examples where scientists have found evidence to support a risk factor being a <u>cause</u> of a disease though.

   > E.g. the fact that <u>smoking</u> can cause <u>lung disease</u> and <u>lung cancer</u> (see next page).

Lifestyle Factors Can Increase the Risk of Non-Communicable Diseases

Exercise
1) Exercise <u>decreases</u> the amount of <u>stored</u> body <u>fat</u>.
   So people who exercise are <u>less likely</u> to suffer from <u>obesity</u> and <u>CVD</u>.
2) A <u>lack</u> of exercise increases the risk of <u>CVD</u> because it increases <u>blood pressure</u>.

Obesity is where you are more than 20% over the recommended body mass.

Diet
1) Eating <u>too much</u> can lead to <u>obesity</u>. Obesity is linked to <u>type 2 diabetes</u>, <u>high blood pressure</u> and <u>CVD</u>. It's also a risk factor for some <u>cancers</u>.
2) Too much <u>fat</u> in your diet can <u>increase</u> your <u>blood cholesterol level</u>. Your body needs <u>cholesterol</u> to function properly. However, <u>too much</u> of a type of <u>cholesterol</u> (known as <u>'bad' cholesterol</u>) can cause <u>fat</u> to build up inside <u>arteries</u>. This can lead to <u>coronary heart disease</u> (see p.78).
3) Eating <u>too little</u> can cause problems too. If you don't get enough of the right vitamins or minerals you can get <u>deficiency diseases</u>. E.g. a lack of <u>vitamin C</u> can cause problems with the skin, joints and gums.

Best put down that cake and go for a run...

You might be asked to interpret data about risk factors. Remember, correlation doesn't necessarily mean cause.

Q1   Explain how exercising can reduce the risk of obesity.   [1 mark]

More on Non-Communicable Diseases

Sadly, you're not finished with risk factors just yet. Here are some more examples of lifestyle factors that can increase the risk of getting non-communicable diseases...

Alcohol and Smoking Can Also Lead to Non-Communicable Diseases

Alcohol

1) Alcohol is broken down by enzymes in the liver. Some of the products are toxic. If you drink too much alcohol over a long period of time these products can cause a liver disease called cirrhosis.
2) Drinking too much alcohol increases blood pressure. This can lead to cardiovascular disease (CVD).
3) Many cancers have been linked to drinking too much alcohol.

Smoking

Burning cigarettes produce things such as nicotine, carbon monoxide and tar. These can cause problems such as:

1) CVD — carbon monoxide reduces the amount of oxygen that can be carried in the blood. If the heart muscle doesn't get enough oxygen it can lead to a heart attack (see next page). Nicotine causes the heart to contract more often. This increases blood pressure, which increases the risk of CVD.
2) Cancer — tar from cigarette smoke is full of toxic chemicals. Some of these can cause cancer.
3) Lung diseases — cigarette smoke can damage the lining of the tubes in the lungs.
4) Smoking when pregnant can cause lots of health problems for the unborn baby.

Lifestyle Factors Cause Different Trends

Global

Non-communicable diseases are more common in developed countries than in developing countries. However, these diseases are now becoming much more common in developing countries too. These trends can be linked to lifestyle and income. For example:

In developed countries, people generally have a higher income (more money) and a higher standard of living than people in developing countries.

- Lack of exercise and drinking more alcohol are linked with higher income.
- Deaths related to smoking are more common in poorer countries.
- In developed and developing countries, obesity is linked with higher incomes. This is because people can afford lots of high-fat food. However, obesity is now linked with lower incomes too, as people are eating cheaper, less healthy foods.

National

Non-communicable diseases are the biggest cause of death in the UK. However, there are differences across the country. For example:

- People from poorer areas are much more likely to smoke, have a poor diet, and not exercise than those who have more money. This means that heart disease, obesity, type 2 diabetes, and cancer are more common in those areas.
- People from poorer areas are also more likely to suffer from alcohol-related disorders.

Local

- People's lifestyle choices affect non-communicable diseases at the local level.
- If you choose to smoke, drink, not exercise or have a poor diet, then the risk increases.

Too many exams are a risk factor for stress...

Trends in non-communicable diseases are often to do with income, because it can have a big effect on lifestyle.

Q1 Give two non-communicable diseases that drinking too much alcohol is a risk factor for. [2 marks]

Treating Cardiovascular Disease

Cardiovascular disease is a big, big problem in the UK. The good news is there are lots of ways to treat it.

Cardiovascular Disease Affects The Heart and Blood Vessels

1) Too much cholesterol (a fatty substance) can cause fatty deposits to build up in arteries. This makes the arteries narrower. CORONARY HEART DISEASE is when the coronary arteries have become narrower. This reduces blood flow to the heart.

See p.29-30 for more on the heart and blood vessels.

2) Sometimes bits of the fatty deposits can break off. This can cause a blood clot. Blood clots can block blood flow.

3) If an artery gets completely blocked it can lead to a HEART ATTACK. This is where part of the heart muscle doesn't get enough oxygen. If the blockage occurs in the brain, it can cause a STROKE.

4) High blood pressure can damage blood vessels. This can also cause blood clots to form.

There are Different Ways of Treating CVD

Healthy Lifestyle

1) People with CVD are encouraged to eat a healthy diet that is low in fat.
2) They may also be encouraged to exercise regularly and stop smoking.

Drugs

Sometimes drugs are needed to help control the effects of CVD. For example:
1) STATINS — these reduce the amount of cholesterol in the blood.
2) ANTICOAGULANTS — these make blood clots less likely to form.
3) ANTIHYPERTENSIVES — these reduce blood pressure.
A problem with these drugs is that they can cause side effects.

Surgery

1) STENTS are tubes that are put inside arteries to keep them open. This means that blood can pass through to the heart muscle:

  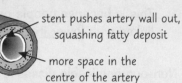

normal artery

deposits of fat build up

space in centre of artery shrinks

stent pushes artery wall out, squashing fatty deposit

more space in the centre of the artery

Stents can lower the risk of a heart attack in people with coronary heart disease. But over time, the artery can narrow again. The patient also has to take drugs to stop blood clotting on the stent.

2) If part of a blood vessel is blocked, a piece of healthy vessel can be put into the heart. This lets blood flow around the blocked part. This is called CORONARY BYPASS SURGERY.

3) The whole heart can be replaced with a DONOR HEART. However, the new heart can be rejected. This is because the immune system recognises it as 'foreign'. Drugs have to be taken to stop this from happening. These drugs can have side effects.

Heart surgery is a major operation. All surgeries have risks such as bleeding, clots and infection.

Look after yerselves me hearties...

...and make sure you know the drawbacks as well as the advantages for the ways of treating CVD.

Q1   Statins can treat CVD. Why might a patient not want to take these drugs?   [1 mark]

Stem Cells in Medicine

You might remember <u>stem cells</u> from page 24. Turns out they might be <u>really useful</u> little things...

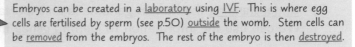

Stem Cells May Be Able to Cure Many Diseases

<u>Stem cells</u> could be really useful in treating some medical conditions. This is because they can <u>differentiate</u> (see page 24) into <u>different cell types</u>.

1) Medicine <u>already</u> uses adult stem cells to cure some <u>diseases</u>.

2) Scientists can also remove stem cells from very <u>early human embryos</u> and <u>grow</u> them.

Embryos can be created in a <u>laboratory</u> using <u>IVF</u>. This is where egg cells are fertilised by sperm (see p.50) <u>outside</u> the womb. Stem cells can be <u>removed</u> from the embryos. The rest of the embryo is then <u>destroyed</u>.

3) These embryonic stem cells could be used to <u>replace faulty cells</u> in sick people. For example, you could make:

- <u>beating heart muscle cells</u> for people with <u>heart disease</u>,
- <u>insulin-producing cells</u> for people with <u>diabetes</u>,
- <u>nerve cells</u> for people with <u>spinal injuries</u>.

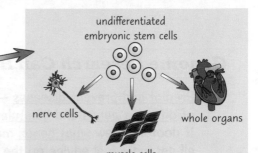

undifferentiated embryonic stem cells

nerve cells

muscle cells

whole organs

4) Tissues and organs grown from <u>embryonic stem cells</u> or from <u>donated adult stem cells</u> can be <u>transplanted</u> (put into) a patient.

5) But there are worries that doing this could lead to <u>rejection</u>. This happens when the patient's immune system recognises the cells as <u>foreign</u> and <u>attacks them</u> (see p.71).

6) However, if a patient's <u>own adult stem cells</u> can be used (from elsewhere in their body) it's thought that there'll be <u>less risk</u> of <u>rejection</u>.

Some People Are Against Stem Cell Research

1) Some people are <u>against</u> stem cell research. They feel that human embryos <u>shouldn't</u> be used for experiments since each one is a <u>potential human life</u>.

2) Other people think that curing patients who already <u>exist</u> and who are <u>suffering</u> is more important than the rights of <u>embryos</u>.

3) Sometimes <u>unwanted embryos</u> from <u>fertility clinics</u> are used for research. One argument in favour of stem cell research is that if these embryos weren't used by scientists they would probably just be <u>destroyed</u>.

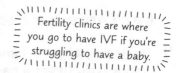

Fertility clinics are where you go to have IVF if you're struggling to have a baby.

4) As there is debate over the use of stem cells, <u>governments</u> often make <u>laws</u> about how they can be used for <u>research</u> and <u>medicine</u>.

But florists cell stems, and nobody complains about that...

The potential of stem cells is huge — but it's early days yet. There's still lots of work to be done getting stem cells to behave as we want them. And you've got lots of work to be doing too — this page isn't going to learn itself.

Q1 Tissues can be grown from donor stem cells or embryonic stem cells and transplanted into a patient. Explain why these tissues can be rejected by the patient. [1 mark]

Q2 Give one reason why some people are against stem cell research. [1 mark]

Using Genome Research in Medicine

Wow. Science is <u>amazing</u>. Scientists might be able to use <u>genes</u> to <u>predict diseases</u> and provide us with <u>new and better drugs</u>. How cool is that. Alright, maybe I should get out more...

The Human Genome Project Identified All Our Genes

See pages 48-49 for more on DNA and the genome.

1) Human DNA is made up of about <u>25 000 genes</u>.

2) The <u>Human Genome Project</u> (HGP) was a 13 year long project. It identified <u>all of the genes</u> found in <u>human DNA</u> (the human genome).

3) <u>Understanding</u> the human genome is an important tool for <u>science</u> and <u>medicine</u>. We can use the information to <u>identify genes</u> that are involved in <u>disease</u>.

Genome Research Can Help Us To Predict and Treat Disease...

1) <u>Predict and prevent diseases</u> — many <u>diseases</u> are caused by the <u>interaction</u> of <u>different genes</u> and <u>lifestyle factors</u> (see pages 76-77). If doctors knew <u>what genes</u> made people more likely to get <u>certain diseases</u>, we could all get <u>individual</u> advice on the best diet and lifestyle to avoid our likely problems.

> <u>Inheriting particular genes</u> increases your <u>risk</u> of developing certain <u>cancers</u>. If a person <u>knows</u> they have these genes, it might help them to make <u>choices</u> that could <u>reduce the risk</u> of the disease developing.

Doctors could also check us regularly to ensure early treatment if we do develop the diseases we're more likely to get.

2) <u>Develop new and better medicines</u> — scientists can use <u>information</u> about the <u>genes</u> that cause diseases to develop <u>new medicines</u>. The new medicines could <u>target</u> the genes <u>responsible</u>.

3) Genome research has also shown <u>common genetic differences</u> between people. Some of these <u>differences</u> mean that some drugs <u>work less well</u> for some people. Scientists can use this knowledge to <u>design new drugs</u> that work better for these people.

... But There are Risks with Using Gene Technology in Medicine

1) <u>Increased stress</u> — imagine if someone knew from an early age that they're genetically more likely to get a nasty brain disease. They could <u>panic</u> every time they get a <u>headache</u> (even if they never get the disease).

2) <u>Gene-ism</u> — people with genetic problems could come under <u>pressure</u> not to have <u>children</u>.

3) <u>Discrimination</u> — <u>employers</u> may not offer a job to someone who is genetically likely to get a <u>disease</u>.

4) <u>Unfair health system</u> — creating <u>specific</u> drugs for <u>different people</u> will increase costs for drug companies. So the <u>new drugs</u> will be more <u>expensive</u>. This could lead to only wealthy people being able to afford these new drugs.

Skinny, bootcut, hipster — there's loads of different genes...

These new medicines are only possibilities — some may happen soon, some will take ages, and others might not happen at all. You must know the benefits and the risks. No problem — you were going to learn it all anyway.

Q1   Type 2 diabetes is caused by a combination of genetic and lifestyle factors. Explain how our understanding of the human genome may help doctors prevent more cases of type 2 diabetes.   [2 marks]

Revision Questions for Topic B6

Wow, that was a massive topic. It's time to put yourself to the test and find out <u>how much you really know</u>.

• Try these questions and <u>tick off each one</u> when you <u>get it right</u>.

• When you've done <u>all the questions</u> under a heading and are <u>completely happy</u> with it, tick it off.

<u>Investigating Distribution and Abundance (p.57-61)</u> ☑

1) What would you use a sweep net for? ☑
2) Describe how you would use a quadrat to compare the distribution of dandelions in two areas. ☑
3) Give two abiotic factors that can affect the distribution of organisms. ☑
4) Describe how you can estimate the percentage cover of an organism in a quadrat. ☑

<u>Ecosystems and Maintaining Biodiversity (p.62-64)</u> ☑

5) Give three human activities which can damage ecosystems. ☑
6) Describe how preventing the introduction of harmful species can help protect biodiversity. ☑
7) Give two reasons why maintaining biodiversity by setting up conservation schemes can be difficult. ☑

<u>Selective Breeding and Genetic Engineering (p.65-66)</u> ☑

8) What is selective breeding? ☑
9) Give one example of how crops could be genetically modified to increase yields. ☑
10) Describe two concerns related to the genetic engineering of animals. ☑

<u>Health and Disease (p.67-71)</u> ☑

11) What is a communicable disease? ☑
12) Name four types of pathogen. ☑
13) Give three ways that disease can be spread. ☑
14) Give three ways that the spread of disease in plants can be controlled. ☑
15) Explain how the production of antibodies helps the body defend itself against disease. ☑

<u>Treating Disease and the Development of Medicines (p.72-75)</u> ☑

16) What is injected into the body in a vaccination? ☑
17) What are antiseptics? ☑
18) Describe an experiment you could do to investigate the effectiveness of different antibiotics. ☑
19) Give the formula you need to calculate the area of a clear zone when investigating antimicrobials. ☑
20) Give three things that new drugs are tested on in the pre-clinical stage of development. ☑

<u>Non-Communicable Diseases and Advances in Medicine (p.76-80)</u> ☑

21) Give three health problems that are linked to eating too much. ☑
22) Describe a global trend in non-communicable diseases. ☑
23) Describe the risks of using surgery to treat cardiovascular disease. ☑
24) Why do scientists think that stem cells could be useful in the treatment of disease? ☑
25) Give three possible risks of using gene technology in medicine. ☑

States of Matter

Materials come in three different forms — solid, liquid and gas. These are the three states of matter. The particle model describes how the particles behave in solids, liquids and gases. Here it is...

States of Matter Depend on the Forces Between Particles

Solids

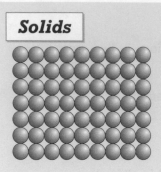

1) There are strong forces of attraction between particles. These forces hold them in fixed positions in a regular pattern.

2) The particles don't move from their positions. All solids keep a set shape and volume — solids don't flow like liquids.

3) The particles can vibrate, but they stay in their positions. The hotter the solid becomes, the more they vibrate.

4) If you heat the solid this gives the particles more energy. After a while the solid will melt and become liquid.

Liquids

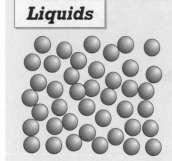

1) There are weak forces of attraction between the particles. They're free to move past each other, but they stay close together.

2) Liquids don't keep a set shape. They will flow to fill the bottom of a container. But they do keep the same volume.

3) The particles move about randomly all the time. The hotter the liquid gets, the faster the particles move.

4) If you cool a liquid, it will freeze and become solid. If you heat a liquid enough, it will evaporate (or boil) and become a gas.

Gases

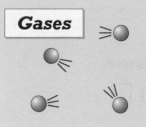

1) There's almost no force of attraction between the particles. They're free to move about and are spaced far apart.

2) Gases don't keep a set shape or volume. They will fill any container.

3) The particles move about randomly all the time. The hotter the gas gets, the faster the particles move.

4) If you cool a gas, it will condense (become a liquid).

Atoms are Rearranged During Chemical Reactions

1) When a substance changes from one state of matter to another (for example when it boils or melts) it's a physical change. No new substances are made — the chemicals just change state.

2) Physical changes are easy to undo by heating or cooling. Chemical reactions are a bit different...

3) During a chemical reaction, bonds between atoms break and the atoms change places.

4) The atoms from the substances you start off with (the reactants) rearrange themselves to form different chemicals (the products).

5) Compared to physical changes, chemical changes are often hard to reverse.

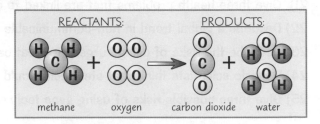

I felt like changing state, so I moved from Texas to Michigan...

After all this stuff about chemical reactions, let's see how you react to a practice question...

Q1   Describe the forces between the particles and the arrangement of the particles in a liquid.   [3 marks]

The History of the Atom

Atoms are pretty tiny. But what exactly are they like? Scientists have been trying to work it out for <u>years</u>...

The Theory of Atomic Structure Has Changed

1) At the start of the 19th century, <u>John Dalton</u> described atoms as <u>solid balls</u>. He thought that each <u>element</u> was a different type of ball.

2) In 1897, <u>J J Thomson</u> worked out that atoms contained even smaller, negatively charged particles — <u>electrons</u>. So they <u>weren't</u> solid balls.

3) His new theory was called the '<u>plum pudding model</u>'. This model showed the atom as a <u>ball</u> of <u>positive charge</u> with <u>electrons scattered</u> in this ball.

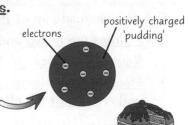

delicious pudding

Rutherford Showed that the Plum Pudding Model Was Wrong

1) In 1909, Ernest <u>Rutherford</u> and his students, Hans <u>Geiger</u> and Ernest <u>Marsden</u>, conducted the famous <u>gold foil experiment</u>. They fired positively charged particles at a very thin sheet of gold.

2) From the plum pudding model, they <u>predicted</u> that most of the particles would <u>go straight through</u> the sheet, but that a few would <u>change direction</u> by a <u>small amount</u>.

3) But they found that some particles <u>bounced backwards</u>. So the plum pudding model <u>couldn't</u> be right.

4) Rutherford came up with the <u>nuclear model</u> of the atom to explain this new evidence.

5) In this theory there's a tiny, positively charged <u>nucleus</u> at the centre of the atom. This nucleus is surrounded by a 'cloud' of negative electrons.

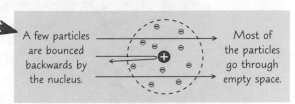

A few particles are bounced backwards by the nucleus.

Most of the particles go through empty space.

The Bohr Model Explains a Lot

1) Niels Bohr realised that Rutherford's model where the electrons are in a 'cloud' around the nucleus <u>didn't work</u>. The electrons would be <u>attracted</u> to the positive nucleus and the atom would <u>collapse</u>.

2) So he came up with a new model of the atom where the electrons move around the nucleus in <u>fixed shells</u>.

3) Bohr's theory helped to explain the <u>observations</u> of lots of other scientists at the time.

nucleus   shells

electrons

Scientific Theories Have to be Backed Up by Evidence

1) Our current model of the atom is <u>different</u> to what people thought the atom looked like in the past. These different ideas were <u>accepted</u> because they fitted the <u>evidence</u> available at the time.

2) As scientists did more <u>experiments</u>, new evidence was found and our theory of the <u>structure</u> of the atom was <u>changed</u> to fit it. This is nearly always the way <u>scientific knowledge</u> develops — new evidence leads to people coming up with new, <u>improved ideas</u>.

3) Scientists also put their ideas up for <u>peer-review</u> (see page 1). This means that other scientists get a chance to check the research for <u>errors</u> before it gets published in a <u>journal</u>.

I love a good model — Kate Moss is my personal favourite...

This is a great example of how science works. Scientists building on the work of other scientists. Lovely.

Q1   Name the model of atomic structure that JJ Thomson developed.   [1 mark]

Q2   Draw and label a diagram to show the Bohr model of the atom.   [2 marks]

The Atom

There are quite a few different <u>modern models</u> of the atom — but chemists tend to like this model best. You can use it to <u>explain</u> loads of things in chemistry, which is nice. Well, here goes...

The Atom is Made Up of Protons, Neutrons and Electrons

The atom is made up of three different <u>particles</u> — protons, neutrons and electrons.

- <u>Protons</u> are <u>heavy</u> and <u>positively charged</u>.
- <u>Neutrons</u> are <u>heavy</u>. They are <u>neutral</u> (have no charge).
- <u>Electrons</u> have <u>hardly any mass</u> and are <u>negatively charged</u>.

Particle	Relative Mass	Relative Charge
Proton	1	+1
Neutron	1	0
Electron	0.0005	−1

Protons and neutrons are still teeny tiny. They're just heavy compared to electrons.

The Nucleus

1) The nucleus is in the <u>middle</u> of the atom.
2) It contains <u>protons</u> and <u>neutrons</u>.
3) It has a <u>positive charge</u> because of the protons.
4) Almost the <u>whole</u> mass of the atom is in the nucleus.
5) Compared to the size of the atom, the nucleus is <u>tiny</u>.

The Electrons

1) Electrons move <u>around</u> the nucleus in electron <u>shells</u>.
2) They're <u>negatively charged</u>.
3) They're <u>tiny</u>, but their shells cover <u>a lot of space</u>.
4) The atomic radius of an atom is the distance from the centre of the atom to the outer edge. Atoms have an <u>atomic radius</u> of about 10^{-10} m (0.0000000010 m).
5) Electrons have almost <u>no</u> mass.

Shells can also be called 'energy levels'.

Molecules Form When Atoms Bond Together

1) <u>Molecules</u> are made up of two or more atoms.
2) Molecules can be made of the <u>same element</u> (e.g. hydrogen), or <u>different elements</u> (e.g. ammonia).
3) Simple molecules (see page 93) are pretty tiny. The <u>bonds</u> that form between these molecules are generally a similar length to the atomic radius — <u>about 10^{-10} m</u>.

hydrogen molecule

ammonia molecule

Don't trust atoms — they make up everything...

You need to learn what's in that table with the relative masses and charges of the different parts of the atom. Try remembering **P**rotons are **P**ositive, **N**eutrons are **N**eutral and **E**lectrons are **E**... Never mind.

Q1 What is the charge on: a) a proton,   b) a neutron,   c) an electron?   [1 mark]

Q2 Where would you find most of the mass of an atom?   [1 mark]

Atomic Numbers and Mass Numbers

Hmm, these sound <u>tricky</u>, but don't worry — <u>all will be revealed</u> on this page. Here's what they mean...

Atomic Number and Mass Number Describe an Atom

The <u>nuclear symbol</u> of an atom tells you its <u>atomic number</u> and <u>mass number</u>.
For example, here's the nuclear symbol for an atom of <u>sodium</u>:

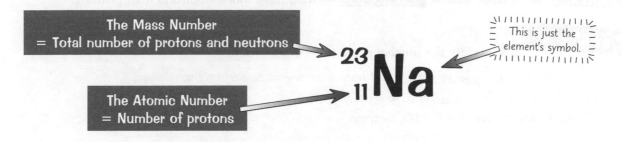

**The Mass Number
= Total number of protons and neutrons**

$$^{23}_{11}\text{Na}$$

**The Atomic Number
= Number of protons**

This is just the element's symbol.

1) The <u>atomic number</u> tells you how many <u>protons</u> there are in the atom.

2) Atoms of the <u>same</u> element all have the <u>same</u> number of <u>protons</u>.
Atoms of <u>different</u> elements will have <u>different</u> numbers of protons.

- Sodium (Na) has an atomic number of <u>11</u>. So every atom of sodium contains <u>11 protons</u>.
- Iron (Fe) has an atomic number of <u>26</u>. So every atom of iron contains <u>26 protons</u>.
- Sodium and iron have different numbers of protons because they're <u>different elements</u>.

3) The <u>mass number</u> is the <u>total number</u> of <u>protons and neutrons</u> in the atom. The mass number is <u>always bigger</u> than the atomic number.

Except for ordinary hydrogen atoms, whose atomic number and mass number are both 1.

4) To find the number of <u>neutrons</u> in an atom, just subtract the <u>atomic number</u> from the <u>mass number</u>.

EXAMPLE: Use the table on the right to calculate the number of neutrons in an atom of bromine.

Number of neutrons = mass number − atomic number
= 80 − 35
= 45 neutrons

Bromine	
Mass number	80
Atomic number	35

5) Neutral atoms have <u>no charge</u> overall.

6) This is because they have the <u>same number</u> of <u>protons</u> as <u>electrons</u>. The charge on the electrons is the same size as the charge on the protons, but opposite — so the charges <u>cancel out</u>.

7) So, the number of electrons in a neutral atom is also <u>equal</u> to the <u>atomic number</u>.

Element	Atomic number	Number of protons	Number of electrons
sodium	11	11	11
iron	26	26	26

Bert's high proton diet was causing his atomic mass to increase...

There's a bit of maths here, but it's just some adding and subtracting, so don't worry too much.

Q1 Work out the number of neutrons in the following atoms: a) $^{16}_{8}\text{O}$, b) $^{40}_{20}\text{Ca}$, c) $^{27}_{13}\text{Al}$. [3 marks]

Ions and Isotopes

Ions and isotopes are pretty <u>different</u> things even though their names sound a bit <u>similar</u>.
They're both to do with the <u>particles</u> that make up atoms. Engage your brain and read on...

Ions have Different Numbers of Protons and Electrons

1) Ions form when atoms (or groups of atoms) <u>gain</u> or <u>lose electrons</u> (see page 89 for more).

2) <u>Negative ions</u> form when atoms <u>gain electrons</u> — they have more electrons than protons.

 **EXAMPLE:**

Calculate the number of electrons in an F^- ion.

1) F^- has a <u>single negative charge</u>, so it must have one more electron than protons.
2) F has an <u>atomic number</u> of <u>9</u>, so it has 9 protons.
3) So F^- must have 9 + 1 = 10 electrons

3) <u>Positive ions</u> form when atoms <u>lose electrons</u> — they have more protons than electrons.

 **EXAMPLE:**

Calculate the number of electrons in an Fe^{2+} ion.

1) Fe^{2+} has a <u>2+ charge</u>, so it must have two more protons than electrons.
2) Fe has an <u>atomic number</u> of <u>26</u>, so it has 26 protons.
3) So Fe^{2+} must have 26 − 2 = 24 electrons

Isotopes are the Same Except for the Number of Neutrons

> Isotopes are different forms of the same element, which have the same number of protons but a different number of neutrons.

1) Isotopes have the <u>same atomic number</u> but <u>different mass numbers</u>.
2) If they had <u>different</u> atomic numbers, they'd be <u>different</u> elements altogether.
3) The two main isotopes of carbon are a famous example:

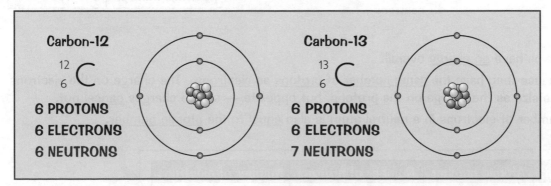

Carbon-12
$^{12}_{6}C$
6 PROTONS
6 ELECTRONS
6 NEUTRONS

Carbon-13
$^{13}_{6}C$
6 PROTONS
6 ELECTRONS
7 NEUTRONS

Na^+ was positive that he'd lost one of his electrons...

Remember, <u>ions</u> have different numbers of electrons and protons. <u>Isotopes</u> have a different number of neutrons.

Q1   Chlorine has an atomic number of 17. It has two main isotopes, chlorine-35 and chlorine-37.
      How many protons are there in: a) one atom of chlorine-35,   b) one atom of chlorine-37?   [2 marks]

Q2   Bromine has an atomic number of 35. How many electrons are there in a Br^- ion?   [1 mark]

The Periodic Table

We haven't always known as much about chemistry as we do now. Take the <u>periodic table</u> as an example. Early chemists tried to understand <u>patterns</u> in the properties of the elements to learn more about them.

Dmitri Mendeleev Made the First Proper Periodic Table

1) In <u>1869</u>, <u>Dmitri Mendeleev</u> took the 50 or so elements known at the time and arranged them into his <u>Table of Elements</u>.

2) Mendeleev put the elements in order of <u>atomic mass</u>.

3) To keep elements with <u>similar properties</u> in the same <u>columns</u>, he had to <u>swap</u> one or two elements round and leave a few <u>gaps</u>.

Mendeleev's Table of the Elements

H																	
Li	Be											B	C	N	O	F	
Na	Mg											Al	Si	P	S	Cl	
K	Ca	*	Ti	V	Cr	Mn	Fe	Co	Ni	Cu	Zn	*	*	As	Se	Br	
Rb	Sr	Y	Zr	Nb	Mo	*	Ru	Rh	Pd	Ag	Cd	In	Sn	Sb	Te	I	
Cs	Ba	*	*	Ta	W	*	Os	Ir	Pt	Au	Hg	Tl	Pb	Bi			

a column

This is How the Periodic Table Looks Today

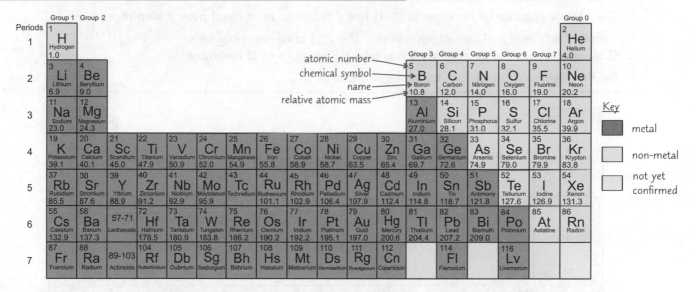

atomic number
chemical symbol
name
relative atomic mass

Key
■ metal
□ non-metal
□ not yet confirmed

1) Once <u>protons</u> and <u>electrons</u> were discovered, the <u>atomic number</u> (see page 85) of each element oould be found, based on the number of protons in its nucleus.

2) The <u>modern</u> periodic table shows the elements in order of increasing <u>atomic number</u> — and they fit the same <u>patterns</u> that Mendeleev worked out.

3) The periodic table is laid out so elements with <u>similar chemical properties</u> form <u>columns</u> — these are called <u>groups</u>. (Elements with similar chemical properties <u>react</u> in similar ways.)

4) The <u>group</u> that each element belongs to is the <u>same</u> as the <u>number of electrons</u> it has in its <u>outer shell</u>. E.g. <u>Group 1</u> elements have <u>1</u> outer shell electron, <u>Group 7</u> elements have <u>7</u>. This doesn't work with <u>Group 0</u> elements though. They have <u>full</u> outer shells of <u>8</u> electrons (except helium which has 2).

5) The rows are called <u>periods</u>.

6) The period to which the element belongs corresponds to the <u>number of shells</u> of electrons it has.

I'm in a chemistry band — I play the symbols...

Because of how the periodic table is organised in groups and periods, you can see the trends in the reactivity (and other properties) of the elements and therefore make predictions on how reactions will occur. How neat is that?

Q1   Using a periodic table, state how many electrons beryllium (Be) has in its outer shell.   [1 mark]

Q2   Based on its position in the periodic table, would you expect potassium (K) to have similar chemical properties to sodium? Explain your answer.   [1 mark]

Electron Shells

Like snails, <u>electrons</u> live in <u>shells</u>. Unlike snails, electrons won't nibble on your daisies...

Electron Shell Rules:

1) Electrons occupy <u>shells</u> (sometimes called <u>energy levels</u>).

2) The <u>lowest</u> energy levels are <u>always filled first</u>.

3) Only <u>a certain number</u> of electrons are allowed in each shell:

1st shell	2nd shell	3rd shell
<u>2</u> electrons	<u>8</u> electrons	<u>8</u> electrons

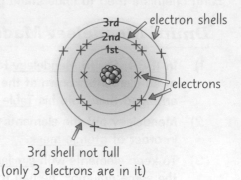

3rd shell not full
(only 3 electrons are in it)

Working Out Electronic Structures

1) The <u>electronic structures</u> for the first <u>20</u> elements are shown in the diagram below.

2) You can work these out from the <u>atomic number</u> of each element: For example, take nitrogen:

- The atomic number of nitrogen is <u>7</u>. It has <u>7</u> protons, so it must have <u>7</u> electrons.
- Follow the 'Electron Shell Rules' above. The <u>first</u> shell can only take 2 electrons and the <u>second</u> shell can take a <u>maximum</u> of 8 electrons.
- So the electronic structure for nitrogen must be <u>2.5</u>.

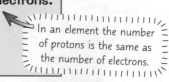

In an element the number of protons is the same as the number of electrons.

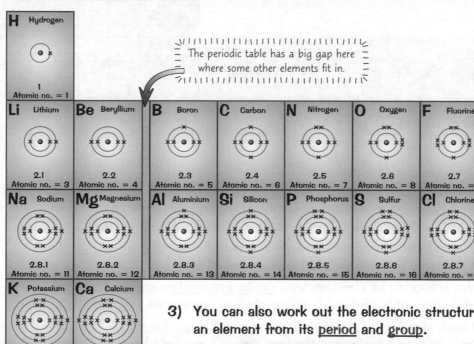

The periodic table has a big gap here where some other elements fit in.

H Hydrogen							He Helium
1							2
Atomic no. = 1							Atomic no. = 2

Li Lithium	Be Beryllium	B Boron	C Carbon	N Nitrogen	O Oxygen	F Fluorine	Ne Neon
2.1	2.2	2.3	2.4	2.5	2.6	2.7	2.8
Atomic no. = 3	Atomic no. = 4	Atomic no. = 5	Atomic no. = 6	Atomic no. = 7	Atomic no. = 8	Atomic no. = 9	Atomic no. = 10

Na Sodium	Mg Magnesium	Al Aluminium	Si Silicon	P Phosphorus	S Sulfur	Cl Chlorine	Ar Argon
2.8.1	2.8.2	2.8.3	2.8.4	2.8.5	2.8.6	2.8.7	2.8.8
Atomic no. = 11	Atomic no. = 12	Atomic no. = 13	Atomic no. = 14	Atomic no. = 15	Atomic no. = 16	Atomic no. = 17	Atomic no. = 18

K Potassium	Ca Calcium
2.8.8.1	2.8.8.2
Atomic no. = 19	Atomic no. = 20

3) You can also work out the electronic structure of an element from its <u>period</u> and <u>group</u>.

4) The <u>number of shells</u> which contain electrons is the same as the <u>period</u> of the element.

5) The <u>group number</u> tells you <u>how many electrons</u> occupy the <u>outer shell</u> of the element.

- Sodium is in <u>period 3</u>, so it has <u>3</u> shells occupied — so the first two shells must be full (2.8).
- It's in <u>Group 1</u>, so it has <u>1</u> electron in its outer shell. So its electronic structure is <u>2.8.1</u>.

The electronic structure of the fifth element — it's a bit boron...

Electronic structures may seem a bit complicated at first, but after plenty of practice they'll get easier to work out.

Q1   Give the electronic structure of aluminium (atomic number = 13).   [1 mark]

Simple Ions

Ions are all over the place in chemistry — some atoms just can't wait to get rid of electrons, others want more.

Simple Ions Form When Atoms Lose or Gain Electrons

1) Ions are charged particles — they can be single atoms (e.g. Cl⁻) or groups of atoms (e.g. NO₃⁻).
2) When atoms lose or gain electrons to form ions, all they're trying to do is get a full outer shell (also called a "stable electronic structure"). Atoms like full outer shells — it's atom heaven.
3) When metals form ions, they lose electrons to form positive ions.
4) When non-metals form ions, they gain electrons to form negative ions.
5) The number of electrons lost or gained is the same as the charge on the ion.
   E.g. If 2 electrons are lost the charge is 2+. If 3 electrons are gained the charge is 3−.

Groups 1 & 2 and 6 & 7 are the Most Likely to Form Ions

1) The elements that most readily form ions are those in Groups 1, 2, 6 and 7.
2) Group 1 and 2 elements are metals. They lose electrons to form positive ions (cations).
3) Group 6 and 7 elements are non-metals. They gain electrons to form negative ions (anions).
4) As you know already, elements in the same group all have the same number of outer electrons.
5) So elements in the same group have to lose or gain the same number of electrons to get a full outer shell. This means that they form ions with the same charges.

Group 1 elements form 1+ ions.
Group 7 elements form 1− ions.
Group 2 elements form 2+ ions.
Group 6 elements form 2− ions.

H																	He
Li	Be											B	C	N	O	F	Ne
Na	Mg											Al	Si	P	S	Cl	Ar
K	Ca	Sc	Ti	V	Cr	Mn	Fe	Co	Ni	Cu	Zn	Ga	Ge	As	Se	Br	Kr
Rb	Sr	Y	Zr	Nb	Mo	Tc	Ru	Rh	Pd	Ag	Cd	In	Sn	Sb	Te	I	Xe
Cs	Ba	La	Hf	Ta	W	Re	Os	Ir	Pt	Au	Hg	Tl	Pb	Bi	Po	At	Rn
Fr	Ra	Ac	Rf	Db	Sg	Bh	Hs	Mt	Ds	Rg	Cn		Fl		Lv		

6) As you go down each group you add electron shells to the electronic structure. This means the outer electrons get further from the nucleus.

• For Groups 1 and 2, this means that it gets easier to remove the outer electrons to form ions. The elements get more reactive as you go down the groups.
• But for Groups 6 and 7, it means that it gets harder for the nucleus to attract extra electrons to form ions. The elements get less reactive as you go down the groups.

I've got my ion on you...

If you can't remember when positive and negative ions form, remember that electrons are negatively charged...
When an atom loses some of these negatively charged electrons it becomes positively charged (a positive ion).
If an atom gains some of these negatively charged electrons it becomes negatively charged (a negative ion).

Q1 What is the charge on a potassium (K) ion? [1 mark]

Ionic Bonding

Particles with opposite charges are <u>attracted to each other</u> — just like me and digestive biscuits...

Ions with Opposite Charges Form Ionic Bonds

1) When a <u>metal</u> and a <u>non-metal</u> react, the metal <u>loses</u> electrons to form a <u>positively charged ion</u>. The non-metal <u>gains</u> electrons to form a <u>negatively charged ion</u>.

2) These oppositely charged ions are then <u>strongly attracted</u> to one another by <u>electrostatic forces</u> (the attraction between positive and negative ions) and form an <u>ionic bond</u>.

3) To find the <u>formula</u> of an ionic compound, you need to <u>balance</u> the positive and the negative charges of the ions that it's made from. For example:

Sodium chloride	Magnesium chloride	Potassium oxide
$Na^+ + Cl^- \longrightarrow NaCl$	$Mg^{2+} + 2Cl^- \longrightarrow MgCl_2$	$2K^+ + O^{2-} \longrightarrow K_2O$
The <u>sodium</u> ion has a 1+ charge and the <u>chloride</u> ion has a 1– charge, so they balance.	The <u>magnesium</u> ion has a 2+ charge and the <u>chloride</u> ion has a 1– charge, so you need <u>two</u> Cl⁻ ions to balance the Mg^{2+} ion.	The <u>potassium</u> ion has a 1+ charge and the <u>oxygen</u> ion has a 2– charge, so you need <u>two</u> K⁺ ions to balance the O^{2-} ion.

You Can Show Ionic Bonding Using Dot and Cross Diagrams

1) Dot and cross diagrams show the <u>arrangement</u> of electrons in an atom or ion.

2) They can also show what happens to the electrons when atoms <u>react</u> with each other.

3) Each electron is shown as a <u>dot</u> or a <u>cross</u>.

<u>Sodium Chloride (NaCl)</u>
- The <u>sodium</u> atom gives up its outer electron, becoming an <u>Na⁺</u> ion.
- The <u>chlorine</u> atom picks up the electron, becoming a Cl⁻ (chloride) ion.

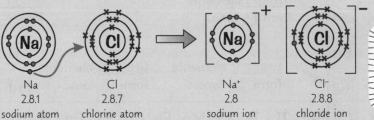

Here, the dots represent the Na electrons and the crosses represent the Cl electrons.

<u>Magnesium Chloride (MgCl₂)</u>
- The <u>magnesium</u> atom gives up its <u>two</u> outer electrons, becoming an Mg^{2+} ion.
- The two <u>chlorine</u> atoms pick up <u>one electron each</u>, becoming <u>two</u> Cl⁻ (chloride) ions.

4) Dot and cross diagrams are really useful for showing how ionic compounds are formed, but they <u>don't</u> show the <u>structure</u> of the compound. For that, you'll need a different type of diagram (see next page).

The name's Bond — Ionic Bond...

Remember, in ionic bonding ions with opposite charges (one negative and one positive) are attracted to each other.

Q1 Potassium forms K⁺ ions and bromine forms Br⁻ ions. Give the formula of potassium bromide. [1 mark]

Topic C2 — Elements, Compounds and Mixtures

Ionic Compounds

Compounds made of ions that are bonded to each other are known as <u>ionic compounds</u>. Here's a bit more about them and the <u>properties</u> that make them special...

Ionic Compounds Have a Giant Lattice Structure

1) The ions in an ionic compound form a <u>closely packed structure</u> — this is called an <u>ionic lattice</u>. When <u>lots</u> of ions come together it's called a <u>giant ionic lattice</u>.

2) There are very strong <u>electrostatic forces of attraction</u> between <u>oppositely charged</u> ions, in <u>all directions</u>.

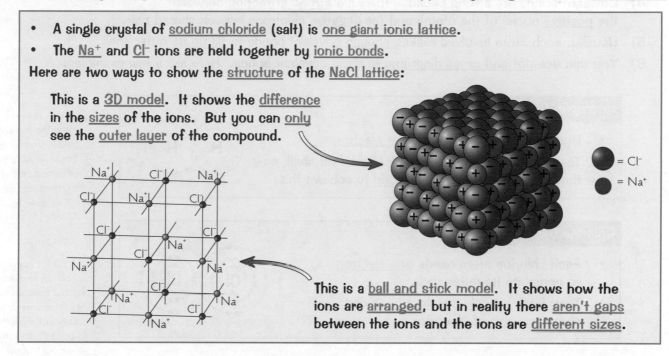

- A single crystal of <u>sodium chloride</u> (salt) is <u>one giant ionic lattice</u>.
- The <u>Na⁺</u> and <u>Cl⁻</u> ions are held together by <u>ionic bonds</u>.

Here are two ways to show the <u>structure</u> of the <u>NaCl lattice</u>:

This is a <u>3D model</u>. It shows the <u>difference</u> in the <u>sizes</u> of the ions. But you can <u>only</u> see the <u>outer layer</u> of the compound.

= Cl⁻
= Na⁺

This is a <u>ball and stick model</u>. It shows how the ions are <u>arranged</u>, but in reality there <u>aren't gaps</u> between the ions and the ions are <u>different sizes</u>.

Ionic Compounds All Have Similar Properties

1) Ionic compounds have <u>high melting</u> and <u>boiling points</u> due to the <u>strong attraction</u> between the ions. It takes a large amount of <u>energy</u> to separate the ions (and cause the compound to melt or boil — see page 82).

2) Solid ionic compounds <u>don't</u> conduct electricity because the ions are fixed in place and can't move. But when an ionic compound <u>melts</u>, the ions are <u>free to move</u> so an electric <u>current</u> can flow.

3) Many also <u>dissolve easily</u> in water. The ions <u>separate</u> and are all <u>free to move</u> in the solution, so an electric <u>current</u> can flow.

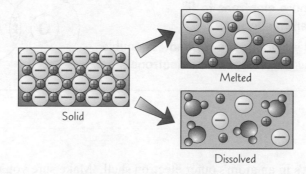

Solid

Melted

Dissolved

Giant ionic lattices — all over your chips...

You need to know about the different ways that ionic compounds can be shown. Dot and cross diagrams were covered on the previous page. On this page we've covered ball and stick and 3D models of ionic compounds.

Q1   Explain why ionic compounds conduct electricity when they are molten.   [1 mark]

Covalent Bonding

Ionic bonding isn't the only way atoms join together. They can also <u>share</u> electrons to form <u>covalent bonds</u>.

Covalent Bonds — Sharing Electrons

1) When <u>non-metal atoms</u> join together they form <u>covalent bonds</u> by <u>sharing</u> pairs of electrons.
2) This way <u>both atoms</u> feel that they have <u>a full outer shell</u>, and that makes them happy.
3) <u>Each</u> covalent bond provides <u>one extra</u> shared electron for each atom.
4) Covalent bonds are strong because there's a <u>strong attraction</u> between the <u>positive</u> nuclei of the atoms and the <u>negative</u> electrons in each shared pair.
5) Usually, each atom involved makes <u>enough</u> covalent bonds to <u>fill up</u> its outer shell.
6) You can use <u>dot and cross diagrams</u> to show covalent bonds. Here are a few examples:

Hydrogen Gas (H$_2$)

- Hydrogen atoms have just <u>one electron</u>.
- They need <u>one more</u> to complete the first shell, so they form a <u>single covalent bond</u> to achieve this.

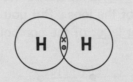

As in the dot and cross diagrams for ionic bonds on page 90, the dots and crosses here represent electrons from different atoms.

Chlorine Gas (Cl$_2$)

- Each chlorine atom needs <u>one electron</u> to complete its outer shell.
- They form a <u>single covalent bond</u> and share <u>one pair</u> of electrons.

You can also draw dot and cross diagrams like these ones so that they just show the outer shell of electrons in each atom.

Water (H$_2$O)

- Oxygen needs <u>two</u> more electrons to fill its outer shell.
- In a molecule of water, it <u>shares</u> electrons with two hydrogen atoms, forming two single covalent bonds.

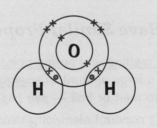

In all the diagrams, you can see that each atom has a full outer shell.

Carbon Dioxide (CO$_2$)

- Carbon needs <u>four</u> more electrons to fill its outer shell, oxygen needs <u>two</u>.
- So <u>two double covalent bonds</u> are formed. A double covalent bond has <u>two shared pairs</u> of electrons.

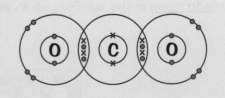

Sharing is caring...

Covalent bonding is all about what's in an atom's outer electron shell. Make sure you're up to speed with electronic structures (see page 88) so you can work out how many covalent bonds an atom can form.

Q1 Fluorine atoms have the electronic structure 2.7. Draw a dot and cross diagram to show the covalent bonding in a fluorine molecule, F$_2$. [1 mark]

Q2 In a molecule of hydrogen chloride (HCl) a hydrogen atom is covalently bonded to a chlorine atom. Draw a dot and cross diagram to show the bonding in a molecule of HCl. [1 mark]

Simple Molecules

Substances containing covalent bonds are usually <u>simple molecules</u>. This page is all about their <u>properties</u>.

Simple Molecular Substances Have Low Melting and Boiling Points

1) Substances formed with <u>covalent bonds</u> usually have <u>simple molecular structures</u>, like CO_2 and H_2O.

2) The atoms within the molecules are held together by <u>very strong covalent bonds</u>.

3) By contrast, the forces of attraction <u>between</u> these molecules are <u>very weak</u>.

4) It's these <u>weak intermolecular forces</u> that you have to break to <u>melt</u> or <u>boil</u> a simple covalent substance.

5) So the melting and boiling points are <u>very low</u>, because the molecules are <u>easily parted</u> from each other.

6) Most simple molecular substances are <u>gases or liquids</u> at room temperature.

7) Simple molecular substances <u>don't conduct electricity</u>, because they <u>don't</u> have free electrons or ions.

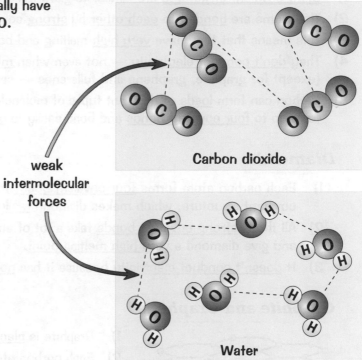

weak intermolecular forces

Carbon dioxide

Water

<u>Ball and stick models</u> show how the atoms in covalent molecules are connected. You can make them with plastic molecular model kits, or as computer models.

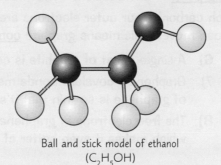

Ball and stick model of ethanol
(C_2H_5OH)

- They're great for helping to <u>see</u> the structure of molecules, as they show you the shape of the molecule in <u>3D</u>.

- They're <u>more realistic</u> than 2D drawings, but they're still a bit <u>misleading</u>.

- They make it look like there are <u>massive gaps</u> between the atoms — in reality this is where the <u>electron clouds</u> are.

'Electron clouds' is just a way of describing the space where you find electrons in an atom.

Is it just me, or does ethanol look like a little doggie...

Make sure you understand what affects the melting and boiling point of a simple molecular substance.
Hint: it's all about the intermolecular forces between molecules.

Q1   Using your knowledge of their structure, explain why simple molecules boil at low temperatures. [2 marks]

Giant Covalent Structures and Fullerenes

Most of the <u>covalent molecules</u> you'll meet at GCSE contain only a few atoms. But not these ones...

Giant Covalent Structures Contain Many Covalent Bonds

1) <u>Giant covalent structures</u> are similar to giant ionic lattices (see p.91) <u>except</u> they have <u>no charged ions</u>.
2) The atoms are <u>bonded</u> to <u>each other</u> by <u>strong</u> covalent bonds.
3) This means that they have <u>very high</u> melting and boiling points.
4) They <u>don't conduct electricity</u> — not even when <u>molten</u> (except for graphite, graphene and fullerenes — see below).
5) <u>Carbon</u> can form <u>loads</u> of different types of molecule. This is because carbon atoms can form up to <u>four covalent bonds</u> and bond easily to <u>other carbon atoms</u> to make <u>chains</u> and <u>rings</u>.

Diamond

1) Each carbon atom forms <u>four covalent bonds</u> in a <u>very rigid</u> giant covalent structure, which makes diamond <u>really hard</u>.
2) All those <u>strong covalent bonds</u> take a lot of energy to break and give diamond a <u>very high melting point</u>.
3) It <u>doesn't conduct electricity</u> because it has <u>no free electrons</u> or ions.

Graphite and Graphene

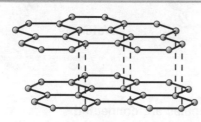

1) Graphite is <u>black</u> and <u>opaque</u>, but still kind of <u>shiny</u>.
2) Each carbon atom only forms <u>three covalent bonds</u>, creating <u>sheets of carbon atoms</u> which are free to <u>slide over each other</u>.
3) The layers are held together weakly so are <u>slippery</u> and can be <u>rubbed off</u> onto paper to leave a black mark — that's how a pencil works.
4) Graphite's got a <u>high melting point</u> — the covalent bonds need <u>loads of energy</u> to break.
5) Since only three out of each carbon's four outer electrons are used in bonds, there are lots of free <u>electrons</u> that can move. This means graphite <u>conducts electricity</u>.

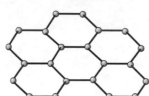

6) A single sheet of graphite is called <u>graphene</u>.
7) Graphene's covalent bonds make it extremely <u>strong</u>. A sheet of graphene is so thin that it's <u>transparent</u> and incredibly <u>light</u>.
8) The free electrons in graphene can move anywhere within the sheet, which makes it even better at <u>conducting electricity</u> than graphite.

Fullerenes are Large Carbon Molecules

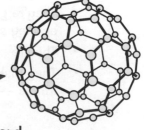

1) <u>Fullerenes</u> are another form of <u>carbon</u>. They aren't giant covalent structures — they're large <u>molecules</u> shaped like <u>hollow balls</u> or <u>tubes</u>. Different fullerenes contain <u>different numbers</u> of carbon atoms.
2) The carbon atoms in fullerenes are arranged in <u>rings</u>. They have <u>free electrons</u>, so they can <u>conduct electricity</u>.
3) Their <u>melting</u> and <u>boiling points</u> aren't anything like as high as those of diamond and graphite. However, they're still <u>pretty high</u> for <u>molecular substances</u> — this is because fullerenes are big molecules (and bigger molecules have more <u>intermolecular forces</u>).

So that pencil I gave her was just the same as a diamond, really...

Before you go on, make sure you can explain the properties of all of these different types of carbon molecule.

Q1   Give two differences between the structure and properties of diamond and graphite.   [2 marks]

Polymers and Properties of Materials

Polymers are yet another type of structure that you'll come across. They're a type of covalent molecule. But they behave a bit differently to simple covalent substances because their molecules are very long.

Plastics are Long-Chain Molecules Called Polymers

1) Polymers are formed when lots of small molecules called monomers join together. This reaction is called polymerisation — and it usually needs high pressure and a catalyst.

2) Plastics are polymers. They're usually carbon-based and their monomers are often alkenes (a type of hydrocarbon containing a carbon-carbon double bond).

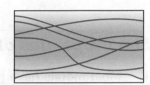

Squawk! Pretty polymers!

Forces Between Molecules Give Polymers Their Properties

Strong covalent bonds hold the atoms together in polymer chains. But it's the forces between the different chains that determine the properties of the plastic.

Weak Forces:

- If the plastic is made up of chains that are only held together by weak intermolecular forces, then the chains will be free to slide over each other.

- This means that the plastic can be stretched easily, and will have a low melting point.

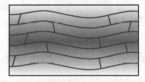

Strong Forces:

- Some plastics have stronger bonds between the polymer chains — these might be covalent bonds (sometimes called cross-links).

- These plastics have higher melting points, are rigid and can't be stretched, as the cross-links hold the chains firmly together.

Properties of Materials Depend on Structure and Bonding

1) All the different types of material in this topic have their own special properties. What they've all got in common is the fact that their properties are down to the structures and bonding in the material.

2) The individual atoms in the material don't have these properties themselves — it's the type and strength of the bonds in a material that decides what properties it has.

> For example, chlorine is pretty good at forming both ionic and covalent bonds.
>
> - It's found in many common ionic compounds, like sodium chloride. The ionic bonds in sodium chloride are really strong because there's a strong electrostatic attraction between the ions. This means that sodium chloride has a high melting and boiling point (see page 91).
>
> - Chlorine also forms simple molecular substances such as chloromethane. The intermolecular forces which attract the molecules to each other are weak (see page 93). This means chloromethane has a low melting and boiling point.
>
> - Some polymers, such as polyvinyl chloride (PVC), also contain chlorine. PVC is strong and rigid, because the intermolecular forces between the polymer chains in PVC are relatively strong.

My cat Molly loves plastics — in fact, Molly purrs for polymers...

Polymers are really useful. So useful in fact that I think they deserve their own question. Oh, and here's it is...

Q1 Two polymers, A and B, are made up of carbon and hydrogen atoms. Polymer A only has intermolecular forces between polymer chains, but polymer B has covalent bonds between chains. Which polymer will have the higher melting point? [1 mark]

Topic C2 — Elements, Compounds and Mixtures

Metals

BONG. Here is the news. BONG. <u>Metals</u> have some really <u>useful properties</u>. BONG. These properties come from the <u>bonding</u> in metals. BONG. Okay, I'll stop hitting myself with this metal pan now.

Metals Have a Crystal Structure

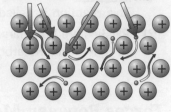

Metal ions   Free electrons

1) <u>All</u> metals have the <u>same</u> basic properties, due to the <u>special type of bonding</u> that exists in metals.

2) In metals, the <u>outer electron(s)</u> of each atom can move freely. The atoms become <u>positive ions</u> in a 'sea' of free <u>electrons</u>.

3) <u>Metallic bonding</u> is the <u>electrostatic attraction</u> (attraction between positive and negative things) between these ions and electrons. The ions are surrounded by the electrons, so the attraction acts in <u>all directions</u>.

Metals are generally found on the <u>left-hand side</u> of the <u>periodic table</u>. Elements on this side of the table normally get a <u>full outer shell</u> by <u>losing electrons</u> (see p.89). This explains the bonding in solid metals — the electrons they give up form the electron 'sea'.

The Properties of Metals are due to Metallic Bonding

1) Most metals have <u>high melting</u> and <u>boiling points</u>, and <u>high density</u>.
   - Metals are very <u>hard</u>, <u>dense</u> and <u>shiny</u>.
   - They generally have <u>high melting</u> and <u>boiling points</u> because of these <u>strong metallic bonds</u>. You need to use a lot of <u>energy</u> to break them apart.

2) Metals are <u>strong</u>, but also <u>bendy</u> and <u>malleable</u>.
   - Metals are <u>strong</u> and <u>hard to break</u>.
   - But they can also be <u>hammered</u> into different shapes (they're <u>malleable</u>).

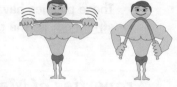

3) Metals are good <u>conductors</u> of <u>heat</u> and <u>electricity</u>.
   - This is due to the 'sea' of <u>free electrons</u> which move freely through the metal, carrying the <u>electrical charge</u>.
   - They can also carry <u>heat energy</u> through the metal.

Don't try this at home. You'll die.

4) Most metals can react with <u>oxygen</u> to form <u>metal oxides</u>.

5) Metals can be <u>mixed</u> with other <u>elements</u> to make <u>alloys</u>.
   - <u>Pure metals</u> often aren't quite right for certain jobs. You can change their <u>properties</u> by mixing them with <u>other elements</u> (either metals or non-metals) to make <u>alloys</u>.
   - Alloys have <u>different properties</u> from the main metal (or metals) they contain.

<u>Non-metal</u> elements generally have different <u>properties</u> from <u>metals</u>. Non-metals usually have <u>low</u> melting and boiling points. When solid, they tend to be <u>weak</u> and <u>brittle</u>. They have <u>lower densities</u> than metals and <u>don't conduct electricity</u>. (But there are exceptions, e.g. <u>carbon</u> breaks some of these rules — see p.94.)

I saw a metal on the bus once — he was the conductor...

If your knowledge of metals is still feeling a bit malleable, the question below might help. Give it a go...

Q1   Copper is a metal. State one property of copper that makes it suitable for use in electrical circuits, and explain why it has this property.   [2 marks]

States, Structure and Bonding

Bridge vs lighthouse... Phone box vs pyramid... It's time to start <u>comparing</u> different types of structure...

Structure and Bonding Affect Melting and Boiling Points

1) The <u>type of bonding</u> in a substance affects its <u>melting point</u> and <u>boiling point</u>.

2) The <u>stronger</u> the <u>bonds</u> are that keep the particles together in a solid or liquid, the more <u>heat energy</u> you need to put in to break these bonds and separate the particles.

3) <u>Simple covalent</u> substances have strong bonds <u>within</u> each molecule, but only <u>weak</u> <u>intermolecular forces</u> between the molecules (see p.93). It <u>doesn't</u> take much <u>energy</u> to <u>break these forces</u>, so simple covalent substances melt and boil at fairly <u>low temperatures</u>.

4) Most <u>metals</u> have high melting and boiling points. This is because the metal ions are very strongly attracted to the <u>'sea' of free electrons</u> (see previous page).

5) The positive and negative ions in <u>ionic lattices</u> are strongly attracted to each other. This strong attraction means ionic substances have <u>high</u> melting and boiling points.

6) <u>Giant covalent lattices</u> are held together by <u>strong covalent</u> <u>bonds</u>. These bonds take a lot of energy to break, so giant covalent substances have <u>very high</u> melting and boiling points.

Structure	Melting / boiling point
simple covalent	low
metallic	high
ionic	high
giant covalent	high

Making Predictions about Substances from Their Properties

You might be asked to use data about substances to work out things about them. Here's an example:

The table below gives information about the properties of four different substances.

Substance	Melting point / °C	Boiling point / °C	Good electrical conductor?
A	−218	−183	No
B	1535	2750	Yes
C	1410	2355	No
D	801	1413	When molten

How well different types of substance conduct electricity is covered on p.91, 93, 94 and p.96.

a) Predict the structure of substance C.

1) C has a <u>high</u> melting and boiling point, so it's <u>unlikely</u> to be a <u>simple molecular</u> substance.

2) It <u>doesn't</u> conduct electricity well, so that means it's <u>unlikely</u> to be a <u>metal</u>. <u>Ionic</u> substances don't conduct electricity when they're solid, but they do when they're liquid, so we can <u>rule out</u> ionic too.

3) <u>Giant covalent</u> structures <u>don't</u> usually conduct electricity, and they have <u>high</u> melting and boiling points, so this is probably the structure of C.

Substance C is likely to have a giant covalent structure.

b) Predict the state of substance D at 1000 °C.

1) The <u>melting point</u> of D is 801 °C and its <u>boiling point</u> is 1413 °C.

2) That means it's a solid <u>below 801 °C</u>, a gas <u>above 1413 °C</u>, and a liquid <u>in between</u>.

3) <u>1000 °C</u> is between 801 °C and 1413 °C, so D is a <u>liquid</u> at this temperature.

Substance D will be a liquid at 1000 °C.

I predict a tall, dark examiner will set you a question on this...

Questions on this sort of stuff may well require you to put all the bits of info from the last few pages together. Remember, you need to know what properties the different types of structure have <u>and</u> why they have them too.

Q1 Using the table in the example above, predict the states of substances A, B and C at 1500 °C. [3 marks]

Purity

Purity — one of those special <u>science words</u> that has a special <u>science meaning</u> that doesn't quite match the normal meaning people use in real life... *sigh*...

Pure Substances Contain Only One Thing

1) In <u>everyday life</u>, the word 'pure' is often used to mean 'clean' or 'natural'.

2) In <u>chemistry</u>, it's got a more <u>specific</u> meaning — a substance is <u>pure</u> if it's completely made up of a <u>single element or compound</u>.

3) If you've got <u>more than one</u> compound present, or different elements that aren't all part of a single compound, then you've got a <u>mixture</u>, not a pure substance.

4) So, for example, <u>fresh air</u> might be thought of as nice and 'pure', but it's <u>chemically impure</u> because it's a mixture of different gases.

5) Lots of <u>mixtures</u> are really <u>useful</u> — <u>alloys</u> (see page 96) are a great example. But sometimes chemists need to get a <u>pure sample</u> of a substance.

Having impure thoughts again, Henry?

When you dissolve a solid in a liquid, the solution contains both the liquid and the thing you dissolved in it — so it's a mixture.

Test for Purity Using Boiling and Melting Points

1) Every <u>pure</u> substance has a <u>specific melting point</u> and <u>boiling point</u>. For example, pure ice melts at 0 °C, and pure water boils at 100 °C.

2) So you can test the <u>purity</u> of a sample of a substance by comparing the <u>actual</u> melting or boiling point of the sample to the <u>expected value</u>.

- If a substance is <u>impure</u>, the <u>melting point</u> will be too <u>low</u>. So if some ice melts at −2 °C, it's probably got an impurity in it (e.g. salt).

- The <u>boiling point</u> of an impure substance will be too <u>high</u>. For example, seawater contains salt (and other impurities). Its boiling point tends to be around 100.6 °C.

3) You can also sometimes tell if a sample of a solid or liquid is a <u>mixture</u> by <u>heating it up</u>. In a mixture, the <u>different components</u> will melt or boil at <u>different temperatures</u>, so part of the mixture will melt or boil first, while the rest will stay in its original state for longer. This means mixtures will often melt over a <u>range</u> of temperatures. For example:

> Adil is testing a sample of a compound for <u>purity</u> by determining its <u>melting point</u>. The <u>pure compound</u> has a melting point of <u>55 °C</u>. Adil believes his sample contains a small number of <u>impurities</u>.
>
> If Adil is correct, which of the following results should he expect from his test?
>
> A. The sample melts at a temperature <u>below 55 °C</u>.
> B. The sample melts at <u>exactly 55 °C</u>.
> C. The sample melts at a temperature <u>above 55 °C</u>.
> D. The sample melts gradually over a <u>range of temperatures</u> which includes 55 °C.
>
> Answer: Impurities <u>lower</u> the melting point of a substance, so if his sample is impure, Adil should expect it to melt <u>below</u> the normal value.
>
> A. The sample melts at a temperature below 55 °C.

If in doubt, heat it up until it melts — that's my motto...

There are lots of ways to get a pure substance out of a mixture. The ones you need to know about are covered over the next few pages. But first, let's check you've got your head around this purity stuff.

Q1   Substance X has a melting point of 850 °C when pure. A sample of substance X is made that contains some impurities. How would you expect the melting point of the sample to differ from the melting point of a pure sample of substance X? Explain your answer.   [2 marks]

 **PRACTICAL** # Simple Distillation

Distillation is used to separate mixtures that contain <u>liquids</u>.
The first type that you need to know about is <u>simple</u> distillation.

Simple Distillation is Used to Separate Out Solutions

1) <u>Simple distillation</u> is used for separating out a <u>liquid</u> from a <u>solution</u>.

2) Here's how to use simple distillation to get <u>pure water</u> from <u>seawater</u> (a mixture containing water and salt):

> 1) Firstly, pour your sample of seawater into the <u>distillation flask</u>.
>
> 2) Set up the <u>equipment</u> as shown in the diagram below. Connect the bottom end of the <u>condenser</u> to a cold tap using <u>rubber tubing</u>. Run <u>cold water</u> through the condenser to keep it cool.
>
> 3) Gradually heat the distillation flask. The part of the solution that has the lowest boiling point will <u>evaporate</u> (turn from a liquid to a gas) — in this case, that's the water.
>
> 4) The water <u>vapour</u> passes into the condenser where it <u>cools</u> and <u>condenses</u> (turns back into a liquid). It then flows into the beaker where it is <u>collected</u>.
>
> 5) Eventually you'll end up with just the <u>salt</u> left in the flask.

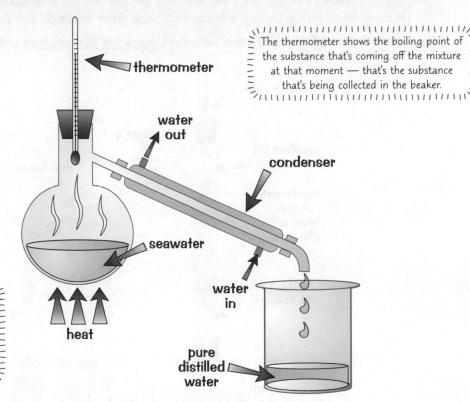

The thermometer shows the boiling point of the substance that's coming off the mixture at that moment — that's the substance that's being collected in the beaker.

If the liquid is flammable, don't use a Bunsen burner to heat it — it could catch fire. Use an electric heater instead (or a water bath if the substance you're collecting has a boiling point of less than 100 °C).

3) The <u>problem</u> with simple distillation is that you can only use it to separate things with <u>very different</u> boiling points.

4) If you have a <u>mixture of liquids</u> with <u>similar boiling points</u>, you need another method to separate them — like fractional distillation (see next page)...

Simple distillation — not so simple if you are wearing mittens...

In some very dry countries, simple distillation is used to make drinking water from seawater (see p.148 for more).

Q1 Describe how you could use simple distillation to obtain pure water from a solution of sodium carbonate. [4 marks]

Q2 A student tried to use simple distillation to separate a mixture of propanol (boiling point = 97 °C) and water (boiling point = 100 °C). This method didn't work. Suggest why. [1 mark]

Fractional Distillation

Here's <u>another type</u> of distillation to learn about. It's a bit <u>different</u> to the one you met on the last page though, so <u>read on</u> to find out more. At least there's a <u>nice big diagram</u> to show what's happening...

Fractional Distillation is Used to Separate a Mixture of Liquids

1) If you've got a <u>mixture of liquids</u> with <u>similar boiling points</u>, you can separate them out using <u>fractional distillation</u>.

2) Here's an experiment that can be done in the lab to show how <u>fractional distillation of crude oil</u> happens at an oil <u>refinery</u>:

1) Put your <u>mixture</u> in a flask. Attach a <u>fractionating column</u> and condenser above the flask as shown below.

2) Gradually heat the flask. The <u>different liquids</u> will all have <u>different boiling points</u> — so they will evaporate (turn from liquid to gas) at <u>different temperatures</u>.

3) The liquid with the <u>lowest boiling point</u> evaporates first. When the temperature on the thermometer matches the boiling point of this liquid, it will reach the <u>top</u> of the column.

4) Liquids with <u>higher boiling points</u> might also start to evaporate. But the column is <u>cooler</u> towards the <u>top</u>, so they will only get part of the way up before <u>condensing</u> (turning back into a liquid) and running back down towards the flask.

5) When the first liquid has been collected, <u>raise the temperature</u> until the <u>next one</u> reaches the top.

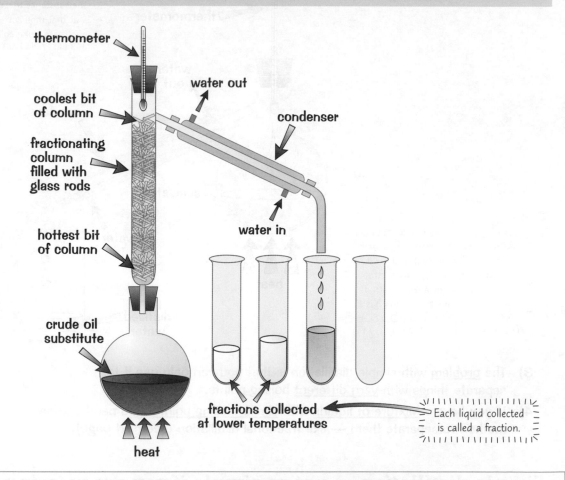

thermometer

water out

coolest bit of column

condenser

fractionating column filled with glass rods

water in

hottest bit of column

crude oil substitute

fractions collected at lower temperatures

Each liquid collected is called a fraction.

heat

Fractionating — sounds a bit too much like maths to me...

The industrial method for fractional distillation of crude oil isn't quite as basic as the one shown here. If you're desperate to find out what goes on in an oil refinery, have a look at page 141.

Q1   A student uses fractional distillation to separate a mixture of liquids. Liquid A has a boiling point of 35 °C, liquid B has a boiling point of 65 °C and liquid C has a boiling point of 49 °C. Which liquid will be collected first?   [1 mark]

Filtration and Crystallisation

If you've mixed a <u>solid</u> with a <u>liquid</u>, it should be pretty easy to <u>separate</u> them out again. Which <u>method</u> you'll need to use depends on whether or not the solid can <u>dissolve</u> in the liquid.

Filtration is Used to Separate an Insoluble Solid from a Liquid

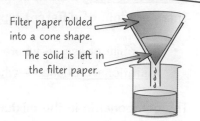

1) If the <u>product</u> of a reaction is an <u>insoluble solid</u> (a solid that can't be dissolved in water), you can use <u>filtration</u> to separate it out from the <u>liquid reaction mixture</u>.

2) All you do is pop some <u>filter paper</u> into a <u>funnel</u> and pour your mixture into it. The liquid part of the mixture <u>runs through</u> the paper, and the <u>solid</u> is left in the paper cone.

Filter paper folded into a cone shape.

The solid is left in the filter paper.

Crystallisation Separates a Soluble Solid from a Solution

If a solid <u>can be dissolved</u> it's described as being <u>soluble</u>. To separate a dissolved solid from a solution you can use <u>crystallisation</u>. Here's how:

1) Pour the solution into an <u>evaporating dish</u> and gently <u>heat</u> the solution. As the <u>solvent</u> (a liquid that can dissolve another substance, usually water) evaporates the solution will get more <u>concentrated</u>.

2) Once about half of the solvent has evaporated (<u>or</u> when you see crystals start to form), remove the dish from the heat and leave the solution to <u>cool</u>.

3) The salt should start to form <u>crystals</u> as it becomes <u>less soluble</u> in the cool, highly concentrated solution.

4) <u>Filter</u> the crystals out of the solution, and leave them in a warm place to <u>dry</u> (or use a <u>drying oven</u>).

evaporating dish

Choose the Right Purification Method

1) You might have to pick one of the <u>techniques</u> covered in this section to separate a mixture.

2) The best technique to use will depend on the <u>properties</u> of the <u>substances</u> in the mixture. For example:

Choose wisely...

A <u>mixture</u> is composed of two substances, X and Y.
<u>Substance X</u> is a <u>liquid</u> at room temperature, has a <u>melting point</u> of 5 °C and a <u>boiling point</u> of 60 °C. <u>Substance Y</u> is a <u>solid</u> at room temperature. It has a <u>melting point</u> of 745 °C and a <u>boiling point</u> of 1218 °C. Substance Y <u>dissolves completely</u> in substance X.

Suggest a <u>purification method</u> you could use to obtain:
a) A pure sample of substance X,   b) A pure sample of substance Y.

<u>Answers:</u>

a) To get X on its own, you need to <u>distil it</u> from the solution. You can use <u>simple distillation</u> here — there's no need for fractional distillation as there's only <u>one liquid</u> in the solution.
You could obtain a pure sample of substance X using simple distillation.

b) To get the <u>soluble solid</u> (Y) out of the solution, you should use <u>crystallisation</u>.
Distillation could work for this but crystallisation's better for getting a <u>pure sample</u> of a solid from a solution.
You could obtain a pure sample of substance Y using crystallisation.

Revise mixtures — just filter out the important bits....

Some mixtures are made up of several components, so you might need to use a combination of the methods covered in this section to get all the different components out.

Q1   Name a method you could use to make pure copper sulfate crystals from copper sulfate solution.   [1 mark]

Chromatography

Chromatography is another practical method that you need to know inside out and upside down... read on.

Chromatography uses Two Phases

1) Chromatography is a method used to separate and identify the substances in a mixture.

2) There are lots of different types of chromatography — but they all have two 'phases':

   • A mobile phase — where the molecules can move. This is always a liquid or a gas.
   • A stationary phase — where the molecules can't move. This can be a solid or a really thick liquid.

3) The components in the mixture separate out as the mobile phase moves over the stationary phase.

4) This happens because each of the chemicals in a mixture will spend different amounts of time dissolved in the mobile phase and stuck to the stationary phase. This is known as its 'distribution' between the phases.

In Thin-Layer Chromatography the Mobile Phase is a Solvent — PRACTICAL

1) In thin-layer chromatography (TLC), the stationary phase is a thin layer of a solid (e.g. silica gel or aluminium oxide powder) on a glass or plastic plate. The mobile phase is a solvent (e.g. ethanol).

2) Here's the method for setting it up:

   1) Draw a line near the bottom of the plate. (Use a pencil to do this — pencil marks won't react or dissolve in the solvent.)

   2) Put a spot of the mixture to be separated on the line.

   3) Put some of the solvent into a beaker.

   4) Dip the bottom of the plate (not the spot) into the solvent.

   5) Put a watch glass over the beaker. This acts as a lid and stops any solvent from evaporating away.

   6) The solvent will start to move up the plate. When the chemicals in the mixture dissolve in the solvent, they will move up the plate too.

   7) You will see the different chemicals in the sample separate out, forming spots at different places on the plate.

   8) Remove the plate from the beaker before the solvent reaches the top. Mark the distance the solvent has moved (the solvent front) in pencil.

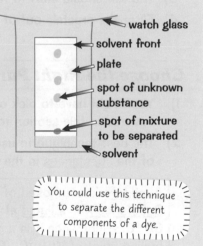

watch glass
solvent front
plate
spot of unknown substance
spot of mixture to be separated
solvent

You could use this technique to separate the different components of a dye.

Paper Chromatography is Similar to TLC

1) Paper chromatography is very similar to TLC, but the stationary phase is a sheet of chromatography paper (often filter paper).

2) The mobile phase is a solvent such as ethanol (just like in TLC).

What's up with Barry?

He's going through a stationery phase.

Give that mixture a bit of TLC, baby...

You might get asked about TLC or paper chromatography in the exams — lucky they're so similar then...

Q1   Why is a pencil used to mark the line drawn during chromatography?   [1 mark]

Q2   What is used as the stationary phase in paper chromatography?   [1 mark]

Interpreting Chromatograms

So, what use is chromatography, apart from making a pretty pattern of spots? Let's find out...

You can Calculate the R_f Value for Each Chemical

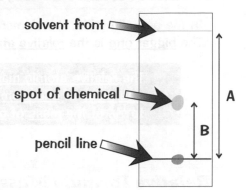

1) The result of doing chromatography is called a chromatogram.

2) You need to know how to work out the R_f values for spots on a chromatogram.

3) An R_f value is the ratio between the distance travelled by the dissolved substance and the distance travelled by the solvent.

4) You can find R_f values using the formula:

$$R_f = \frac{\text{distance travelled by substance}}{\text{distance travelled by solvent}}$$

R_f value of this chemical
$= B \div A$

- To find the distance travelled by the substance (B on the diagram), measure from the pencil line to the centre of the spot.
- To find the distance travelled by the solvent (A on the diagram), measure from the pencil line to the solvent front.

5) Chromatography is often carried out to see if a certain substance is present in a mixture. You run a pure sample of the substance alongside the unknown mixture. If the R_f values match, the substances may be the same (although it doesn't definitely prove they are the same).

6) A pure substance won't be separated by chromatography — it'll always move as one spot, while a mixture can produce multiple spots.

Gas Chromatography is a Bit More High-Tech

1) Gas chromatography (GC) is used to analyse unknown substances too.

2) If they're not already gases, then they have to be made into a gas.

3) The mobile phase is an unreactive gas, such as nitrogen.

4) The stationary phase is a viscous (thick) liquid, such as an oil.

The chromatogram from GC is a graph. Each peak on the graph represents a different chemical.

- The distance along the x-axis is the retention time. These can be looked up to find out what the chemical is.
- The relative areas under the peaks show you the relative amounts of each chemical in the sample.

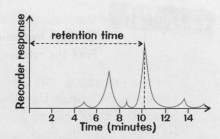

Relative amounts just means you can compare the amount of each substance detected, but you can't work out the actual amounts of each substance.

- There's one peak for each chemical. So a sample of a pure substance will produce a single peak.

J'aime la chromatographie... hmm, I think I need an interpreter...

Gas chromatography is used a lot by scientists in real-life chemical analysis. Just don't try it in your oven at home.

Q1   On a paper chromatogram, chemical X travelled 2.1 cm, chemical Y travelled 3.6 cm and the solvent front travelled 6.0 cm. Calculate the R_f value of chemical Y.   [2 marks]

Relative Masses

The <u>mass of an atom</u> is really, really tiny. To make it easier to <u>calculate</u> with and <u>compare</u> the masses of different atoms, you usually use <u>relative masses</u> instead of their actual masses.

Relative Atomic Mass, A_r — Describes an Element

In the periodic table, the elements all have <u>two</u> numbers next to them. The <u>bigger one</u> is the <u>relative atomic mass</u> (A_r) of the element.

> The <u>relative atomic mass</u> of an element is the <u>average mass</u> of <u>one atom</u> of the element, compared to $\frac{1}{12}$ of the <u>mass</u> of <u>one atom</u> of <u>carbon-12</u>.

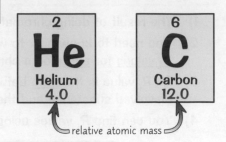

2	6
He	**C**
Helium	Carbon
4.0	12.0

relative atomic mass

Relative Formula Mass, M_r — Describes a Compound

The <u>relative formula mass</u>, <u>M_r</u>, of a compound is all the relative atomic masses in its formula <u>added together</u>.

> For simple covalent compounds, the relative formula mass is usually called the relative molecular mass.

EXAMPLE:

a) Find the relative formula mass of magnesium chloride, $MgCl_2$.

1) Find the <u>relative atomic masses</u> of magnesium and chlorine in the <u>periodic table</u>.

A_r of Mg = 24.3 A_r of Cl = 35.5

2) <u>Add up</u> all the relative atomic masses of each of the atoms in the compound.

M_r of $MgCl_2$ = Mg + (2 × Cl)
= 24.3 + (2 × 35.5)
= 24.3 + 71.0 = 95.3

b) Find the relative molecular mass of ethanoic acid, CH_3COOH.

1) Find the <u>relative atomic masses</u> of carbon, hydrogen and oxygen in the <u>periodic table</u>.

A_r of C = 12.0 A_r of H = 1.0 A_r of O = 16.0

2) <u>Add up</u> all the relative atomic masses of each of the atoms in the compound.

M_r of CH_3COOH = C + (3 × H) + C + O + O + H
= 12.0 + (3 × 1.0) + 12.0 + 16.0 + 16.0 + 1.0
= 60.0

Compounds with Brackets in...

EXAMPLE:

Calcium hydroxide has the formula $Ca(OH)_2$.
Find the relative formula mass of calcium hydroxide.

The <u>small number 2</u> after the bracket in the formula $Ca(OH)_2$ means that there's <u>two of everything inside the brackets</u>.

A_r of C = 12.0 A_r of O = 16.0 A_r of H = 1.0
M_r of $Ca(OH)_2$ = Ca + [(O + H) × 2]
= 40.1 + [(16.0 + 1.0) × 2]
= 40.1 + 34.0 = 74.1

This page is a relative masterpiece...

This stuff comes up a fair bit in chemistry, so make sure you've got to grips with it by doing loads of practice questions. Start with these. Use the periodic table inside the back cover to find the A_r values you need.

Q1   Find the relative formula mass of sodium chloride, NaCl.   [1 mark]

Q2   Find the relative formula mass of magnesium hydroxide, $Mg(OH)_2$.   [2 marks]

Molecular and Empirical Formulas

Three types of <u>formula</u> to cover here. You should already be familiar with <u>molecular</u> and <u>displayed</u> formulas.
<u>Empirical formulas</u> are not fun at all, because they involve ratios. But I'm sure you'll learn to love them...

Molecular Formulas and Displayed Formulas Show Numbers of Atoms

You can work out <u>how many atoms</u> of each type there are in a substance when you're given its <u>formula</u>.

This is called a <u>molecular formula</u>. It shows the <u>number</u> and <u>type</u> of <u>atoms</u> in a molecule.

CH_4

<u>Methane</u> contains 1 carbon atom and 4 hydrogen atoms.

$$H-C-H$$ (with H above and below)

This is called a <u>displayed formula</u>. It shows the <u>atoms</u> and the <u>covalent bonds</u> in a molecule as a picture.

Don't panic if a molecular formula has <u>brackets</u> in it — here's what they mean:

$CH_3(CH_2)_2CH_3$

- The <u>2</u> after the bracket means there are <u>2 lots of CH_2</u> — so you could write this out as $CH_3CH_2CH_2CH_3$.
- In total there are 4 carbon atoms and 10 hydrogen atoms.

The Empirical Formula is the Simplest Ratio of Atoms

An <u>empirical formula</u> of a compound tells you the <u>smallest whole-number ratio</u> of atoms in the compound.

EXAMPLE:

Find the empirical formula of ethane, C_2H_6.

The numbers in the <u>molecular formula</u> of <u>ethane</u> are <u>2</u> and <u>6</u>.

To simplify the ratio, just divide by the largest number that goes into 2 and 6 <u>exactly</u> — that's <u>2</u>.

C: $2 \div 2 = 1$
H: $6 \div 2 = 3$

The empirical formula of ethane is CH_3.

You can use the <u>empirical formula</u> of a compound, together with its M_r, to find its molecular formula.

EXAMPLE:

Compound X has the empirical formula CH. The M_r of compound X is 78.
Find the molecular formula of compound X.

1) Start by finding the M_r of the <u>empirical formula</u>.
   The A_r of carbon is <u>12.0</u>, the A_r of hydrogen is <u>1.0</u>.

   M_r of CH $= (1 \times C) + (1 \times H)$
   $= (1 \times 12.0) + (1 \times 1.0)$
   $= 12.0 + 10 = 13.0$

2) Divide the M_r of compound X by the M_r of the empirical formula.

   $78 \div 13.0 = 6$

3) Now to get the <u>molecular formula</u> of compound X, you just <u>multiply</u> everything in the empirical formula by your answer to step 2 — in this case, that's <u>6</u>.

   C: $1 \times 6 = 6$
   H: $1 \times 6 = 6$

   The molecular formula of compound X is C_6H_6.

I believe in empiricals...

Another page with lots of maths — which means the best way to learn this stuff is by doing some questions.
Wait, what's that on the next line? A question on empirical formulas? It's almost like it's your destiny to answer it...

Q1   What is the empirical formula of a compound with the molecular formula H_2O_2?   [1 mark]

Revision Questions for Topics C1 and C2

That's <u>Topic C1</u> and <u>Topic C2</u> done and dusted. Time to take a look back at the best bits.

*   Try these questions and <u>tick off each one</u> when you <u>get it right</u>.
*   When you've done <u>all the questions</u> under a heading and are <u>completely happy</u> with it, tick it off.

States of Matter and the Atom (p.82-86) ☑

1) What are the three states of matter?
2) Which scientist developed the nuclear model of the atom?
3) Draw a diagram of an atom. Label the nucleus and the electrons on your diagram.
4) What does the mass number tell you about an atom?
5) True or false? Negative ions form when atoms lose electrons.

The Periodic Table and Electronic Structures (p.87-88) ☑

6) Outline how Mendeleev arranged the elements in his version of the periodic table.
7) How many electrons would you expect an element in Group 7 to have in its outer shell?
8) What's the maximum number of electrons that each of the first three electron shells will hold?
9) The atomic number of argon is 18. What is its electronic structure?

Structure, Bonding and Properties of Materials (p.89-97) ☑

10) What is an ion?
11) Why does magnesium form ions with a 2+ charge, while sodium only forms ions with a 1+ charge?
12) What type of structure do ionic compounds form?
13) Describe how a covalent bond forms.
14) What do ball and stick models show?
15) List two typical properties of giant covalent structures.
16) Name three substances that have a giant covalent structure.
17) Name the type of molecules that plastics are made from.
18) List three typical properties of metals that are due to their metallic bonding.
19) Out of the four main types of structure (ionic, simple covalent, giant covalent and metallic), which one is most likely to have a low melting point?

Purity and Separating Mixtures (p.98-103) ☑

20) In chemistry, what is meant by the term 'a pure substance'?
21) Does adding an impurity to a substance raise or lower its boiling point?
22) List the equipment that you would need to do a fractional distillation in the lab.
23) What would you use filtration to separate?
24) In chromatography, what does the term 'mobile phase' mean?
25) Describe the method for separating a mixture by thin-layer chromatography.
26) What is the formula used to calculate R_f values?

Relative Masses and Formulas (p.104-105) ☑

27) What is the 'relative atomic mass' of an element?
28) How do you work out the relative formula mass of a compound?
29) What is the empirical formula of a compound?

Conservation of Mass

You've probably realised by now that you can't <u>magic</u> stuff out of thin air. It can't magically <u>disappear</u>, either.

In Chemical Reactions, Mass is Always Conserved (Stays the Same)

1) During a chemical reaction <u>no atoms are destroyed</u> and <u>no atoms are created</u>.

2) There are the <u>same number</u> of each <u>type of atom</u> on both sides of the equation.

3) Because of this <u>no mass is lost or gained</u> during a reaction — you can say that mass is <u>conserved</u>.

4) You can add up the <u>relative formula masses</u> (see page 104) on each side of the equation to show that mass is conserved.

There's more about equations on page 110.

EXAMPLE:

Use relative formula masses to show that mass is conserved in this reaction: $2Li + F_2 \rightarrow 2LiF$

1) Add up the <u>relative formula masses</u> of all the <u>reactants</u>.

M_r reactants $= 2 \times A_r(Li) + M_r(F_2)$
$= (2 \times 6.9) + (2 \times 19.0) = 51.8$

2) Add up the <u>relative formula masses</u> of all the <u>products</u>.

M_r products $= 2 \times M_r(LiF)$
$= 2 \times (6.9 + 19.0) = 51.8$

3) <u>Compare</u> the <u>relative formula masses</u> of the reactants and products.

M_r reactants $= M_r$ products, so the mass has been conserved.

If the Mass Seems to Change, There's Usually a Gas Involved

If you use a beaker or flask <u>without a lid</u>, it might look like there's been a <u>change of mass</u> during a reaction. There are two reasons why this happens:

1 If the mass seems to <u>increase</u>, it's probably because one of the <u>reactants</u> is a <u>gas</u> that's found in air (e.g. oxygen) and the products are solid or liquid. For example, look at the following reaction:

$$copper_{(s)} + oxygen_{(g)} \rightarrow copper\ oxide_{(s)}$$

- When you do this reaction in a container <u>without a lid</u>, <u>oxygen from the air</u> will join to the copper in your container.

- It will look like the <u>products</u> weigh <u>more</u> than the <u>reactants</u> did.

- But in fact the mass of the copper oxide will be the <u>same</u> as the mass of the copper <u>plus</u> the mass of the oxygen from the air.

I have literally no idea what I'm doing.

2 If the mass seems to <u>decrease</u>, it's probably because some of the reactants are solids or liquids and at least one of the <u>products</u> is a <u>gas</u>. For example, look at the following reaction:

$$copper\ carbonate_{(s)} \rightarrow copper\ oxide_{(s)} + carbon\ dioxide_{(g)}$$

- When you do this reaction in a container <u>without a lid</u>, the carbon dioxide gas will <u>escape</u> as soon as it's made.

- It will look like the <u>products</u> weigh <u>less</u> than the <u>reactants</u> did.

- But in fact the mass of the copper oxide plus the mass of the carbon dioxide will be the <u>same</u> as the mass of the copper carbonate.

Remember the particle model from page 82? A gas will expand to fill any container it's in. So if the container isn't sealed, the gas will carry on expanding and escape into the air around.

Conservation of Mass — protecting mass for future generations...

Never forget that, in a reaction, the total mass of reactants is the same as the total mass of products.

Q1   Use relative formula masses to show that mass is conserved in this reaction: $2Cu + O_2 \rightarrow 2CuO$ [3 marks]

Chemical Formulas

Make sure you've really got your head around the idea of <u>ionic bonding</u> (page 90) before you start this.

You Need to be Familiar with Some Common Ions

1) You met <u>ions</u> back on page 89. They form when atoms, or groups of atoms, lose or gain electrons.

2) Here are some common ions you may meet during the course.

Positive Ions		Negative Ions	
1+ ions	2+ ions	2– ions	1– ions
Lithium, Li^+	Magnesium, Mg^{2+}	Carbonate, CO_3^{2-}	Hydroxide, OH^-
Sodium, Na^+	Calcium, Ca^{2+}	Sulfate, SO_4^{2-}	Nitrate, NO_3^-
Potassium, K^+		Oxide, O^{2-}	Fluoride, F^-
		Sulfide, S^{2-}	Chloride, Cl^-
			Bromide, Br^-
			Iodide, I^-

Look back at page 89 for how to predict what ion an element will form from its position in the periodic table.

3) Any of the positive ions can <u>react</u> with any of the negative ions to form an <u>ionic compound</u> (see page 90).

4) For example, a positive sodium ion (Na^+) can react with a negative chloride ion (Cl^-) to form sodium chloride ($NaCl$).

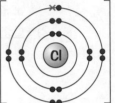
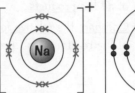

You Can Work Out the Formula of an Ionic Compound

1) Ionic compounds are made up of a <u>positively charged</u> part and a <u>negatively charged</u> part.

2) The <u>overall charge</u> of <u>any ionic compound</u> is <u>zero</u>.
So the <u>negative charges</u> in the compound must <u>balance</u> the <u>positive charges</u>.

3) You can use the charges on the <u>ions</u> to work out the formula of an ionic compound.

EXAMPLE:

What is the chemical formula of calcium nitrate?

1) Write out the <u>formulas</u> of the <u>calcium</u> and <u>nitrate</u> ions. | calcium ion = Ca^{2+} nitrate ion = NO_3^-

2) The <u>overall charge</u> on the compound must be <u>zero</u>. So work out how many NO_3^- ions you need to <u>balance out</u> the charge on one Ca^{2+} ion. | To balance the 2+ charge on one Ca^{2+} ion, you need two NO_3^- ions (because $2 + (2 \times -1) = 0$).

3) Use that information to write out the <u>formula</u>. | The formula is: $Ca(NO_3)_2$

The brackets show that you need <u>two</u> of the <u>whole nitrate ion</u>.

You Need to Learn the Formulas of Some Molecules

It's a good idea to <u>learn</u> the chemical formulas of these common molecules. They crop up all the time.

- Water — H_2O
- Ammonia — NH_3
- Carbon dioxide — CO_2
- Hydrogen — H_2
- Chlorine — Cl_2
- Oxygen — O_2

Group 1 ions — positively wonderful, but for a small charge...

Chemical formulas pop up everywhere. Make sure you can handle them, or you'll be stumped in the exam.

Q1   Write the formula, with the charge, of the following ions:
a) bromide ion,   b) carbonate ion,   c) lithium ion. [3 marks]

Q2   What is the chemical formula of the ionic compound magnesium hydroxide? [1 mark]

Chemical Equations

If you're going to get anywhere in chemistry you need to know about <u>chemical equations</u>...

Chemical Changes are Shown Using Chemical Equations

1) One way to show what's happening in a chemical reaction is to write a <u>word equation</u>.

2) A word equation shows you the <u>names</u> of the chemicals that are <u>reacting</u> and <u>being made</u>.

Here's an example — <u>methane</u> burns in <u>oxygen</u> giving <u>carbon dioxide</u> and <u>water</u>:

The molecules on the <u>left</u> of the equation are called the <u>reactants</u> (because they react with each other).

methane + oxygen → carbon dioxide + water

The molecules on the <u>right</u> are called the <u>products</u> (because they're produced from the reactants).

Symbol Equations Show the Atoms on Both Sides

1) Chemical <u>reactions</u> can also be shown using <u>symbol equations</u>.

2) Symbol equations show the <u>chemical symbols</u> and <u>formulas</u> of the <u>reactants</u> and <u>products</u>.

For example, here's the <u>symbol equation</u> for the reaction of <u>methane</u> with oxygen:

$$CH_4 + 2O_2 \rightarrow CO_2 + 2H_2O$$

The <u>oxygen</u> (O_2) and <u>water</u> (H_2O) formulas have <u>numbers</u> in front of them. These numbers keep the equation <u>balanced</u> (so you have the <u>same number</u> of each type of <u>atom</u> on <u>both sides</u> of the equation). There's more about balancing equations coming up on the next page.

State Symbols Tell You the State of a Substance in an Equation

1) Symbol equations can also include <u>state symbols</u> next to each substance.

2) State symbols tell you what <u>state of matter</u> the reactants and products are in.

3) The four state symbols you'll see are:

(s) — solid   (l) — liquid   (g) — gas   (aq) — aqueous

'Aqueous' means 'dissolved in water' — so it's a solution.

<u>Example</u>: <u>Solid zinc</u> reacts with a <u>solution</u> of <u>hydrochloric acid</u>.
The reaction produces a <u>solution</u> of <u>zinc chloride</u> and <u>hydrogen gas</u>.
So the equation for this reaction <u>with state symbols</u> is:

$$Zn_{(s)} + 2HCl_{(aq)} \rightarrow ZnCl_{2(aq)} + H_{2(g)}$$

Me + Doughnuts → Happiness — one equation I can get behind...

Without equations we wouldn't have a way of showing what is happening in a reaction. You'll need to understand both word and symbol equations, so it's a good idea to get to grips with them both before moving on.

Q1   Hydrogen and oxygen molecules are formed in a reaction where water splits apart.
     The symbol equation for this reaction is: $2H_2O_{(l)} \rightarrow 2H_{2(g)} + O_{2(g)}$
     a) Write the word equation for this reaction.   [1 mark]
     b) What state is the hydrogen in?   [1 mark]

Balancing Chemical Equations

If you thought that was all there was to know about <u>chemical equations</u>, prepare to be disappointed...

Symbol Equations Need to be Balanced

1) There must always be the <u>same</u> number of atoms on <u>both sides</u> of a symbol equation — atoms can't just <u>disappear</u>.

2) You <u>balance</u> the equation by putting numbers <u>in front</u> of the formulas where needed. Take this equation for reacting sulfuric acid with sodium hydroxide:

$$H_2SO_4 + NaOH \rightarrow Na_2SO_4 + H_2O$$

3) The <u>formulas</u> are all correct, but the numbers of some of the atoms <u>aren't the same</u> on both sides.

Left-hand side	Right-hand side
H = 3	H = 2
S = 1	S = 1
O = 5	O = 5
Na = 1	Na = 2

4) You <u>can't</u> solve this by changing the numbers <u>inside</u> the <u>formulas</u> (so you <u>can't</u> change H_2SO_4 to H_3SO_4).

5) But you <u>can</u> put numbers <u>in front</u> of a whole formula (so you <u>can</u> change H_2SO_4 to $2H_2SO_4$).

6) So all you do to <u>balance an equation</u> is this:

> 1) Find an element that <u>doesn't balance</u>. <u>Pencil in a number</u> in front of one of the formulas to try and sort it out.
>
> 2) <u>See where that gets you.</u>
>
> 3) If the equation still <u>isn't</u> balanced, don't worry — just pencil in <u>another number</u> and see where that gets you.
>
> 4) Keep doing this until the equation is <u>completely balanced</u>.

$E = mc^2$

EXAMPLE:

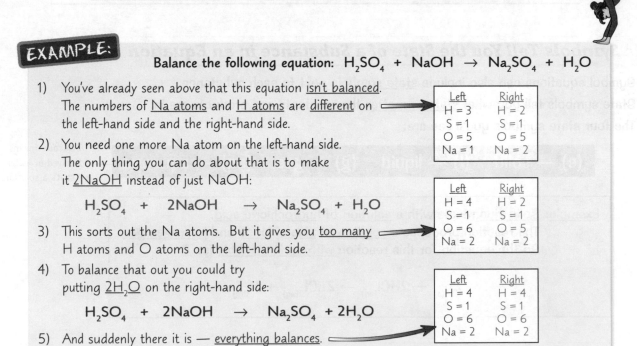

Balance the following equation: $H_2SO_4 + NaOH \rightarrow Na_2SO_4 + H_2O$

1) You've already seen above that this equation <u>isn't balanced</u>. The numbers of <u>Na atoms</u> and <u>H atoms</u> are <u>different</u> on the left-hand side and the right-hand side.

Left	Right
H = 3	H = 2
S = 1	S = 1
O = 5	O = 5
Na = 1	Na = 2

2) You need one more Na atom on the left-hand side. The only thing you can do about that is to make it <u>2NaOH</u> instead of just NaOH:

$$H_2SO_4 + 2NaOH \rightarrow Na_2SO_4 + H_2O$$

Left	Right
H = 4	H = 2
S = 1	S = 1
O = 6	O = 5
Na = 2	Na = 2

3) This sorts out the Na atoms. But it gives you <u>too many</u> H atoms and O atoms on the left-hand side.

4) To balance that out you could try putting <u>2H$_2$O</u> on the right-hand side:

$$H_2SO_4 + 2NaOH \rightarrow Na_2SO_4 + 2H_2O$$

Left	Right
H = 4	H = 4
S = 1	S = 1
O = 6	O = 6
Na = 2	Na = 2

5) And suddenly there it is — <u>everything balances</u>.

Revision is all about getting the balance right...

Balancing equations is all about practice. Handily, I see some practice questions coming up right now...

Q1   Balance the equation: $Na + O_2 \rightarrow Na_2O$ [1 mark]

Q2   Balance the equation: $Fe + Cl_2 \rightarrow FeCl_3$ [1 mark]

Endothermic and Exothermic Reactions

Whenever chemical reactions occur, there are changes in <u>energy</u>.

Reactions are Exothermic or Endothermic

> An <u>EXOTHERMIC reaction</u> is one which <u>gives out heat energy</u> to the surroundings.
> Exothermic reactions increase the <u>temperature</u> of the surroundings.

> An <u>ENDOTHERMIC reaction</u> is one which <u>takes in heat energy</u> from the surroundings.
> Endothermic reactions decrease the <u>temperature</u> of the surroundings.

During a chemical reaction, energy is being <u>transferred</u> between the reaction mixture and the surroundings. Energy <u>isn't</u> being made or lost — just <u>moved around</u>.

Reaction Profiles Show if a Reaction's Exothermic or Endothermic

1) <u>Reaction profiles</u> show the energy levels of the <u>reactants</u> and the <u>products</u> in a reaction.

2) You can use them to work out if a reaction is <u>giving out</u> energy or <u>taking it in</u>.

3) This reaction profile shows an <u>exothermic reaction</u> — the products have <u>less energy</u> than the reactants.

4) The <u>difference in height</u> between the reactants and the products shows the <u>energy given out</u> in the reaction.

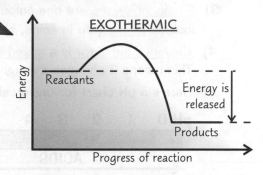

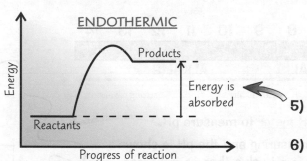

5) This shows an <u>endothermic reaction</u> — the products have <u>more energy</u> than the reactants.

6) The <u>difference in height</u> between the reactants and the products shows the <u>energy taken in</u> during the reaction.

Activation Energy is the Energy Needed to Start a Reaction

1) The <u>activation energy</u> is the <u>smallest</u> amount of energy needed to <u>start a reaction</u>.

2) On a reaction profile, it's the difference between the <u>reactants</u> and the <u>highest point</u> of the curve.

3) It's a bit like having to <u>climb up</u> one side of a hill before you can ski down the <u>other side</u>.

4) If you put in <u>less energy</u> than the activation energy there <u>won't</u> be enough energy to <u>start</u> the reaction — so nothing will happen.

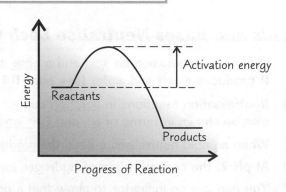

Exothermic reactions are a hot topic right now...

It might help to remember that "exo-" = exit and "-thermic" = heat — so exothermic reactions give out heat.

Q1 During a reaction, the temperature of the reaction mixture increases from 21 °C to 28 °C.
  a) Is the reaction exothermic or endothermic? [1 mark]
  b) Sketch a reaction profile for the reaction.
     Label the energy of the reactants, the energy of the products and the activation energy. [3 marks]

Acids and Bases

Testing the pH of a solution means using an <u>indicator</u> — and that means pretty <u>colours</u>...

The pH Scale Goes from 0 to 14

1) The pH scale is a measure of <u>how acidic or alkaline</u> a solution is.

2) A <u>neutral</u> substance has <u>pH 7</u>.

3) An <u>acid</u> is a substance with a <u>pH less than 7</u>. Acids form H^+ ions in water.

4) A <u>base</u> is a substance with a <u>pH greater than 7</u>.
An <u>alkali</u> is a base that <u>dissolves in water</u>. Alkalis form OH^- ions in water.

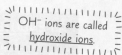
OH^- ions are called hydroxide ions.

5) As the <u>concentration</u> of hydrogen ions <u>increases</u>, the <u>pH decreases</u>.
The higher the hydrogen ion concentration, the <u>more acidic</u> something is, so the lower the pH.

You Can Measure the pH of a Solution

PRACTICAL

1) An <u>indicator</u> is a <u>dye</u> that <u>changes colour</u> depending on whether it's <u>above or below a certain pH</u>.

2) Indicators are simple to use. You just <u>add a few drops</u> to the solution you're testing,
then compare the colour the solution goes to a <u>pH chart</u> for that indicator.

3) <u>Single indicators</u> are one colour in acids and another colour in alkalis. Examples of single indicators
include <u>litmus</u> (red in acids, blue in alkalis) and <u>phenolphthalein</u> (colourless in acids, pink in alkalis).

4) <u>Universal indicator</u> is a <u>mixed indicator</u> — it's made by mixing together several single indicators.
This means it changes through a whole <u>series of colours</u> as you go along the pH scale.

5) Here's a pH chart for universal indicator:

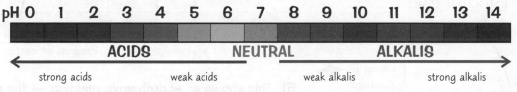

pH 0 1 2 3 4 5 6 7 8 9 10 11 12 13 14

ACIDS   NEUTRAL   ALKALIS

strong acids   weak acids   weak alkalis   strong alkalis

6) You can also use a <u>pH probe</u> attached to a <u>pH meter</u> to measure pH.

7) You place the probe in the solution you are measuring and the pH is shown
on the display. This gives you a <u>more accurate</u> pH value than an indicator.

8) When you use a pH probe, it's important to <u>set it up correctly</u>. Before you
start, make sure the display shows <u>pH 7</u> if you put the probe in pure water.

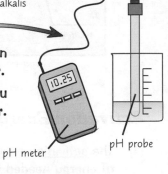

pH meter

pH probe

Acids and Bases Neutralise Each Other

1) The reaction between an <u>acid</u> and a <u>base</u> is called <u>neutralisation</u>.
It produces a <u>salt</u> and <u>water</u> (see page 114 for more on this).

acid + base → salt + water

2) Neutralisation reactions in <u>solution</u> can
also be shown in terms of H^+ and OH^- ions:

$H^+ + OH^- → H_2O$

3) When an acid neutralises a base the <u>products</u> are <u>neutral</u> — they have a <u>pH of 7</u>.

4) At pH 7, the concentration of hydrogen ions <u>equals</u> the concentration of hydroxide ions.

5) You can use an indicator to show that a neutralisation reaction is <u>over</u>.
For example, universal indicator will go <u>green</u> when the reaction is complete.

This page should have all bases covered...

pHew, you got to the end of the page, so here's an interesting(ish) fact — your skin is slightly acidic (pH 5.5).

Q1   a) The pH of an unknown solution is found to be 6. Is the solution acidic or alkaline?   [1 mark]
     b) What colour would the solution go if you added a few drops of universal indicator to it?   [1 mark]

Reactions of Acids

MORE? You want MORE? Well, since I'm so nice, here's some <u>more on acids</u> for you.

Many Metals React with Acids to Give Salts

$$Acid + Metal \rightarrow Salt + Hydrogen$$

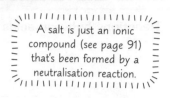

A salt is just an ionic compound (see page 91) that's been formed by a neutralisation reaction.

Hydrochloric Acid Produces Chloride Salts:

$$2HCl + Mg \rightarrow MgCl_2 + H_2$$
hydrochloric acid + magnesium → magnesium chloride + hydrogen

$$6HCl + 2Al \rightarrow 2AlCl_3 + 3H_2$$
hydrochloric acid + aluminium → aluminium chloride + hydrogen

Drat! That's the last time I use acid to polish my leg armour.

Sulfuric Acid Produces Sulfate Salts:

$$H_2SO_4 + Mg \rightarrow MgSO_4 + H_2$$
sulfuric acid + magnesium → magnesium sulfate + hydrogen

$$3H_2SO_4 + 2Al \rightarrow Al_2(SO_4)_3 + 3H_2$$
sulfuric acid + aluminium → aluminium sulfate + hydrogen

Nitric Acid Produces Nitrate Salts, but...

1) The reaction of <u>nitric acid</u> with metals is more complicated.

2) You get a <u>nitrate salt</u>, but instead of hydrogen gas, the other products are usually a mixture of <u>water</u>, <u>NO</u> and <u>NO$_2$</u>.

Metal Carbonates Give Salt + Water + Carbon Dioxide

$$Acid + Metal\ Carbonate \rightarrow Salt + Water + Carbon\ Dioxide$$

Again, hydrochloric acid gives <u>chloride salts</u>, sulfuric acid gives <u>sulfate salts</u> and nitric acid gives <u>nitrate salts</u>:

$$2HCl + Na_2CO_3 \rightarrow 2NaCl + H_2O + CO_2$$
hydrochloric acid + sodium carbonate → sodium chloride + water + carbon dioxide

$$H_2SO_4 + K_2CO_3 \rightarrow K_2SO_4 + H_2O + CO_2$$
sulfuric acid + potassium carbonate → potassium sulfate + water + carbon dioxide

$$2HNO_3 + ZnCO_3 \rightarrow Zn(NO_3)_2 + H_2O + CO_2$$
nitric acid + zinc carbonate → zinc nitrate + water + carbon dioxide

Nitrates — much cheaper than day-rates...

What a lot of reactions. Take a peek back at pages 109-110 if you need help with writing and balancing equations.

Q1   What salt is produced when calcium reacts with hydrochloric acid?   [1 mark]

Neutralisation Reactions

Here is another page on the <u>reactions of acids</u>. I bet you can't wait to get reading. Don't let me stop you...

Acids and Alkalis React to Give a Salt and Water

Reactions between acids and alkalis are <u>neutralisation</u> reactions (see page 112).

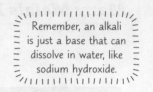
Remember, an alkali is just a base that can dissolve in water, like sodium hydroxide.

$$\text{Acid} + \text{Alkali} \rightarrow \text{Salt} + \text{Water}$$

$$HCl + NaOH \rightarrow NaCl + H_2O$$
hydrochloric acid + sodium hydroxide → sodium chloride + water

$$H_2SO_4 + Zn(OH)_2 \rightarrow ZnSO_4 + 2H_2O$$
sulfuric acid + zinc hydroxide → zinc sulfate + water

$$HNO_3 + KOH \rightarrow KNO_3 + H_2O$$
nitric acid + potassium hydroxide → potassium nitrate + water

You can Make Soluble Salts Using Acid + Alkali Reactions

PRACTICAL

1) You can make a <u>soluble salt</u> (a salt that <u>dissolves in water</u>) by adding an <u>acid</u> to an <u>alkali</u>.

2) With this type of reaction though, you can't <u>see</u> when the reaction has <u>finished</u> — there's no signal that all the alkali has been neutralised.

3) You can't just add an <u>excess</u> (more than you need) of acid to the alkali because you'd end up with a <u>mixture</u> of the salt and the acid rather than just a salt solution.

4) So the first thing you need to do is to find out exactly how much acid is needed to <u>neutralise</u> the alkali.

5) Put a <u>measured amount</u> of your <u>alkali</u> in a flask. Add a few drops of a <u>single indicator</u> like <u>phenolphthalein</u> (see page 112).

6) Then use a <u>burette</u> (see page 218) to add the acid to the alkali bit by bit, until the alkali is <u>neutralised</u>. You will know when this is because the <u>indicator</u> will <u>change colour</u> at the point when the alkali is neutralised.

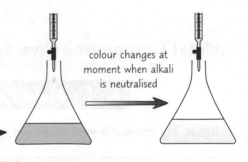
colour changes at moment when alkali is neutralised

7) Now you know what volume of acid is needed to neutralise the alkali. So you can <u>repeat</u> the reaction using exactly the right amount of acid and alkali but with <u>no indicator</u> (so the salt <u>won't</u> have any indicator mixed in with it).

8) The <u>solution</u> that remains when the reaction is complete will only contain the <u>salt</u> and <u>water</u>.

9) If you want <u>pure, dry crystals</u> of the salt you'll have to do a bit more. You'll need to <u>evaporate</u> off some of the water from your solution. Then leave the solution to <u>crystallise</u> (form <u>crystals</u> of <u>solid salt</u>). Finally, you can <u>filter</u> the solid salt out of the solution and <u>dry</u> it.

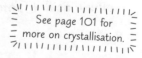
See page 101 for more on crystallisation.

AAAARRGGHH — so many reactions...

I think you'll agree that the only right way to finish a page as thrilling as this one is with a practice question.

Q1   Complete the balanced equation for the reaction of sulfuric acid with potassium hydroxide, shown below.

$$H_2SO_4 + \text{....} \, KOH \rightarrow \text{..........} + \text{....} \, H_2O$$

[2 marks]

Making Salts

<u>Making salts</u> can be tricky. You need a different method depending on whether the salt's <u>insoluble</u> or <u>soluble</u>.

Making Soluble Salts Using an Acid and an Insoluble Base

1) You can make <u>soluble salts</u> by reacting an <u>acid</u> with an <u>insoluble base</u>.
2) You need to pick the right <u>acid</u>, plus an <u>insoluble base</u> (a <u>metal oxide</u> or <u>metal hydroxide</u>).
3) <u>Warm</u> the acid (carefully) and then add the <u>base</u> to the <u>acid</u>.
4) The base and acid will react to produce a <u>soluble salt</u> (and water). When all the acid has been neutralised, the excess solid will <u>sink</u> to the bottom.
5) <u>Filter</u> off the <u>excess</u> solid to get a solution containing only salt and water.
6) <u>Heat the solution gently</u> to slowly <u>evaporate</u> off some of the water, then leave the more concentrated solution to cool and allow the salt to form <u>crystals</u>. Filter off the solid and leave it to <u>dry</u>.

<u>Example:</u> You can add <u>copper oxide</u> to <u>hydrochloric acid</u> to make <u>copper chloride</u>:
$$CuO_{(s)} + 2HCl_{(aq)} \rightarrow CuCl_{2(aq)} + H_2O_{(l)}$$

Making Insoluble Salts — Precipitation Reactions

1) To make a pure, dry sample of an <u>insoluble</u> salt, you can use a <u>precipitation reaction</u>.
2) You just pick the right two <u>soluble salts</u> and mix them. They will <u>react</u> to form your <u>insoluble salt</u>.

<u>Example:</u> to make <u>lead chloride</u> (insoluble), mix <u>lead nitrate</u> and <u>sodium chloride</u> (both soluble).

lead nitrate + sodium chloride → lead chloride + sodium nitrate

<u>Method</u>:

1) Add 1 spatula of <u>lead nitrate</u> to a test tube. Add <u>deionised water</u> (that's water that's had all the ions removed from it, so they don't interfere with the reaction). <u>Shake well</u> until all the lead nitrate has <u>dissolved</u>.
2) In a separate test tube, do the same with 1 spatula of <u>sodium chloride</u>.
3) Tip the <u>two solutions</u> into a beaker and stir them to make sure the solutions are mixed together. The lead chloride should <u>precipitate</u> out.
4) Put a folded piece of <u>filter paper</u> into a <u>filter funnel</u>, and stick the funnel into a <u>conical flask</u>.
5) <u>Pour</u> the contents of the beaker into the middle of the filter paper. Make sure that the level of the solution doesn't go above the filter paper — otherwise some of the solid could dribble down the side.
6) <u>Rinse the beaker</u> with more deionised water and tip this into the filter paper. This is to make sure you get <u>all the product</u> from the beaker.
7) Then <u>rinse the solid</u> with deionised water to wash off any leftover <u>sodium nitrate solution</u>.
8) Take the filter paper out. Scrape the <u>lead chloride</u> onto a new bit of filter paper and leave it to <u>dry</u>.

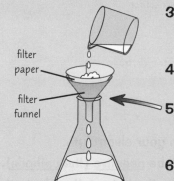

I was attacked by a nasty lead chloride — it was a-salt...

The theory may seem dull, but you'll probably get to make some nice salts in your class, and that's pretty cool.

Q1 Iron nitrate is a soluble salt that can be made from iron oxide (an insoluble base) and nitric acid. Describe how you would make pure, solid iron nitrate from these reactants. [5 marks]

Oxidation, Reduction and Electrolysis

There are three ideas to get your head round on this page: reduction, oxidation and electrolysis.

Substances can be Oxidised or Reduced

1) Oxidation is the addition of oxygen. Reduction is the removal of oxygen.

> Example: iron oxide can react with carbon monoxide to produce iron and carbon dioxide.
> $$Fe_2O_3 + 3CO \rightarrow 2Fe + 3CO_2$$
> In this reaction: • the iron oxide is reduced to iron — oxygen is removed from it.
>   • the carbon monoxide is oxidised to carbon dioxide — oxygen is added to it.

2) The thing that gives up its oxygen (gets reduced) is sometimes called the oxidising agent (because it oxidises the other substance). In the example above, the oxidising agent is the iron oxide.

3) The thing that takes the oxygen (gets oxidised) is sometimes called the reducing agent (because it reduces the other substance). In the example above, the reducing agent is the carbon monoxide.

Electrolysis Means 'Splitting Up With Electricity'

1) When an ionic substance is molten (melted) or dissolved, the ions are free to move about. These free ions mean that the liquid can conduct electricity.

2) If you pass an electric current through an ionic substance that's molten or in solution, it breaks down. This is called electrolysis.

3) The molten or dissolved ionic substance that gets broken down is called the electrolyte.

> Solid ionic substances can't conduct electricity because the ions are in fixed positions and can't move.

During Electrolysis the Ions Move Towards the Electrodes

1) To do electrolysis, you need your electrolyte, plus a power source, wires and two electrodes.

2) An electrode is just a solid that conducts electricity. You join the wires to the electrodes and dip the electrodes into the electrolyte to complete the circuit. You set it up like this:

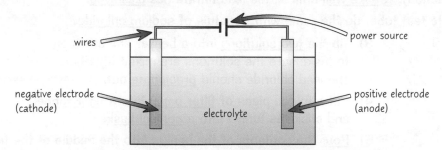

wires

power source

negative electrode (cathode)

positive electrode (anode)

electrolyte

3) You usually use inert electrodes. This means they won't react with your electrolyte.

4) One of the electrodes will be positive (the anode) and the other will be negative (the cathode).

5) The positive ions (cations) in the electrolyte will move towards the cathode (negative electrode). The negative ions (anions) in the electrolyte will move towards the anode (positive electrode).

6) At the electrodes, the ions lose or gain electrons to form uncharged substances.

If only revision could be reduced to nothing...

You'll definitely need to remember that oxidation is the gain of oxygen and reduction is the removal of oxygen. And don't worry if electrolysis seems a bit scary at the moment — there's more about it coming up.

Q1   Look at the following equation: $2CuO + C \rightarrow 2Cu + CO_2$
      State which reactant is being oxidised and which reactant is being reduced.   [2 marks]

Electrolysis

This stuff is electrifying. You'll be on the edge of your seat with all this fun, fun, fun <u>electrolysis</u>.

In Molten Ionic Compounds, You Only Have Two Ions

1) When you electrolyse a <u>molten ionic compound</u>, the products are just the <u>elements</u> it's made up of.

2) A metal will form from the metal ions at the cathode (negative electrode). A gas will form from the non-metal ions at the anode (positive electrode).

For example, if you electrolyse lead bromide ($PbBr_2$) you get:
- beads of <u>molten lead</u> produced at the cathode.
- <u>brown bromine gas</u> produced at the anode.

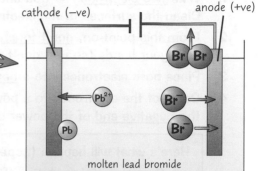

cathode (−ve)

anode (+ve)

molten lead bromide

3) Here are a few more examples:

Molten compound	Product at cathode	Product at anode
lead iodide, PbI_2	lead	iodine
potassium chloride, KCl	potassium	chlorine
aluminium oxide, Al_2O_3	aluminium	oxygen

Electrolysis of Aqueous Solutions is a Bit More Complicated

1) If an ionic compound is <u>dissolved in water</u>, the solution will contain <u>ions</u> from the <u>compound</u> plus <u>hydrogen ions</u> (H^+) and <u>hydroxide ions</u> (OH^-) from the <u>water</u>.

2) This makes predicting the <u>products of electrolysis</u> for a solution a bit tricky. Just follow these rules:

<u>CATHODE</u>:
- At the <u>cathode</u>, <u>hydrogen gas</u> will be formed if the metal is <u>more reactive</u> than hydrogen (e.g. sodium).
- If the metal is <u>less reactive</u> than hydrogen (e.g. copper), a solid layer of the <u>pure metal</u> will be formed instead.

Some reactivity series (see page 127) include hydrogen. You can use these to find out which metals are more or less reactive than hydrogen.

<u>ANODE</u>:
- At the <u>anode</u>, if <u>halide ions</u> (Cl^-, Br^-, I^-) are present, molecules of chlorine, bromine or iodine will be formed.
- If <u>no halide ions</u> are present, <u>oxygen</u> will be formed from the hydroxide ions.

<u>Example: the electrolysis of sodium chloride solution</u>

A solution of <u>sodium chloride</u> (NaCl) contains <u>four different ions</u>: Na^+, Cl^-, OH^- and H^+.

- <u>Sodium</u> metal is more reactive than hydrogen. So at the cathode <u>hydrogen gas</u> is produced.

- <u>Chloride ions</u> are present in the solution. So at the anode <u>chlorine gas</u> is produced.

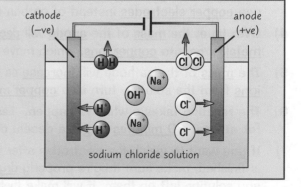

cathode (−ve)

anode (+ve)

sodium chloride solution

Page 119 tells you how to test for chlorine gas and hydrogen gas.

Faster shopping at the supermarket — use Electrolleys...

Electrolysis isn't the easiest of topics — you need to take it slow and make sure you get it.

Q1 Molten sodium bromide ($NaBr_{(l)}$) is electrolysed. What product forms at the cathode? [1 mark]

Q2 Copper chloride solution ($CuCl_{2 (aq)}$) is electrolysed. What product forms at the anode? [1 mark]

Electrolysis of Copper Sulfate Solution

One more page on electrolysis to go — this time it's all about the electrolysis of copper sulfate solution.

Here's How to Set Up an Electrolysis Experiment

PRACTICAL

You'll probably have to do an electrolysis experiment, so you need to know how to set up the equipment. Here's how you'd set it up with copper sulfate solution as the electrolyte:

1) Take two electrodes — you should use inert electrodes, e.g. carbon (graphite). Clean the surfaces of the electrodes using a piece of emery paper.

2) From this point on, don't touch the surfaces of the electrodes with your hands (so you don't get any grease on the electrodes).

3) Place both electrodes into a beaker filled with your electrolyte.

4) Connect the electrodes to a power supply using crocodile clips and wires. The electrode attached to the negative end of the power supply is the cathode. The one attached to the positive end is the anode.

Here's what will happen (hopefully):

- Copper sulfate solution ($CuSO_4$) contains four different ions — Cu^{2+}, SO_4^{2-}, H^+ and OH^-.

- Copper is less reactive than hydrogen. So at the cathode, copper is produced. You'd see a coating of copper forming on the cathode.

- There aren't any halide ions around, so at the anode oxygen and water are produced. You'd see bubbles of oxygen gas forming.

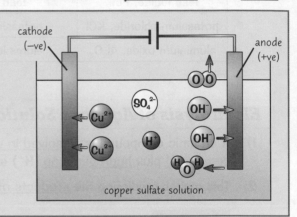

cathode (−ve)

anode (+ve)

copper sulfate solution

The test for oxygen gas is on the next page.

Non-Inert Electrodes Take Part in Electrolysis Reactions

1) Usually in electrolysis you use inert electrodes. But sometimes you might choose to use non-inert electrodes instead. Non-inert electrodes can break down into the electrolyte.

2) For example, you could use copper electrodes in a solution of copper sulfate.

3) You should use the same method and apparatus as for the electrolysis experiment above. But this time, use copper electrodes instead of carbon electrodes.

This method can be used to purify copper — see page 137 for more.

4) Over time, the mass of the anode will decrease as copper metal turns into copper ions, which move into the solution.

5) The mass of the cathode will increase as copper ions from the solution turn into copper metal.

6) The reaction takes a while to happen. Leave it running for at least 30 minutes to get a decent change in mass.

7) If you want to weigh the electrodes after the experiment is finished, make sure they're properly dry first. (If there's any solution left on them, it will make their mass look higher than it really is.)

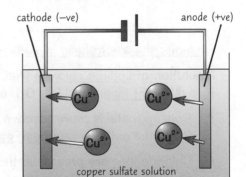

cathode (−ve)

anode (+ve)

copper sulfate solution

Electro-lite — low-fat and packed full of important ions...

You'll probably be glad to know that that's the end of electrolysis. Well, at least this page had a practical on it...

Q1   June sets up an electrolysis experiment using two copper electrodes and a copper sulfate solution. She connects it to a power supply and leaves it for 30 minutes. How would you expect the mass of the cathode to change during the experiment? Explain your answer.   [2 marks]

Tests for Gases

There are lots of ways of <u>testing</u> for different <u>gases</u> — here are the ones you need to know about...

Testing for Gases Can be Dangerous

1) When you're testing a mystery gas, you need to be <u>careful</u>.

2) Some gases (like chlorine) are <u>toxic</u>, so you don't want to just go spewing them out into your classroom.

3) If you don't know what gas you've got, carry out the tests in a <u>fume cupboard</u> to be on the safe side.

Test for Carbon Dioxide Using Limewater

1) You can test to see if a gas is <u>carbon dioxide</u> by bubbling it through <u>limewater</u>.

2) If the gas is carbon dioxide, the limewater will <u>turn cloudy</u>.

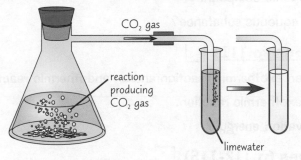

CO_2 gas

reaction producing CO_2 gas

limewater

Test for Hydrogen Using a Lighted Splint

1) Hydrogen makes a '<u>squeaky pop</u>' with a <u>lighted splint</u>.

2) The noise comes from the hydrogen burning with the oxygen in the air to form water.

squeaky pop!

hydrogen

✓ Eeeee! ♪

Test for Oxygen Using a Glowing Splint

You can <u>test</u> for oxygen by checking if the gas will <u>relight</u> a <u>glowing splint</u>.

oxygen

glowing splint

Test for Chlorine Using Damp Blue Litmus Paper

1) You can test to see if a gas is <u>chlorine</u> by holding a piece of <u>damp blue litmus paper</u> over it.

2) If the gas is chlorine, it will <u>bleach</u> the litmus paper, turning it <u>white</u>.

3) It may also turn <u>red</u> for a moment first — that's because a solution of chlorine is <u>acidic</u>.

damp blue litmus paper

chlorine

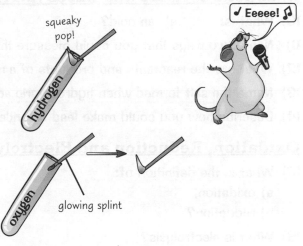

Bleach, cloudy and squeaky pop — the world's worst cereal mascots.

I'm afraid this is just one of those pages where the only thing to do is sit down and learn all four of these gas tests, including what a positive result would be, until they're stuck in your memory. Then try the questions...

Q1 Describe how you could test a gas to see if it was oxygen. State what a positive result would be. [2 marks]

Q2 A student placed a lighted splint into a test tube containing a gas. The gas burned with a squeaky pop. Suggest what gas was present in the test tube. [1 mark]

Topic C3 — Chemical Reactions

Revision Questions for Topic C3

Well, wasn't that enjoyable? Topic C3 has been my favourite topic so far I think.

* Try these questions and tick off each one when you get it right.
* When you've done all the questions under a heading and are completely happy with it, tick it off.

Conservation of Mass (p.107) ☑

1) In a reaction, how does the mass of products compare with the mass of reactants? ☑
2) Why might the mass of a reaction that takes place in an open flask look like it has decreased? ☑

Formulas and Equations (p.108-110) ☑

3) What is the charge on an oxide ion? ☑
4) Give the formula of a sulfate ion. ☑
5) What is the overall charge on an ionic compound? ☑
6) What is the state symbol for an aqueous substance? ☑

Energy Changes In Reactions (p.111) ☑

7) What is the difference between an exothermic reaction and an endothermic reaction? ☑
8) Sketch a reaction profile for an exothermic reaction. ☑
9) What is meant by the term 'activation energy'? ☑

Reactions of Acids and Bases (p.112-115) ☑

10) What is: a) an acid? b) an alkali? ☑
11) Name two ways that you could measure the pH of a solution. ☑
12) What are the reactants and products of a neutralisation reaction? ☑
13) Name the salt formed when hydrochloric acid reacts with aluminium. ☑
14) Describe how you could make lead chloride ($PbCl_2$) using a precipitation reaction. ☑

Oxidation, Reduction and Electrolysis(p.116-118) ☑

15) What is the definition of:
    a) oxidation,
    b) reduction? ☑
16) What is electrolysis? ☑
17) Molten lead bromide is split up into lead and bromine using electrolysis.
    At which electrode will the lead form? ☑
18) Describe how you would set up an experiment to electrolyse
    copper sulfate solution using inert electrodes. ☑
19) Imagine you are electrolysing a solution of copper sulfate using copper electrodes.
    What will happen to the mass of the anode during the experiment? ☑

Tests for Gases (p.119) ☑

20) What is the test for carbon dioxide gas? ☑
21) If you were testing a gas to see if it was chlorine, describe what a positive result would look like. ☑

Group 1 — Alkali Metals

You can predict how different elements will __react__ by looking at where they are in the __periodic table__ — elements in the __same group__ will react in __similar ways__. Time to take a look at some of the groups, starting with __Group 1__...

Group 1 Metals are Known as the 'Alkali Metals'

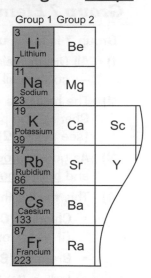

The Group 1 metals are lithium, sodium, potassium, rubidium, caesium and francium.

1) The alkali metals all have __one outer electron__
   — so they have __similar chemical properties__.

2) They all have these __physical properties__:
   - __Low melting points__ and __boiling points__ (compared with other metals).
   - __Low density__ — lithium, sodium and potassium float on water.
   - __Very soft__ — they can be cut with a knife.

3) The alkali metals form __ionic__ compounds (see page 91).

Group 1 Metals are Very Reactive

1) The Group 1 metals easily __lose__ their one __outer electron__ to form a __1+ ion__. This has a __full outer shell__, which means it's nice and __stable__.

2) The __more easily__ a metal loses its outer electrons, the __more reactive__ it is — so the Group 1 metals are very reactive.

3) As you go __down__ Group 1, the alkali metals get __more reactive__.

4) It gets __easier__ for them to __lose__ their __outer electron__ because it's further from the nucleus (the __atomic radius__ is __larger__). So the outer electron is less strongly attracted to the nucleus and __less energy__ is needed to remove it.

Reaction with Cold Water Produces a Hydroxide and Hydrogen Gas

1) When the __alkali metals__ are put in __water__, they react __strongly__.

2) The reaction produces __hydrogen gas__ and a __hydroxide__ of the metal (which is an __alkali__). For example:

Squeaky pop!

A squeaky pop shows H_2 gas is present — see p.119 for more.

$$2Na \ + \ 2H_2O \rightarrow \ 2NaOH \ + \ H_2$$
sodium + water → sodium hydroxide + hydrogen

The same reaction happens with all of the alkali metals — make sure you can write equations for them all.

3) The reactivity of Group 1 metals with water (and dilute acid — see below) increases down the group.
   - __Lithium__ will __move__ around the surface, __fizzing__ like mad.
   - __Sodium__ and __potassium__ do the same, but they also __melt__ in the heat of the reaction. The potassium even gets hot enough to __set fire__ to the hydrogen gas being produced.
   - __Rubidium__ and __caesium__ react __violently__ with water, and tend to __explode__ when they get wet...

The alkali metals also react with __dilute acids__, but with an __acid__ the products are a __salt__ and hydrogen gas.
For example: $\quad 2Na \ + \quad 2HCl \quad \rightarrow \quad 2NaCl \quad + \quad H_2$
$\qquad\qquad\qquad$ sodium + hydrochloric acid → sodium chloride + hydrogen

These reactions are __more violent__ than the ones with water. They are too __dangerous__ to do in a school lab.

And that's why you don't get caesium teaspoons... *Amongst other reasons...*

Alkali metals are really reactive. In fact they have to be stored in oil — otherwise they just react with the air.

Q1   Name the two products made when lithium reacts with water.   [2 marks]

Group 7 — Halogens

Here's a page on another periodic table group that you need to be familiar with — <u>the halogens</u>.

Group 7 Elements are Known as the Halogens

Group 7 is made up of the elements fluorine, chlorine, bromine, iodine and astatine.

1) All Group 7 elements have <u>7 electrons in their outer shell</u> — so they all have <u>similar chemical properties</u>.

2) The halogens exist as <u>molecules that contain 2 atoms</u> (e.g. Cl_2, Br_2, I_2). Sharing one pair of electrons in a <u>covalent bond</u> (see page 92) gives both atoms a <u>full outer shell</u>.

3) As you go <u>down Group 7</u>, the <u>melting points</u> and <u>boiling points</u> of the halogens <u>increase</u>.

4) This means that at <u>room temperature</u>:

- <u>Chlorine</u> (Cl_2) is a fairly reactive, poisonous, <u>green gas</u> (it has a low boiling point).
- <u>Bromine</u> (Br_2) is a poisonous, <u>red-brown liquid</u>.
- <u>Iodine</u> (I_2) is a <u>dark grey solid</u>.

	Group 6	Group 7	Group 0
			He
	O	9 F Fluorine 19	Ne
	S	17 Cl Chlorine 35.5	Ar
	Se	35 Br Bromine 80	Kr
		53 I Iodine 127	Xe
		85 At Astatine 210	Rn

Reactivity Decreases Going Down Group 7

1) A halogen atom only needs to <u>gain one electron</u> to form a <u>1– ion</u> with a <u>full outer shell</u>.

2) The <u>easier</u> it is for a halogen atom to <u>attract</u> an electron, the <u>more reactive</u> the halogen will be.

3) As you go <u>down</u> Group 7, the halogens become <u>less reactive</u>. It gets <u>harder</u> for the atoms to attract the <u>extra electron</u> to fill the outer shell when it's <u>further away</u> from the nucleus (the <u>atomic radius</u> is <u>larger</u>).

$$Cl \quad + \quad e^- \rightarrow \quad Cl^-$$

The Halogens React With Alkali Metals to Form Salts

The halogens will react strongly with alkali metals to form <u>salts</u> called <u>metal halides</u>. For example:

$$2Na \quad + \quad Cl_2 \quad \rightarrow \quad 2NaCl$$
Sodium + Chlorine → Sodium chloride

$$2K \quad + \quad Br_2 \quad \rightarrow \quad 2KBr$$
Potassium + Bromine → Potassium bromide

All the reactions between Group 1 and Group 7 elements follow this pattern — make sure you can write equations for any of them.

The Halogens Take Part in Displacement Reactions

1) A <u>more reactive</u> halogen can <u>displace</u> (push out) a <u>less reactive</u> one from a salt solution.

2) There's loads more about these reactions coming up on the next page...

Halogens — one electron short of a full shell...

Another page, another periodic table group to learn the properties and the trends of. When you're pretty confident that you've got all the stuff from this page in your head, have a go at the questions below, just to check.

Q1 Describe the trend in melting points as you go down Group 7. [1 mark]

Q2 Write a balanced symbol equation for the reaction between sodium metal (Na) and iodine (I_2). [2 marks]

Halogen Displacement Reactions

The halogens are a pretty competitive lot really. In fact the <u>more reactive</u> ones will push the <u>less reactive</u> ones out of a compound. How rude — has nobody ever taught them that it's bad manners to push?

A More Reactive Halogen Will Displace a Less Reactive One

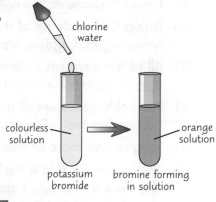

chlorine water

colourless solution → orange solution

potassium bromide   bromine forming in solution

1) The elements in Group 7 take part in <u>displacement reactions</u>.

2) A <u>displacement reaction</u> is where a <u>more reactive</u> element 'pushes out' (<u>displaces</u>) a <u>less reactive</u> element from a compound.

3) For example, <u>chlorine</u> is more reactive than <u>bromine</u>. If you add <u>chlorine water</u> (a <u>solution</u> of Cl_2) to <u>potassium bromide</u> solution, the chlorine will <u>displace</u> the <u>bromine</u> from the salt solution.

4) The <u>chlorine</u> becomes <u>chloride ions</u>. So the salt solution becomes <u>potassium chloride</u>.

5) The <u>bromide ions</u> become <u>bromine</u>, which turns the solution <u>orange</u>.

6) The <u>equation</u> for this reaction is shown below:

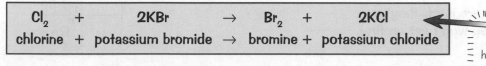

$$Cl_2 + 2KBr \rightarrow Br_2 + 2KCl$$
chlorine + potassium bromide → bromine + potassium chloride

If you ever need to write an equation for a different halogen displacement reaction, they all follow this pattern.

Displacement Reactions Show Reactivity Trends

1) You can use <u>displacement reactions</u> to show the <u>reactivity trend</u> of the halogens.

2) Put a small amount of a <u>halide salt solution</u> (e.g. potassium bromide) in a test tube. Add a few drops of a <u>halogen solution</u> (e.g. chlorine water). <u>Shake</u> the tube gently to mix everything.

3) If you see a <u>colour change</u>, then a <u>reaction</u> has happened — the halogen has <u>displaced</u> the halide from the salt. If you <u>don't</u> see a colour change, then <u>no reaction</u> has happened.

4) The table below shows what should happen when you <u>mix different combinations</u> of <u>halogen solutions</u> with <u>halide salt solutions</u>.

Start with:	Potassium chloride solution $KCl_{(aq)}$ — colourless	Potassium bromide solution $KBr_{(aq)}$ — colourless	Potassium iodide solution $KI_{(aq)}$ — colourless
Add chlorine water $Cl_{2(aq)}$ — colourless	no reaction	orange solution (Br_2) formed	brown solution (I_2) formed
Add bromine water $Br_{2(aq)}$ — orange	no reaction	no reaction	brown solution (I_2) formed
Add iodine water $I_{2(aq)}$ — brown	no reaction	no reaction	no reaction

5) <u>Chlorine</u> displaces both bromine and iodine from salt solutions. <u>Bromine</u> can't displace chlorine, but it does displace iodine. <u>Iodine</u> can't displace chlorine or bromine.

6) This shows the <u>reactivity trend</u> — the halogens get <u>less reactive</u> as you go <u>down</u> the group.

New information displaces old information from my brain...

If you remember that the halogens get less reactive as you go down the group, you can work out what will happen when you mix any halogen with any halide salt. You need to know the colour changes that go with the reactions too.

Q1   A student added a few drops of a halogen solution to some potassium iodide solution. The solution turned brown. She added a few drops of the same halogen solution to some potassium bromide solution. No reaction occurred. Name the halogen solution that the student used.   [1 mark]

Group 0 — Noble Gases

The elements in Group 0 of the periodic table are known as the <u>noble gases</u>. 'Noble' here is just being used in the old chemistry sense of being <u>unreactive</u> — nothing to do with them being particularly good.

Group 0 Elements are All Unreactive, Colourless Gases

1) Group 0 elements are called the <u>noble gases</u>.

2) Group 0 is made up of the elements helium, neon, argon, krypton, xenon and radon.

3) All of the elements in Group 0 are <u>colourless gases</u> at room temperature.

4) The noble gases are all made up of <u>single atoms</u> (not molecules). For example, <u>helium</u> is just <u>He</u>.

5) They're also more or less <u>inert</u> (they <u>don't react</u> with much at all).

6) The reason for this is that they have a <u>full outer shell</u> of electrons. This means they <u>don't</u> easily either <u>give up</u> or <u>gain</u> electrons.

7) As the noble gases are inert, they're <u>non-flammable</u> (they won't set on fire).

Group 6	Group 7	Group 0
		2 **He** Helium
		4
O	F	10 **Ne** Neon
		20
S	Cl	18 **Ar** Argon
		40
	Br	36 **Kr** Krypton
		84
	I	54 **Xe** Xenon
		131
	At	86 **Rn** Radon
		222

There are Patterns in the Properties of the Noble Gases

1) As with the other groups in the periodic table, there are <u>trends</u> in the <u>properties</u> of the noble gases.

2) There are trends in the <u>boiling points</u>, <u>melting points</u> and <u>densities</u> of Group 0 elements. Thankfully they're nice and easy to remember because they're all the <u>same</u>.

Boiling and Melting Points

1) Both boiling point and melting point <u>increase</u> as you go down the group.

2) The increase in boiling and melting points is due to an <u>increase</u> in the <u>size</u> of the atoms as you go down the group.

3) This means that there are <u>greater forces of attraction</u> between the atoms. So more energy is needed to <u>break them apart</u>.

Density

1) Density <u>increases</u> as you go down the group.

2) Helium has the <u>lowest</u> density and radon has the <u>highest</u>.

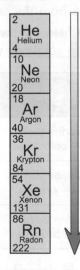

2 **He** Helium
4
10 **Ne** Neon
20
18 **Ar** Argon
40
36 **Kr** Krypton
84
54 **Xe** Xenon
131
86 **Rn** Radon
222

Boiling point, melting point and density all <u>increase</u> as you go down the group.

What's a pirate's favourite element? Arrrrgon...

The noble gases might seem a bit dull because they're so unreactive, but don't let that fool you. They're used in lots of different types of lighting and they've got quite a few different medical uses too. They're even used in lasers. Plus, of course, helium definitely makes balloons far more interesting than if you just fill them with air...

Q1   Which group of the periodic table are the noble gases in?   [1 mark]

Q2   Argon and xenon are two noble gases. Which one has the higher boiling point?   [1 mark]

Topic C4 — Predicting and Identifying Reactions and Products

Predicting Properties of Elements

You can use the <u>trends</u> (patterns) in the properties of a group to <u>predict</u> the properties of an element.

You can Predict the Properties of Different Elements

1) In the exam you could be given information about a particular <u>property</u> of the Group 0, Group 1 or Group 7 elements. For example, <u>boiling point</u>, <u>melting point</u> or <u>density</u>.

2) You might then be asked to use this information to <u>estimate the value</u> of this property for a <u>different element</u> in the group.

3) That sounds a bit tricky, but these examples will <u>guide you through it</u>.

EXAMPLE:

Use the densities of helium (0.2 kg/m³) and argon (1.8 kg/m³) to predict the density of neon.

1) You know that the <u>density</u> of the noble gases <u>increases</u> as you go <u>down the group</u>.

2) Neon comes <u>between</u> helium and argon in group 0. So you can predict that the density of neon will be <u>roughly halfway</u> between the densities of helium and argon.

3) So to predict the density of neon you just need to find the average (mean) of the two densities you know.

Predicted density of neon = (helium density + argon density) ÷ 2
= (0.2 + 1.8) ÷ 2
= 2.0 ÷ 2 = 1.0

Neon should have a density of about 1.0 kg/m³.

There are other methods you could use for these questions, but don't worry — you'd get marks for any sensible answer.

EXAMPLE:

The table below shows the boiling points of the first three Group 7 elements (halogens). Predict the boiling point of the fourth member of the group, iodine.

1) You know that the <u>boiling point</u> of the halogens <u>increases</u> as you go down Group 7, so iodine's boiling point will be <u>higher</u> than bromine's. This means it'll be a <u>larger, positive number</u>.

2) To predict how much larger, look at the <u>gaps</u> between the boiling points of the other elements:

Difference between Cl and F: (−34.6) − (−188) = 153.4

Difference between Br and Cl: (58.8) − (−34.6) = 93.4

Element	Boiling point (°C)
Fluorine (F)	−188
Chlorine (Cl)	−34.6
Bromine (Br)	58.8
Iodine (I)	?

3) The gaps aren't exactly the same, so find the <u>average (mean) gap</u>:

Average gap = (153.4 + 93.4) ÷ 2
(246.8 ÷ 2) = 123.4 °C

4) Now you can just <u>add</u> this average gap to the <u>boiling point</u> of <u>bromine</u>.

Predicted boiling point of iodine = 58.8 + 123.4 = 182.2 = 182 °C (to 3.s.f.)

The actual boiling point of iodine is 184 °C so this is a good estimate.

4) You could be asked about how an element <u>reacts</u> too, so remember — elements in the <u>same group</u> react in <u>similar ways</u>. This is because they all have the same number of <u>electrons</u> in their <u>outer shells</u> (e.g. Group 7 elements have 7 electrons in their outer shells).

5) To find out which group an element is in just look for it on the <u>periodic table</u>.

I predict that this isn't the most exciting page you've ever read...

So, for this page you needed to dust off your calculator and put your maths hat on. Well don't put either the calculator or the maths hat away yet, because here's a question to test out if you've got the hang of predicting stuff.

Q1 The boiling points of the first four noble gases are: helium = −269 °C, neon = −246 °C, argon = −186 °C and krypton = −153 °C. Predict the boiling point of xenon. [1 mark]

Reactivity of Metals

<u>Reactive metals</u> tend to do exciting, fizzy things when you drop them into acid or water. If you do the same with an <u>unreactive metal</u>, it'll just sit there. How boring. Here's a bit more detail on <u>reactivity experiments</u>...

How Metals React With Acids Tells You About Their Reactivity

1) The easier it is for a metal atom to lose its outer electrons and form a <u>positive ion</u>, the <u>more reactive</u> it will be.

2) Here's a classic experiment that you can do to show that some metals are <u>more reactive</u> than others. All you do is put little pieces of different <u>metals</u> into <u>dilute hydrochloric acid</u>:

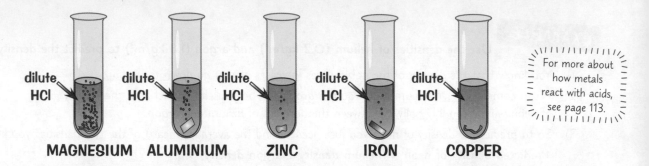

dilute HCl — MAGNESIUM   dilute HCl — ALUMINIUM   dilute HCl — ZINC   dilute HCl — IRON   dilute HCl — COPPER

For more about how metals react with acids, see page 113.

3) The <u>speed</u> of the reaction is shown by the <u>rate</u> at which the <u>bubbles</u> of hydrogen gas are given off.

4) The <u>more reactive</u> the metal, the <u>faster</u> the bubbles will form and the <u>faster</u> the reaction is.

5) Very reactive metals (e.g. <u>magnesium</u>) will <u>fizz strongly</u>. Less reactive metals (e.g. <u>zinc</u>) will <u>bubble a bit</u>. Unreactive metals (e.g. <u>copper</u>) will <u>not</u> react with dilute acids <u>at all</u>.

You could also follow the rate of the reaction by using a gas syringe to measure the volume of gas given off at set time intervals.

Metals Also React With Water

You can also use the <u>reactions</u> of metals with <u>water</u> to work out the order of reactivity for those metals. This is the basic reaction:

> metal + water → metal hydroxide + hydrogen

squeaky pop!
metal
bubbles of H_2 gas
water

1) Very reactive metals like <u>potassium</u>, <u>sodium</u>, <u>lithium</u> and <u>calcium</u> will all react <u>strongly</u> with water.

2) The <u>most reactive</u> metal will react the <u>most strongly</u>. So <u>potassium</u> will react a little more strongly than <u>sodium</u>, then <u>lithium</u>, then <u>calcium</u> (in that order).

3) Less reactive metals like <u>magnesium</u>, <u>zinc</u> and <u>iron</u> won't react much with cold water, but they will react with <u>steam</u> (this time giving a <u>metal oxide</u> and <u>hydrogen</u>).

4) <u>Copper</u> won't react with either water or steam.

I AM NOT HIGHLY REACTIVE — OK...

This stuff isn't too bad — who knows, you might even get to have a go at these experiments in class...

Q1 A student is given small samples of three metals, A, B and C. He places them in dilute hydrochloric acid. Nothing happens to Metal A. Metal B fizzes strongly. Metal C fizzes a bit.
  a) Put the three metals in order, from most reactive to least reactive. [1 mark]
  b) One of the metals was zinc, one was magnesium, and one was copper. Use this information to identify metals A, B and C. [1 mark]

Topic C4 — Predicting and Identifying Reactions and Products

The Reactivity Series and Displacement

There's just time to meet one more type of reaction that can help you to work out how <u>reactive</u> a <u>metal</u> is...

The Reactivity Series Shows How Reactive Metals Are

A <u>reactivity series</u> is just a table that lists <u>metals</u> in order of their <u>reactivity</u>. Here's an example:

The Reactivity Series	
Potassium	K
Sodium	Na
Calcium	Ca
Magnesium	Mg
Aluminium	Al
Zinc	Zn
Iron	Fe
Copper	Cu
Silver	Ag

most reactive

least reactive

The reactivity series can help you to work out the best way of extracting a metal from its ore — see page 136 for more.

I shall not react.

More Reactive Metals Displace Less Reactive Ones

1) If you put a <u>more reactive metal</u> into a salt solution that contains a <u>less reactive metal</u>, the reactive metal will <u>replace</u> the <u>less reactive metal</u> in the salt.

> <u>Example</u>: if you put an <u>iron nail</u> in a solution of <u>copper sulfate</u>, the more reactive iron will "<u>kick out</u>" the less reactive copper from the salt. You end up with <u>iron sulfate solution</u> and <u>copper metal</u>.
>
> copper sulfate + iron → iron sulfate + copper
> $CuSO_4$ + Fe → $FeSO_4$ + Cu

2) If you put a <u>less reactive metal</u> into a salt solution that contains a <u>more reactive metal</u>, <u>nothing</u> happens.

> <u>Example</u>: if you put a small piece of <u>silver</u> metal into a solution of <u>copper sulfate</u>, <u>nothing happens</u>. The more reactive metal (copper) is already in the salt.

3) You can use displacement reactions to <u>work out</u> where in the reactivity series a metal should go.

> <u>Example</u>: A student adds some <u>metals</u> to <u>metal salt solutions</u> and records whether any <u>reactions</u> happen. Use her table of results to work out an <u>order of reactivity</u> for the metals.
>
> | | copper nitrate | magnesium chloride | zinc sulfate |
> |---|---|---|---|
> | copper | no reaction | no reaction | no reaction |
> | magnesium | magnesium nitrate and copper formed | no reaction | magnesium sulfate and zinc formed |
> | zinc | zinc nitrate and copper formed | no reaction | no reaction |
>
> - Magnesium <u>displaces</u> both <u>copper</u> and <u>zinc</u>. So it is <u>more reactive</u> than both.
> - Copper <u>is displaced by</u> both <u>magnesium</u> and <u>zinc</u>. So it is <u>less reactive</u> than both.
> - Zinc <u>can displace copper</u>, but <u>not</u> <u>magnesium</u>. So it must go between them.
>
> The <u>order of reactivity</u>, <u>from most to least</u>, is: <u>magnesium, zinc, copper</u>

And that's why Iron Man never goes swimming in copper sulfate...

You could be given the results of an experiment and have to use them to put the metals into an order of reactivity. Or you could be told their reactivities and then asked to predict how they'll react. Make sure you can do both.

Q1   Tin sits between iron and copper in the reactivity series.
State whether tin would displace zinc from zinc sulfate solution and explain your answer.   [2 marks]

Reaction Rates

Reactions can be <u>fast</u> or <u>slow</u> — you've probably already realised that. It's exciting stuff. Honest.

The Rate of Reaction is a Measure of How Fast the Reaction Happens

1) The <u>rate of a reaction</u> is just <u>how fast</u> it happens.

2) You can find the rate of reaction <u>either</u> by measuring how fast the <u>reactants are used up</u> or how fast the <u>products are formed</u>. Here's the formula for calculating the <u>rate</u> of a reaction:

$$\text{rate of reaction} = \frac{\text{amount of reactant used or amount of product formed}}{\text{time}}$$

You Can Do Experiments to Follow Reaction Rates

There are different ways to <u>measure</u> the rate of a reaction. Here are three examples:

Precipitation

1) This method works for any reaction where mixing <u>two see-through solutions</u> produces a <u>precipitate</u> (a <u>solid</u>). This makes the solution <u>cloudy</u>.

2) You <u>mix</u> the two solutions and put the flask on a piece of paper that has a <u>mark</u> on it.

3) <u>Watch</u> the mark through the mixture and measure how long it takes for the mark to be <u>covered up</u>. The <u>faster</u> it disappears, the <u>faster</u> the reaction.

<u>Example</u>: mixing colourless <u>sodium thiosulfate</u> and colourless <u>hydrochloric acid</u> produces a <u>yellow precipitate</u> of <u>sulfur.</u>

Change in Mass (Usually Gas Given Off)

1) You can use a <u>mass balance</u> to measure the rate of any reaction that <u>produces a gas</u>.

2) As the gas is released, the <u>mass</u> of the reaction mixture will fall.

3) The <u>faster</u> the reading on the balance <u>falls</u>, the <u>faster</u> the reaction.

4) If you record the <u>mass</u> of the reaction at <u>set times</u> (e.g. <u>every 10 s</u>), you can plot a <u>graph</u> of <u>loss in mass</u> against <u>time</u>.

5) The gas that's made is released into the room, so if the gas is <u>harmful</u> you should do the experiment in a <u>fume cupboard</u>.

cotton wool plug — lets gases through but stops any other reactants getting out.

The Volume of Gas Given Off

1) You can use a <u>gas syringe</u> to measure the <u>volume</u> of gas given off by a reaction.

2) The <u>more</u> gas given off during a set amount of <u>time</u>, the <u>faster</u> the reaction.

3) You can use your results to plot a graph of <u>volume of gas</u> produced against <u>time</u>.

gas syringe

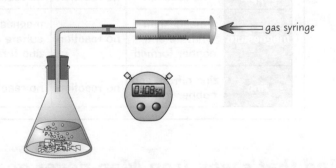

Some reactions are really fast — o t h e r r e a c t i o n s a r e s l o w...

So we have three different ways to follow reaction rates here. Precipitation, mass change and volume of gas made.

Q1   Describe how you could follow the rate of a reaction where mixing two solutions gives a precipitate. [2 marks]

PRACTICAL

Rate Experiments

You'll probably have to <u>measure</u> the <u>rate of a reaction</u> in class at some point. Time to learn how to do it...

Reaction of Hydrochloric Acid and Calcium Carbonate

You can use this experiment to show how <u>surface area</u> affects <u>reaction rate</u>.

1) Set the equipment up as shown in the diagram on the right.

2) Use the <u>gas syringe</u> to measure the <u>volume</u> of gas produced. Take readings at <u>set time intervals</u>. Record your results in a table.

3) Now <u>repeat</u> the experiment using the <u>same volume</u> and <u>concentration</u> of acid and the <u>same mass</u> of <u>chalk powder</u>.

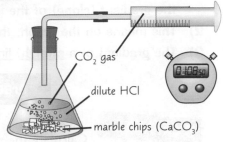

CO₂ gas
dilute HCl
marble chips (CaCO₃)

Finer Particles of Solid Mean a Higher Rate

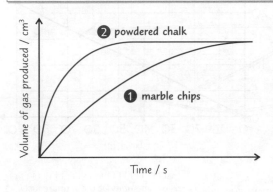

2 powdered chalk
1 marble chips

Volume of gas produced / cm³
Time / s

1) You can plot a <u>graph</u> to show your results. Put <u>time</u> on the <u>x-axis</u> and <u>volume of gas</u> on the <u>y-axis</u>.

2) The <u>fastest</u> reaction will be the line with the <u>steepest slope</u> at the <u>start</u>. (The line goes <u>flat</u> when the reaction <u>finishes</u>.)

3) Using <u>finer particles</u> (<u>chalk powder</u> instead of <u>marble chips</u>) gives the solid a <u>larger surface area</u> for the same volume.

4) Look at the graph on the left. <u>Line 2</u> is much steeper at the start than <u>line 1</u>. So the <u>finer</u> the particles are (the <u>greater</u> the surface area of the solid), the <u>faster</u> the reaction goes.

Reaction of Magnesium Metal with Dilute HCl

You can use this experiment to show how <u>concentration</u> affects <u>reaction rate</u>.

1) The reaction gives off <u>hydrogen gas</u>, so you can measure the <u>change in mass</u> as the gas is formed using a <u>mass balance</u>.

2) Take <u>readings</u> of the <u>mass</u> at <u>set time intervals</u>.

3) Put the results in a <u>table</u>. Work out the <u>loss in mass</u> for each reading.

4) Now <u>repeat</u> the experiment using a different <u>concentration</u> of the acid. You must keep the <u>volume</u> of the acid and the <u>mass</u> and <u>surface area</u> of the magnesium <u>the same</u>.

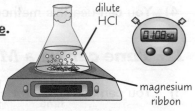

dilute HCl
magnesium ribbon

More Concentrated Solutions Mean a Higher Rate

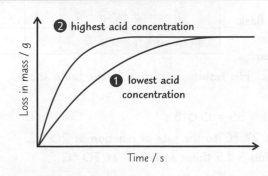

2 highest acid concentration
1 lowest acid concentration

Loss in mass / g
Time / s

1) You can plot a <u>graph</u> to show your results for this experiment too. Put <u>time</u> on the <u>x-axis</u> and <u>loss in mass</u> on the <u>y-axis</u>.

2) Look at the graph on the left. <u>Line 2</u> is much steeper at the start than <u>line 1</u>. So the <u>higher</u> the concentration of the acid is, the <u>faster</u> the reaction goes.

3) You could <u>repeat</u> the experiment with <u>other concentrations</u> of acid and add those results to your graph too.

I prefer chalk to marble chips — I like the finer things in life...

Alright, I think that's definitely enough graphs for one page. Time for a question instead, I reckon...

Q1   A student adds zinc to two flasks containing different concentrations of acid to see how concentration affects reaction rate. Name two things she must keep the same for both flasks to make it a fair test. [2 marks]

Topic C5 — Monitoring and Controlling Chemical Reactions

Calculating Rates

You can work out rates of reaction using <u>graphs</u> or <u>tables</u>. The choice is yours. (Well, it's the examiner's really.)

Faster Rates of Reaction are Shown by Steeper Gradients

1) On a graph that shows the <u>amount of product formed</u> or <u>reactant used up</u> against <u>time</u>, the <u>gradient</u> (<u>slope</u>) of the line is equal to the <u>rate</u> of the reaction.

2) This means on the graph, the <u>steeper</u> the slope of the line is, the <u>faster</u> the rate of reaction.

3) The gradient of a <u>straight line</u> is given by the equation:

$$\text{gradient} = \text{change in } y \div \text{change in } x$$

EXAMPLE:

Calculate the rate of the reaction shown on the graph on the right.

1) Find two <u>points on the line</u> that are <u>easy to read</u> the x and y values of (ones that pass through grid lines). The two points should also be a <u>good distance apart</u>.

2) Draw a line straight <u>down</u> from the higher point and straight <u>across</u> from the lower one to make a <u>triangle</u>.

3) The <u>height</u> of your triangle = <u>change in y</u>
The <u>base</u> of your triangle = <u>change in x</u>
Change in y = 16 cm^3 − 5 cm^3 = 11 cm^3
Change in x = 65 s − 20 s = 45 s

4) Use the formula to work out the <u>gradient</u> of the line, which is also the rate.
Rate = change in y ÷ change in x = 11 cm^3 ÷ 45 s = 0.24 cm^3/s

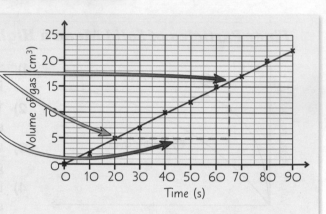

The units of the rate are just 'units of y-axis ÷ units of x-axis'.

4) You can use this method to find the gradient of <u>any straight line</u> (even a <u>straight bit</u> on a <u>curved graph</u>).

1 ÷ Time can be a Measure of Rate

1) You can use $\dfrac{1}{\text{time}}$ (or $\dfrac{1}{t}$) as a measure of the <u>rate of a reaction</u>.

2) The <u>larger</u> the value of $\dfrac{1}{t}$, the <u>faster</u> the reaction is going.

3) This is a useful when you have an experiment where you can <u>only</u> measure the <u>time</u> the reaction takes to <u>finish</u> (like the disappearing mark) and <u>not</u> how much product is made over time.

If you measure the time in seconds, the units of $\frac{1}{t}$ will be $\frac{1}{s}$ — this can also be written as s^{-1}.

EXAMPLE:

A student added sodium thiosulfate to hydrochloric acid in a flask. A yellow precipitate of sulfur formed. He placed a mark under the flask and timed how long it took for the mark to disappear.

Temperature (°C)	20	27
Time for mark to disappear (s)	81	55

The student carried out the experiment at 20 °C and 27 °C. His results are shown in the table above.

a) Find 1/t for both temperatures.
At 20 °C: 1 ÷ t = 1 ÷ 81 = 0.012 s^{-1} At 27 °C, 1 ÷ 55 = 0.018 s^{-1}

b) Using the values for 1/t, compare the rate of reaction at 27 °C to the rate of reaction at 20 °C.
(0.018 ÷ 0.012) = 1.5. So, at 27 °C the rate of reaction is 1.5 times as fast as at 20 °C.

My rate of revision increases if you bring me tea...

Make sure you've got the hang of how to work out a gradient. And remember — steeper gradient = faster rate.

Q1   A graph shows the volume of gas made in a reaction against time. What does the gradient tell you? [1 mark]

Collision Theory

The rate of a reaction can be affected by <u>temperature</u>, the <u>concentration</u> of the reactants (or the <u>pressure</u> for gases) and the <u>size of the particles</u> (for solids). Want to know why? Read on...

Particles Must Collide with Enough Energy in Order to React

1) <u>Reaction rates</u> are explained by <u>collision theory</u>.

2) A <u>collision</u> is just when two particles <u>hit each other</u>.

3) <u>The rate of a chemical reaction</u> depends on:

   • The <u>frequency</u> of collisions between the particles (<u>how often</u> they collide). The <u>more</u> successful collisions there are, the <u>faster</u> the reaction is.

   • The <u>energy</u> of the collisions. Particles have to collide with <u>enough energy</u> for the collision to be <u>successful</u>.

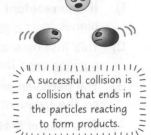

A successful collision is a collision that ends in the particles reacting to form products.

The More Successful Collisions, the Higher the Rate of Reaction

1) Reactions happen when particles <u>collide</u> with <u>enough energy</u> to react.

2) If you <u>increase</u> the <u>number</u> of collisions, the reaction happens <u>more quickly</u> (the <u>rate increases</u>).

Increasing the Temperature Increases Rate

1) When the <u>temperature is increased</u>, the particles <u>move faster</u>.

2) If the particles move faster, they're going to <u>collide more often</u>.

3) Higher temperatures also increase the <u>energy</u> of the collisions, since the particles are moving <u>faster</u>.

4) This means that at <u>higher</u> temperatures there will be more <u>successful collisions</u> — <u>more particles</u> will <u>collide</u> with <u>enough energy</u> to react.

5) So <u>increasing</u> the temperature <u>increases</u> the rate of reaction.

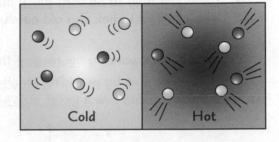

Cold Hot

Increasing Concentration (or Pressure) Increases Rate

1) If a <u>solution</u> is made more <u>concentrated</u>, it means that there are <u>more particles</u> in the same volume.

2) This makes collisions <u>more likely</u>. So <u>increasing concentration</u> increases the reaction rate.

3) In a <u>gas</u>, increasing the <u>pressure</u> means that the particles are <u>more crowded</u>.

4) More particles in the same volume of gas means that the frequency of <u>collisions</u> between particles will <u>increase</u>. So the rate of reaction will also <u>increase</u>.

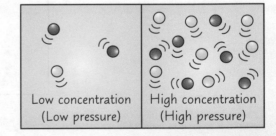

Low concentration (Low pressure) High concentration (High pressure)

Collision theory — it's always the other driver...

Increasing the number of collisions that happen always increases reaction rate. Increasing the energy that the particles have increases the rate too, because then more of them will have enough energy to react when they collide.

Q1   Explain why raising the temperature increases the rate of a reaction.   [3 marks]

Collision Theory and Catalysts

Here's another page on collision theory, plus a chunk about <u>catalysts</u> to spice it up a bit.
Catalysts are very important — they <u>increase reaction rate</u> and <u>reduce energy costs</u> in industrial reactions.

Smaller Solid Particles (or More Surface Area) Means a Higher Rate

1) If one reactant is a <u>solid</u>, breaking it into <u>smaller</u> pieces <u>increases its surface area to volume ratio</u>.

2) This just means that a <u>crushed up solid</u> has a <u>bigger</u> <u>surface area</u> than the same amount of solid in <u>one lump</u>.

3) The particles around it will have <u>more area to hit</u>, so the frequency of collisions will <u>increase</u>.

4) This means that the rate of reaction is faster for solids with a larger <u>surface area to volume ratio</u>.

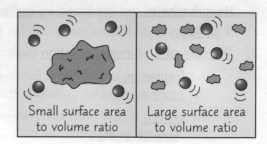

Small surface area to volume ratio | Large surface area to volume ratio

A Catalyst Increases the Rate of a Reaction

A <u>catalyst</u> is a substance which increases the <u>rate of a reaction</u> <u>without</u> being chemically changed or used up in the reaction.

1) Because it <u>isn't</u> used up, you only need a <u>tiny bit</u> to catalyse large amounts of reactants.

2) Catalysts tend to be very <u>fussy</u> about which reactions they catalyse. You can't just stick any old catalyst in a reaction and expect it to work.

• Catalysts work by <u>decreasing</u> the <u>activation energy</u> (see page 111) needed for a reaction to happen.

• They do this by providing an <u>alternative reaction pathway</u> (a different way for the reaction to happen) that has a <u>lower activation energy</u>. You can see this if you look at a <u>reaction profile</u>:

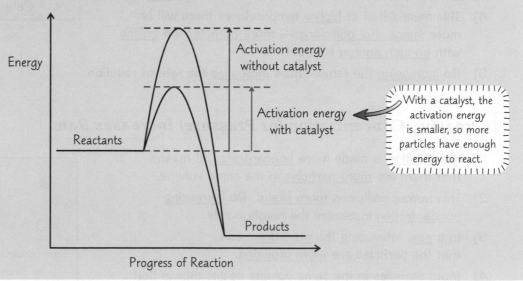

With a catalyst, the activation energy is smaller, so more particles have enough energy to react.

Catalysts are chemical stars — but success won't change them...

A key thing to remember here is that catalysts don't get used up by the reaction.
They increase the rate of reaction by lowering the activation energy.

Q1   Would you expect the rate of reaction between an acid and a metal to be faster with the metal in the form of powder or pieces of metal ribbon? Explain your answer. [3 marks]

Q2   What is a catalyst? [2 marks]

Identifying Catalysts

Working out whether a substance is a <u>catalyst</u> for a reaction is as simple as sticking it into the reaction and seeing what happens. But remember to keep <u>everything the same</u> except for the substance you're testing.

You can Identify Catalysts in Chemical Reactions

1) To find out if a substance is a catalyst for a reaction, you can do an <u>experiment</u>.

2) For example, weigh out a set mass of a <u>solid</u> that you think might be a catalyst for a reaction between two <u>solutions</u>. Measure the <u>reaction rate</u> without the solid. Then <u>add the solid</u> and measure the reaction rate again.

3) If the rate <u>increases</u> and the solid appears to be <u>unchanged</u>, it could be a catalyst.

4) To make it a <u>fair test</u>, you need to keep everything else the same, so that nothing else can affect the rate of reaction. That means keeping the <u>volumes</u> and <u>concentrations</u> of solutions and the <u>temperature</u> the same.

5) You can check that none of the solid has been <u>used up</u> by <u>filtering</u> it out at the end of the experiment. Then you can <u>dry</u> it and measure the <u>mass</u> to check it's all still there.

EXAMPLE:

Hydrogen peroxide (H_2O_2) can break down into water and oxygen:

$$2H_2O_{2(l)} \rightarrow 2H_2O_{(l)} + O_{2(g)}$$

At room temperature this reaction happens very slowly. A catalyst can be used to speed it up. A student tested three different solids to see if they were catalysts for this reaction. Her results are shown in the table below.

Substance added	Amount of oxygen gas released after 1 minute
No substance added	0 cm^3
MnO_2	44 cm^3
KI	32 cm^3
ZnO	0 cm^3

After each experiment the appearance and mass of the added solid was unchanged. Which of these substances could be catalysts for the reaction? Explain your answer.

MnO_2 and KI could both be catalysts for this reaction. Both of these substances increased the amount of oxygen gas collected in 1 minute compared to the reaction without a catalyst. Both were unchanged at the end of the reaction.

Enzymes Control Cell Reactions

1) <u>Enzymes</u> are <u>biological catalysts</u>.

2) This means that they <u>catalyse</u> (<u>speed up</u>) the <u>chemical reactions</u> in living cells.

3) Reactions catalysed by enzymes include:

   • <u>respiration</u> — a process that living things use to produce energy.

   • <u>photosynthesis</u> — a process that plants use to make their own food.

Potato peel will speed up the hydrogen peroxide reaction too...

That's chemistry for you — weird. There's also a more fun version of that H_2O_2 experiment using washing-up liquid. Try asking your teacher to give a demonstration of the 'elephant's toothpaste' reaction. You won't regret it.

Q1   A student adds some dark brown lead dioxide powder to a flask of hydrogen peroxide solution. Lead dioxide is a catalyst for the breakdown of hydrogen peroxide. With reference to the catalyst, describe what you would expect to see in the flask after the reaction had finished.   [1 mark]

Dynamic Equilibrium

<u>Reversible reactions</u> — products forming from reactants and reactants forming from products. I can't keep up...

Reversible Reactions can go Forwards and Backwards

A <u>reversible reaction</u> is one where the <u>products</u> can react with each other to produce the original <u>reactants</u>.
In other words, <u>it can go both ways</u>.

$$A + B \rightleftharpoons C + D$$

The '$\rightleftharpoons$' symbol shows that the reaction goes both ways.

Reversible Reactions Will Reach Equilibrium

1) As the <u>reactants</u> (A and B) react, their <u>concentrations fall</u> — so the <u>forward reaction</u> will <u>slow down</u>.

2) As more and more of the <u>products</u> (C and D) are made, their <u>concentrations rise</u> — so the <u>backward reaction</u> will <u>speed up</u>.

3) After a while the forward reaction will be going at <u>exactly the same rate</u> as the backward one — this is <u>equilibrium</u>.

4) At equilibrium <u>both</u> reactions are still <u>happening</u>, but there's <u>no overall effect</u>. A and B are reacting to make C and D at the same rate as C and D are reacting to make A and B.

5) This is called a <u>dynamic equilibrium</u>.

6) A dynamic equilibrium means the <u>concentrations</u> of reactants and products have reached a balance and <u>won't change</u>.

7) Equilibrium can only be reached if the reversible reaction happens in a '<u>closed system</u>'.

8) A <u>closed system</u> just means that none of the reactants or products can <u>escape</u>.

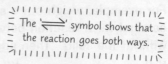

Forward Reaction

Same rate at equilibrium

Backward Reaction

The Position of Equilibrium can be on the Right or the Left

1) When a reaction's at equilibrium it <u>doesn't</u> mean the amounts of reactants and products are <u>equal</u>.

2) Sometimes the equilibrium will <u>lie to the right</u>.
This means that, at equilibrium, there are <u>lots of the products</u> and <u>not much of the reactants</u> around.

3) Sometimes the equilibrium will <u>lie to the left</u>.
This means that, at equilibrium, there are <u>lots of the reactants</u> but <u>not much of the products</u> around.

4) The exact <u>position of equilibrium</u> depends on the <u>conditions</u> (as well as the reaction itself).

Three Things Can Change the Position of Equilibrium

These three things can <u>change</u> the <u>position of equilibrium</u>:

1) **Temperature**
2) **Pressure** (if your reaction involves gases)
3) **Concentration**

By changing these things you can end up with <u>more of the reactants</u> (or <u>more of the products</u>).

Dynamic equilibrium — lots of activity, but not to any great effect*...

Keep an eagle eye out for that arrow that shows you that a reaction is reversible. I'd hate you to miss it.

Q1   Explain what is meant by the term 'reversible reaction'.   [1 mark]

Q2   What does it mean if a reaction takes place in a closed system?   [1 mark]

Revision Questions for Topics C4 and C5

Hooray, that's <u>Topic C4</u> and <u>Topic C5</u> done — now have a go at these questions to see how much you remember.
- Try these questions and <u>tick off each one</u> when you <u>get it right</u>.
- When you've done <u>all the questions</u> under a heading and are <u>completely happy</u> with it, tick it off.

Group 1 — Alkali Metals (p.121) ☑

1) List three physical properties of the alkali metals. ☑
2) Describe why Group 1 metals are so reactive. ☑
3) Write a balanced symbol equation to show the reaction between sodium and water. ☑

Group 7 — Halogens (p.122-123) ☑

4) How many electrons do halogens have in their outer shells? ☑
5) Describe the appearance of iodine at room temperature. ☑
6) Describe how the reactivity of the elements changes as you go down Group 7. ☑
7) Chlorine (Cl_2) can displace bromine from potassium bromide (KBr).
   Describe the colour change that you would see when this reaction happened. ☑
8) Can iodine displace bromine from potassium bromide solution? ☑

Group 0 — Noble Gases and Predicting Properties (p.124-125) ☑

9) Why are the elements in Group 0 inert (unreactive)? ☑
10) Would you expect argon to have a higher melting point than neon? Explain your answer. ☑

Metals and Reactivity (p.126-127) ☑

11) True or false? The easier it is for a metal atom to form a positive ion, the more reactive it will be. ☑
12) Describe how you could test the reactivity of different metals in the lab using hydrochloric acid. ☑
13) Iron is above copper in the reactivity series.
    Would any reaction happen if a piece of copper metal was put in iron sulfate solution? ☑

Rates of Reactions (p.128-130) ☑

14) What is the 'rate' of a reaction? ☑
15) Describe how you would set up an experiment to follow the rate of a reaction
    where the mass of the reaction mixture falls over the course of the reaction. ☑
16) If you draw a graph showing the volume of gas produced by a reaction over time,
    which variable should go on the x-axis? ☑
17) Describe how you would find the rate of a reaction from a straight line graph. ☑

Collision Theory and Catalysts (p.131-133) ☑

18) State how the frequency of successful collisions affects the rate of a reaction. ☑
19) What effect will increasing the concentration of the reactants have on the rate of a reaction? ☑
20) What effect does a catalyst have on the activation energy needed for a reaction to take place? ☑
21) Sketch a reaction profile showing the same reaction with and without a catalyst. ☑
22) What is an enzyme? ☑

Dynamic Equilibrium (p.134) ☑

23) Draw the symbol which shows that a reaction is reversible. ☑
24) If the position of equilibrium for a reversible reaction lies to the right,
    what does that tell you about the relative amounts of reactants and products present? ☑

Topic C5 — Monitoring and Controlling Chemical Reactions

Extracting Metals from Their Ores

A few <u>unreactive metals</u>, like gold, are found in the Earth as the metal itself, rather than as a compound. But most metals have to be <u>extracted</u> from <u>rocks</u> — I bet you're just itching to find out how...

Row faster men!

We can't — it's these cursed metal oars.

Ores Contain Enough Metal to Make Extraction Worthwhile

1) A <u>metal ore</u> is a <u>rock</u> which contains <u>enough metal</u> to make it worth <u>extracting</u> the metal from it.

2) In many cases the ore is an <u>oxide</u> of the metal. For example, the main <u>aluminium ore</u> is called <u>bauxite</u> — it's made up of <u>aluminium oxide</u> (Al_2O_3).

Metals Need to be Extracted from Their Ores

1) Some metals are <u>extracted</u> (separated out) from their ores by <u>reduction with carbon</u> (see below).

2) Other metals are extracted using <u>electrolysis</u> (splitting a compound apart with electricity — see pages 116-118). <u>Electrolysis</u> can also be used to <u>purify</u> metals (see next page).

3) There are other ways to extract metals too. Some metals can be extracted from their ores using <u>displacement reactions</u> (see page 127).

Some Metals are Extracted by Reduction with Carbon

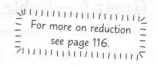

For more on reduction see page 116.

1) A metal can be <u>extracted</u> from its ore chemically by <u>reduction</u> using <u>carbon</u>.

2) Reducing an ore just means <u>removing the oxygen</u> from the metal compound that's in it. This is usually done by <u>heating</u> the metal ore with <u>carbon</u>. For example:

$$2CuO \quad + \quad C \quad \rightarrow \quad 2Cu \quad + \quad CO_2$$
copper oxide + carbon → copper + carbon dioxide

3) Whether or not you can extract a metal from its ore by reducing it with carbon depends on the position of the metal in the <u>reactivity series</u> (see page 127).

- Metals <u>BELOW</u> carbon in the reactivity series can be extracted from their ores by <u>reduction</u> with <u>carbon</u>. For example, <u>iron oxide</u> is reduced in a <u>blast furnace</u> to make <u>iron</u>.

- This is because carbon <u>can only take the oxygen</u> away from metals which are <u>less reactive</u> than carbon <u>itself</u> is.

- Metals <u>ABOVE</u> carbon in the reactivity series have to be extracted using <u>electrolysis</u> (see next page). This is more expensive.

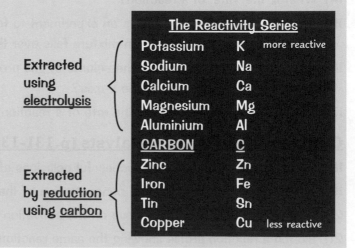

The Reactivity Series		
Potassium	K	more reactive
Sodium	Na	
Calcium	Ca	
Magnesium	Mg	
Aluminium	Al	
CARBON	**C**	
Zinc	Zn	
Iron	Fe	
Tin	Sn	
Copper	Cu	less reactive

Extracted using electrolysis

Extracted by reduction using carbon

[Please insert ore-ful pun here]...

Make sure you've got that reactivity series stuff clear in your head. If a metal's below carbon in the reactivity series, then it's less reactive than carbon and can be extracted from its ore by reduction using carbon.

Q1   Could you extract tin from its metal ore by reducing it with carbon? Explain your answer.   [1 mark]

Extracting Metals with Electrolysis

Electrolysis is expensive. But it's also really useful for extracting reactive metals from their ores...

Some Metals have to be Extracted by Electrolysis

1) Metals that are more reactive than carbon are extracted from their ores using electrolysis. (See pages 116-118 for more on electrolysis.)

2) First the metal ore is melted. Then an electric current is passed through it.

3) The metal is produced at the cathode. A non-metal, usually oxygen, will be made at the anode.

4) Electricity is expensive, so this process costs a lot more than reduction with carbon.

Example: Extracting aluminium from aluminium oxide (Al_2O_3).

1) Aluminium oxide has a very high melting point. It's mixed with another aluminium compound called cryolite to lower the melting point. The molten ore is then electrolysed.

2) The aluminium ions move to the cathode where they form aluminium atoms.

3) The oxide ions move to the anode where they react to form oxygen molecules.

4) The molten (liquid) aluminium metal sinks to the bottom of the tank, where it is collected.

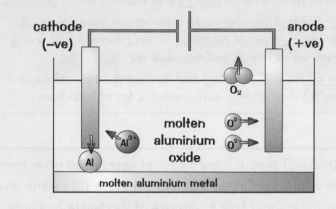

Copper Can be Purified Using Electrolysis

1) Copper can be easily extracted by reduction with carbon.

2) However, the copper produced this way is impure.

3) So electrolysis is also used to purify it, even though it's quite expensive.

4) This produces very pure copper.

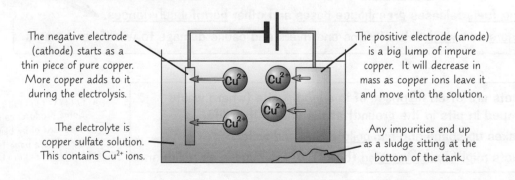

The negative electrode (cathode) starts as a thin piece of pure copper. More copper adds to it during the electrolysis.

The electrolyte is copper sulfate solution. This contains Cu^{2+} ions.

The positive electrode (anode) is a big lump of impure copper. It will decrease in mass as copper ions leave it and move into the solution.

Any impurities end up as a sludge sitting at the bottom of the tank.

This is just the same as the electrolysis of copper sulfate solution using non-inert electrodes — you saw that on page 118.

Metal Extraction — it will cost you more than a few coppers...

More electrolysis? It's just cropping up everywhere. That means there's no excuse not to know it.

Q1   When aluminium oxide is electrolysed, at which electrode is aluminium formed?   [1 mark]

Life-Cycle Assessments

If a company wants to make a new product, it will carry out a <u>life-cycle assessment</u> (LCA).
This looks at every stage of the product's life to assess the <u>impact</u> it would have on the <u>environment</u>.

Life-Cycle Assessments Show the Environmental Cost of Making a Product

1) A <u>life-cycle assessment (LCA)</u> looks at the impact that a product
has on the <u>environment</u> at each stage of its life.

2) These stages are:
  - making the <u>material</u> from natural raw materials
    (For example, if you want to make a product using copper, you'll have to consider
    the effect of mining the copper ore and extracting the metal from it.)
  - making the <u>product</u> from the material
  - <u>using</u> the product
  - <u>disposing</u> of the product.

Making the material

1) <u>Metals</u> have to be <u>mined</u> and <u>extracted</u> from their ores.
   These processes need a lot of <u>energy</u> and cause a lot of <u>pollution</u>.

2) <u>Raw materials</u> for making chemicals often come from <u>crude oil</u>.
   Crude oil is a <u>non-renewable resource</u> (it isn't formed fast enough
   to replace what we're using) and supplies are <u>decreasing</u>.

3) Getting <u>crude oil</u> from the ground and turning it into useful raw
   materials uses a lot of <u>energy</u> and creates a lot of pollution.

Making the product

1) <u>Manufacturing</u> (making) products uses a lot of <u>energy</u> and other resources.

2) It can also cause a lot of <u>pollution</u>, e.g. <u>harmful gases</u> (like sulfur dioxide).

3) You also need to think about how to <u>dispose</u> of any <u>waste</u> products.

4) Some waste can be <u>recycled</u> and turned into other <u>useful chemicals</u>.
   This reduces the amount that ends up polluting the environment.

5) Most chemical manufacture needs <u>water</u>. Businesses have to make sure they
   don't put <u>polluted</u> water back into the environment at the end of the process.

Using the product

<u>Using</u> the product can also damage the environment. For example:

1) <u>Paint</u> can give off <u>toxic fumes</u>.

2) <u>Burning fuels</u> releases <u>greenhouse gases</u> and other <u>harmful substances</u>.

3) <u>Fertilisers</u> can <u>wash</u> into streams and rivers and cause damage to wildlife and plants.

There's more on greenhouse gases on page 145.

Disposing of the product

1) Products are often <u>disposed</u> of in a <u>landfill</u> site (where waste
   is dumped in pits in the ground) at the end of their life.

2) This takes up space and can <u>pollute</u> land and water.

3) Products might be <u>incinerated</u> (burnt), which causes air pollution.

Some products can be disposed of by being recycled (see page 140).

My cycle assessment — two wheels, a bell, an uncomfortable seat...

Don't get your bicycle and life-cycle assessments confused. Life-cycle assessments are the ones you'll need.

Q1   Name the four stages of a product's life that should be considered by a life-cycle assessment.   [4 marks]

Using Life-Cycle Assessments

On the last page you saw what a <u>life-cycle assessment</u> is. Now you get to see how they can be used to decide what product is the <u>least environmentally damaging</u> to make. Oh yes, it's going to get a little bit crazy...

You Can use Life-Cycle Assessments to Compare Products

1) Once you have gathered data on the environmental impact of different products, the next step is to <u>compare</u> your data.

2) The aim of this is to help you to decide which of the products would cause <u>least harm</u> to the environment to make.

3) Sometimes that will be <u>easy</u>. If one product looks better than the others for all of the things you've measured, it's easy to decide that would be the best product to make.

4) Sometimes it might be more <u>difficult</u>. You might have one product that needs a lot of <u>energy</u> to make but is easy to <u>dispose</u> of, while for another product it's the other way around. Then you'd have to decide which of those things you thought was <u>more important</u>.

5) Here's an example of how you might compare some data from a <u>life-cycle assessment</u>.

EXAMPLE:

A company is carrying out a life-cycle assessment to help decide which car, A, B or C, it should make.

Using the data in the table, suggest which car the company should make to minimise the environmental impact of production.

Car	CO_2 produced in making car (tonnes)	Solid waste produced in making car (kg)	Water used in making car (m^3)	Expected lifespan of car (years)
A	17	10 720	8.2	11
B	21	5900	6.0	17
C	34	15 010	9.5	12

To answer this question, you need to compare the four pieces of data for each of the cars.

<u>Car A:</u>
Making car A produces the least CO_2.
But it also produces the second highest amount of waste solids and uses the second highest amount of water. Car A also has the shortest lifespan.

<u>Car B:</u>
Making car B produces more CO_2 than car A.
But it also produces by far the least waste solid and uses the least water.
Car B also has the longest lifespan.
On balance, this looks a better choice than car A.

<u>Car C:</u>
Making car C produces the most CO_2 and produces the most waste solid.
It also uses the most water. Car C has almost as short a lifespan as car A.
This looks like the worst choice.

So, on balance, **car B** looks like the one that will have the least environmental impact.

I go life-cycling at the weekend — it's really good exercise...

Make sure you've got your head around the example on this page. Looking at a life-cycle assessment and using it to explain which product you think a company should make is just the sort of thing you might be asked to do.

Q1 Look at the example above. Suggest one other thing that isn't in the table that the company might want to consider when doing a life-cycle assessment for the three cars. [1 mark]

Recycling Materials

Recycling's a hot topic. We don't have an endless amount of materials to keep on making things from, so recycling's really important to make sure we don't run out of lots of important materials.

Extracting Raw Materials Requires Energy

1) Extracting raw materials (e.g. mining metals) can take lots of energy. Most of this energy will come from burning fossil fuels.

2) Burning fossil fuels contributes to acid rain and climate change, so it's important to burn as little as possible.

3) Fossil fuels will also run out one day.

4) Recycling materials often uses a tiny amount of the energy needed to extract materials from scratch.

5) Energy doesn't come cheap, so recycling saves money too.

6) As there's a limited amount of many raw materials on Earth, recycling saves these resources from being used up.

7) Recycling materials also cuts down on the amount of rubbish that gets sent to landfill. This is where rubbish is dumped in pits in the ground. Landfill takes up space and pollutes the surroundings.

Example: Recycling Aluminium

In fact, aluminium's about the most cost-effective metal to recycle.

1) If we didn't recycle aluminium, we'd have to mine more aluminium ore — 4 tonnes of ore for every 1 tonne of aluminium needed.

2) But mining makes a mess of the landscape (and these mines are often in rainforests).

3) The ore then needs to be transported, and the aluminium extracted (which uses loads of electricity).

4) Don't forget the cost of sending your used aluminium to landfill.

5) So recycling aluminium saves energy and materials, protects the environment, reduces waste and saves money.

Sometimes Recycling isn't Straightforward

1) Recycling isn't an energy-free process. You need energy to reprocess the materials into new forms.

2) Often, items will need sorting to separate out different materials. For example, glass sometimes needs to be sorted into different colours, and different plastics often need to be separated out before recycling too.

3) To decide whether recycling a material is better than just disposing of it and starting from scratch, you need to compare how much energy is used for both of these processes.

4) Generally, you want to go for the option which uses the least energy.

5) You also need to think about any possible harmful effects of putting materials in landfill, and whether the material is renewable (can be replaced) or not.

CGP Jokes — 85% recycled since 1996...

There's only so much of all sorts of raw materials, like metal and oil, on Earth. So we definitely need to think about this kind of thing now, before they run out. Otherwise there won't be any left for us to use...

Q1   Give two advantages of recycling materials.   [2 marks]

Crude Oil

Crude oil can be used to make loads of useful things, like fuels. But you can't just stick crude oil in your car. First, the different hydrocarbons have to be separated — that's where fractional distillation comes in.

Crude Oil is Separated into Different Hydrocarbon Fractions

1) Hydrocarbons are molecules made from carbon and hydrogen atoms only.

2) Crude oil is a mixture of lots of different hydrocarbons.
   Most of them are different length alkane molecules.

3) Alkanes have the general formula C_nH_{2n+2} (e.g. an alkane with two C atoms has the formula C_2H_6).

4) Crude oil is formed from dead plants and animals that are buried for millions of years. It's a fossil fuel.

5) Crude oil is our main source of hydrocarbons and is used to create lots of useful chemicals.

6) The different compounds in crude oil can be separated using a process called fractional distillation.
   Here's what happens:

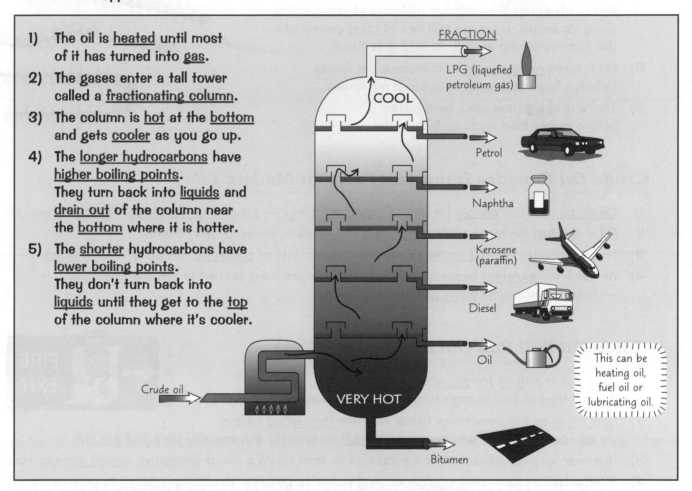

1) The oil is heated until most of it has turned into gas.

2) The gases enter a tall tower called a fractionating column.

3) The column is hot at the bottom and gets cooler as you go up.

4) The longer hydrocarbons have higher boiling points.
   They turn back into liquids and drain out of the column near the bottom where it is hotter.

5) The shorter hydrocarbons have lower boiling points.
   They don't turn back into liquids until they get to the top of the column where it's cooler.

FRACTION

COOL

LPG (liquefied petroleum gas)

Petrol

Naphtha

Kerosene (paraffin)

Diesel

Oil

This can be heating oil, fuel oil or lubricating oil.

Crude oil

VERY HOT

Bitumen

7) You end up with the crude oil mixture separated out into different groups of hydrocarbons.

8) These groups are called fractions. The separated fractions are much more useful than crude oil.

9) Each fraction contains a mixture of hydrocarbons (mostly alkanes) of a similar size and with similar boiling points.

How much petrol is there in crude oil? Just a fraction...

Crude oil is pretty useful, so it's worth having a good read of this page to make sure you know all about it.
I'm afraid you need to know the whole lot for your exams — even the names of all the fractions.

Q1 Give the general formula of the alkanes. [1 mark]

Q2 Name the fraction of crude oil which has the lowest boiling point. [1 mark]

Hydrocarbons

Fractional distillation works because different hydrocarbons have different boiling points. Time to find out why...

Crude Oil Fractions Separate Because of Different Intermolecular Forces

1) When crude oil is heated, the hydrocarbon molecules are supplied with extra energy. This makes the molecules move about more.

2) Eventually a molecule might have enough energy to overcome (break) the intermolecular forces that keep it with the other molecules. It can now go whizzing off as a gas.

3) The intermolecular forces of attraction are much stronger between big molecules than they are between small molecules.

4) This is because even if a big molecule can overcome the forces attracting it to another molecule at some points along its length, there are still lots of other places where the force is strong enough to hold it in place.

5) So it takes more energy to overcome the forces between large molecules than small molecules.

6) That's why big molecules have higher boiling points than small molecules do.

The covalent bonds holding each molecule together are much stronger than the intermolecular forces, so they don't break. That's why you don't end up with lots of little molecules.

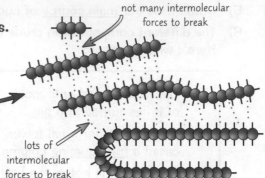

not many intermolecular forces to break

lots of intermolecular forces to break

Crude Oil Provides Important Fuels for Modern Life

1) Crude oil provides energy for lots of important things — generating electricity, heating homes, etc.

2) Oil is the fuel for most modern transport too — cars, trains, planes, the lot.

3) It also provides the raw materials needed to make lots of chemicals, including most plastics.

4) As Earth's population increases, more fossil fuels are being burned to provide electricity — both for increased home use and in industry.

Crude Oil Will Run Out Eventually... Eeek

1) Crude oil is a finite (or non-renewable) resource — it's not formed fast enough to replace the amount we're using.

2) New reserves are sometimes found and new technology means we can get to oil that was once too difficult to extract. But one day we'll just run out.

3) However long the oil lasts, it's a good idea to start thinking about alternative energy sources now.

4) Alternatives include using nuclear or wind power to generate electricity, ethanol to power cars and solar energy to heat water.

5) These alternatives aren't without problems, but we need them to be ready when the oil runs out.

6) Some people think we should stop using oil for fuel (where we have alternatives that we can use) and keep it for making plastics and other chemicals.

Unfortunately our jokes are non-renewable and we've just run out

Crude oil's really useful, but burning it isn't without its problems. Not only will it run out one day but burning oil puts loads of carbon dioxide into the air — and that can lead to climate change (see page 146).

Q1 Crude oil is a finite resource. Explain what this means. [1 mark]

Q2 Two straight-chain alkanes have the chemical formulas C_5H_{12} and $C_{50}H_{102}$. Which of these alkanes you would expect to have a higher boiling point? Explain your answer. [2 marks]

Cracking

Long-chain hydrocarbon molecules can be split up into smaller molecules — this is called cracking.

Cracking is Splitting Up Long-Chain Hydrocarbons

1) Long-chain hydrocarbons are thick gloopy liquids like tar.

2) Cracking turns long alkane molecules into smaller hydrocarbon molecules.

3) It's a thermal decomposition reaction. This is when one substance breaks down into at least two new ones when you heat it.

4) A lot of the long alkane molecules produced in fractional distillation are cracked into smaller alkanes. The smaller molecules are more in demand than the longer ones because they tend to be more useful.

5) Cracking also produces alkene molecules. Alkenes are another type of hydrocarbon. They're used to make polymers (mostly plastics).

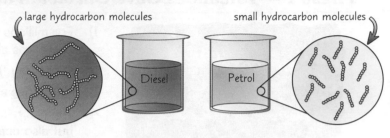

Cracking Involves Heat, Moderate Pressures and a Catalyst

1) Hydrocarbon gases can be passed over a hot aluminium oxide catalyst to crack them.

2) In industry, this is done at a temperature of 400 °C – 700 °C and a pressure of 70 atmospheres.

Example: Decane can be cracked to give octane (a smaller alkane) and ethene (an alkene).

Decane (ten C atoms) → Octane (eight C atoms) + Ethene

Cracking Helps Match Supply and Demand

1) Crude oil contains more of the longer hydrocarbon molecules than the shorter hydrocarbon molecules. But demand for the shorter hydrocarbons is greater than demand for the longer hydrocarbons.

2) Cracking is useful because it balances out supply and demand.

EXAMPLE:

The table on the right shows what percentage of crude oil is made up of three different fractions and the percentage demand for these fractions.

Fraction	% in crude oil	% demand
Petrol	8	24
Kerosene	13	8
Diesel	19	23

a) What mass of petrol would be present in 250 kg of crude oil?
Mass of petrol in 250 kg = 250 × (8 ÷ 100) = 20 kg

b) Kerosene is often cracked to make petrol. Diesel is not. Explain why.
The demand for diesel is higher than the supply of it, so all of it is left as diesel. However, there is more kerosene in crude oil than there is demand for it, so some of it can be cracked to make petrol.

Don't crack up — it's not that bad...

My incredible jokes crack me up all the time. Have you heard the one about the alkane and the chicken?

Q1   At what temperature and pressure is cracking carried out in industry?   [2 marks]

The Atmosphere

Scientists have looked at <u>evidence</u> from rocks, fossils and air bubbles in ice to see how our <u>atmosphere</u> has <u>changed</u> over many, many years. Here's one theory about how our atmosphere might have evolved.

Phase 1 — Volcanoes Gave Out Steam and CO_2

Holiday report: Not nice.
Take strong walking boots
and a coat.

1) For millions of years the Earth's surface was <u>molten</u> (liquid). There was almost no atmosphere.

2) Eventually the Earth's surface cooled and a <u>thin crust</u> formed.

3) <u>Volcanoes</u> started erupting, releasing gases from <u>inside the Earth</u>.

4) The gas released was mainly <u>carbon dioxide</u>, but also contained some <u>steam</u>, <u>methane</u> and <u>ammonia</u>.

5) When things eventually settled down, the early atmosphere was <u>mostly CO_2</u> and water vapour. There was very little oxygen.

6) The water vapour later <u>condensed</u> to form the <u>oceans</u>.

Phase 2 — Green Plants Evolved and Produced Oxygen

Holiday Report: A bit slimy.
Take wellies and a lot of
suncream.

1) A lot of the <u>carbon dioxide</u> from the early atmosphere <u>dissolved</u> into the oceans.

2) <u>Green plants</u> evolved over most of the Earth. As they photosynthesised, they <u>removed CO_2</u> and <u>produced O_2</u>.

3) Thanks to the plants, the amount of O_2 in the air gradually <u>built up</u>.

4) Much of the CO_2 eventually got <u>locked up</u> in <u>fossil fuels</u> and <u>rocks</u>.

5) <u>Nitrogen gas</u> (N_2) was also made when ammonia reacted with oxygen. It was released by some bacteria too.

6) <u>N_2</u> isn't very <u>reactive</u>. So the amount of N_2 in the atmosphere <u>increased</u> over time, because it was being <u>made</u> but not <u>broken down</u>.

Today's Atmosphere is Just Right for Us

The Earth's <u>atmosphere</u> today is made up of:

> 78% nitrogen
> and 21% oxygen

The atmosphere also contains small amounts of <u>noble gases</u> (mainly argon) and some <u>water vapour</u>. About 0.04% of the atmosphere is made up of <u>carbon dioxide</u> too.

I went to a restaurant on the Moon — nice view, no atmosphere...

We can breathe easy knowing that our atmosphere has developed into a lovely oxygen-rich one. Much easier than we would breathe in an atmosphere made up of carbon dioxide, steam, methane and ammonia anyway.

Q1   The atmosphere of Earth originally contained little or no oxygen gas.
      Explain how the amount of oxygen gas in the atmosphere increased over time.   [2 marks]

The Greenhouse Effect

The greenhouse effect isn't a bumper crop of tomatoes and a prize-winning marrow...

Human Activity Affects the Composition of Air

1) The human population is increasing. More people means that more energy is needed for lighting, heating, cooking, transport and so on.

2) People's lifestyles are changing too. The amount of energy each person uses is increasing.

3) This extra energy comes mainly from burning fossil fuels, which releases more carbon dioxide.

4) More people also means that more land is needed to build houses and grow food. This space is often made by chopping down trees.

5) But trees take carbon dioxide out of the atmosphere as they photosynthesise. So if you cut down trees, less carbon dioxide is taken out of the atmosphere.

6) This graph shows how CO₂ levels in the atmosphere have risen over the last 300 years.

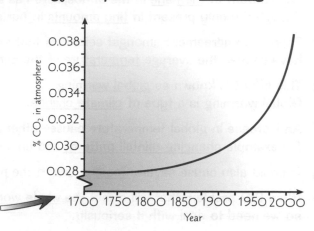

The Greenhouse Effect Helps to Keep the Earth Warm

Here's how the greenhouse effect works:

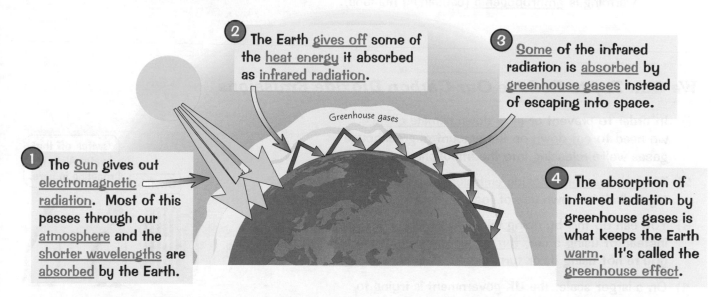

② The Earth gives off some of the heat energy it absorbed as infrared radiation.

③ Some of the infrared radiation is absorbed by greenhouse gases instead of escaping into space.

Greenhouse gases

① The Sun gives out electromagnetic radiation. Most of this passes through our atmosphere and the shorter wavelengths are absorbed by the Earth.

④ The absorption of infrared radiation by greenhouse gases is what keeps the Earth warm. It's called the greenhouse effect.

1) Greenhouse gases are the gases in the atmosphere that can absorb and reflect heat radiation. They're only present in small amounts.

2) Carbon dioxide, water vapour and methane are three greenhouse gases.

3) If the concentration of greenhouse gases in the atmosphere increases, more heat radiation from the Earth is absorbed and less escapes into space. This causes the atmosphere to heat up (see next page).

Where does the president keep his plants? The Green House...

Is all this hot air making you a bit hot and bothered? If so, here are some questions to cheer you up.

Q1   Name three greenhouse gases.   [3 marks]

Q2   Describe how the greenhouse effect works to keep our planet warm.   [4 marks]

Global Warming

Without any greenhouse gases in the atmosphere, the Earth would be too cold for us to live on. But the more greenhouse gases there are in the atmosphere, the warmer we'll get. Is it me, or is it getting hot in here...?

Increasing Greenhouse Gases Causes Climate Change

1) You saw on the last page that the level of carbon dioxide in the atmosphere is increasing.

2) The amount of methane in the atmosphere has also risen lots in recent years. Though it's only present in tiny amounts in our atmosphere, it's a powerful greenhouse gas.

3) There's an agreement amongst scientists that extra greenhouse gases from human activity have caused the average temperature of the Earth to increase.

4) This effect is known as global warming. Global warming is a type of climate change.

5) An increase in global temperature causes other types of climate change, for example changing rainfall patterns and an increase in extreme weather.

6) It could also cause severe flooding due to the polar ice caps melting.

7) It's a BIG problem that will affect the whole world, so we need to deal with it seriously.

- A few scientists believe that the current rises in global temperature are natural and that we don't have enough data to prove that global warming is caused by increasing CO_2 emissions or human activity.

- But most of the scientific community agree that global warming is anthropogenic (caused by humans).

We Can Try to Reduce Our Carbon Dioxide Emissions

1) In order to prevent or slow down climate change, we need to cut down on the amount of greenhouse gases we're releasing into the atmosphere.

2) To reduce carbon dioxide emissions, we can try to limit our own use of fossil fuels.

3) You can do this by doing things like walking or cycling instead of using a car, turning electrical equipment off when you're not using it, or turning your central heating down.

Switch off that heater Alan, it's roasting in here.

OK Tim.

4) On a larger scale, the UK government is trying to encourage the public and industry to use less energy.

5) The government is also helping businesses to save money if they reduce CO_2 emissions and is funding research into new energy sources.

6) Scientists have already developed, or are developing, some alternative energy sources. Many of these alternative energy sources are renewable so, unlike fossil fuels, they won't run out.

Give the climate some privacy — it's changing...

Global warming is a bit scary really. If the Earth keeps on warming up it's likely to cause us all sorts of problems. It's not all depressing news though. There are steps we can take to cut our carbon dioxide emissions — so chin up.

Q1   Give two ways that you could reduce your carbon dioxide emissions.   [2 marks]

Pollutants

When you <u>burn fossil fuels</u>, you make some <u>nasty gases</u> that you don't really want hanging around in the air...

Acid Rain is Caused by Sulfur Dioxide and Oxides of Nitrogen

1) When <u>fossil fuels</u> are burned they release <u>carbon dioxide</u> (which causes <u>global warming</u>).

2) But they <u>also</u> release other harmful gases — especially <u>sulfur dioxide</u> and <u>nitrogen oxides</u>.

3) The <u>sulfur dioxide</u> (SO_2) is made from <u>sulfur impurities</u> in the <u>fossil fuels</u>.
They react with <u>oxygen</u> from the air as the fuel burns.

4) The <u>nitrogen oxides</u> are made when the nitrogen and oxygen <u>in the air</u> react together
at the <u>high temperatures</u> caused by the burning fuel.

5) When these gases <u>mix</u> with <u>water</u> in <u>clouds</u> they form dilute <u>sulfuric acid</u> and dilute <u>nitric acid</u>.
This falls as <u>acid rain</u>.

6) <u>Power stations</u> and <u>car engines</u> produce a lot of sulfur dioxide and nitrogen oxides.

Acid Rain Kills Fish, Trees and Statues

1) <u>Acid rain</u> causes <u>lakes</u> to become <u>acidic</u> and
many plants and animals <u>die</u> as a result.

2) Acid rain kills <u>trees</u> and damages <u>limestone</u> buildings and
ruins some <u>stone statues</u>. It also makes <u>metal</u> corrode.

Oxides of Nitrogen Also Cause Photochemical Smog

1) <u>Photochemical smog</u> is a type of air pollution caused by <u>sunlight</u> acting on <u>oxides
of nitrogen</u>. It is a mixture of lots of different <u>harmful gases</u> including <u>ozone</u> (O_3).

2) Ozone is useful when it's high up in the atmosphere in the <u>ozone layer</u>. But when it
hangs around at <u>ground level</u> and people breathe it in, it can cause <u>breathing problems</u>.

Carbon Monoxide is a Poisonous Gas

1) Carbon monoxide is produced by <u>incomplete combustion</u>.
This is when carbon compounds (like fossil fuels) are burnt <u>without enough oxygen</u>.

2) <u>Car engines</u> produce carbon monoxide.

3) <u>Carbon monoxide</u> (CO) stops your blood doing its proper job of <u>carrying oxygen</u> around the body.

4) If you breathe in <u>a lot</u> of carbon monoxide, you won't be able to transport
<u>enough oxygen</u> around your body. This can lead to <u>fainting</u>, a <u>coma</u> or even <u>death</u>.

Particulate Carbon is Caused by Incomplete Combustion

1) During <u>incomplete combustion</u> (see above), small bits of solids called <u>particulates</u> are released
into the atmosphere. These are just <u>tiny pieces of carbon</u> that <u>float around</u> in the air.

2) If people <u>breathe them in</u>, they can cause or worsen <u>breathing problems</u>.

3) Eventually they fall back to the ground and form a coating of <u>soot</u> on buildings.

Revision and pollution — the two problems with modern life...

Acid rain's bad news for sculptors, fish and trees alike. It's bad news for you too, since you need to know about it...

Q1   Name one pollutant made by burning fossil fuels. State one problem caused by this pollutant.   [2 marks]

Water Treatment

Water, water, everywhere... well, there is if you live in a submarine.

There are a Variety of Limited Water Resources in the UK

1) We need clean water to drink and for loads of other uses in the home (mainly washing things).

2) Water has a lot of uses in industry too. Between half and two thirds of all the fresh water used in the UK goes into industry.

> In the UK, we get our water from:
>
> 1) SURFACE WATER: lakes, rivers and reservoirs. In much of England and Wales, these sources start to run dry during the summer months.
>
> 2) GROUNDWATER: this is water that has been trapped in rocks underground. In parts of the south-east where surface water is very limited, as much as 70% of the water supply comes from groundwater.

3) All these resources are limited. They depend on rainfall, and demand for water increases every year. This means it is important to save water.

4) You can also get clean water by treating waste water (water that's been polluted by any human activity). But not all waste water is easy to treat — it depends what pollutants it contains.

Water is Cleaned in Water Treatment Plants

How clean water is depends on where it comes from — for example, groundwater usually contains fewer impurities than surface water. In the UK, most water is treated using these steps before we drink it:

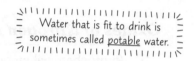
Water that is fit to drink is sometimes called potable water.

1) Filtration: a wire mesh screens out large objects (like leaves and twigs), and then gravel and sand beds filter out any other big solid bits.

2) Sedimentation: special chemicals are added to the water that make fine solid particles clump together. Then the clumps settle at the bottom.

3) Chlorination: chlorine gas is bubbled through to kill harmful bacteria and other microbes.

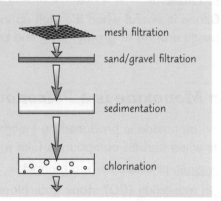
mesh filtration
sand/gravel filtration
sedimentation
chlorination

Some soluble impurities that are dissolved in the water are not removed (because they can't be filtered out). These include minerals which cause water hardness.

You Can Get Fresh Water by Distilling Seawater

1) In some very dry countries, like Saudi Arabia and Kuwait, sea water is distilled to produce drinking water.

2) Distillation needs loads of energy, so it's really expensive and not practical for producing large quantities of fresh water.

If water from the ground is groundwater, why isn't rain skywater?

My huge congratulations on finishing this topic. Now for a celebratory biscuit and a question.

Q1 The first step in treating surface water is filtration.
Explain what happens during the filtration process. [2 marks]

Revision Questions for Topic C6

Topic C6 is a pretty hefty topic, but it's the last chemistry topic, so that makes it a pretty good one I think.
- Try these questions and <u>tick off each one</u> when you <u>get it right</u>.
- When you've done <u>all the questions</u> under a heading and are <u>completely happy</u> with it, tick it off.

Extracting Metals (p.136-137) ☑

1) Write a balanced equation to show how copper is extracted from copper oxide (CuO) using carbon. ☑
2) How can you use a reactivity series to work out which metals can be extracted from their ores using reduction with carbon? ☑

Life-Cycle Assessments and Recycling (p.138-140) ☑

3) What is a life-cycle assessment? ☑
4) Explain why it's better to recycle aluminium (if possible) than to extract more. ☑
5) Name two things you would have to think about when deciding if it was worth recycling a material. ☑

Crude Oil (p.141-143) ☑

6) What is the purpose of fractional distillation? ☑
7) Name three fractions of crude oil. ☑
8) What length of hydrocarbons are collected at the bottom of a fractional distillation column — long ones or short ones? ☑
9) Why do longer hydrocarbons have higher boiling points than shorter hydrocarbons? ☑
10) What happens to an alkane when it's cracked? ☑
11) Name three things that we use crude oil for. ☑

The Atmosphere (p.144) ☑

12) Where did the gases in the Earth's early atmosphere come from? ☑
13) Name the gas that made up most of the Earth's early atmosphere. ☑

The Greenhouse Effect and Global Warming (p.145-146) ☑

14) Give one reason why the amount of carbon dioxide in the Earth's atmosphere is increasing. ☑
15) Describe one possible negative affect of global warming. ☑

Pollutants (p.147) ☑

16) Name one gas that causes acid rain. ☑
17) Give three problems associated with acid rain. ☑
18) Why are carbon particulates bad for human health? ☑

Water Treatment (p.148) ☑

19) Name two different sources of water in the UK. ☑
20) Name three processes that are used to treat water in the UK before we drink it. ☑
21) Suggest a source of water in an area with limited fresh water sources. ☑

The History of the Atom and Atomic Structure

Atoms are the tiny particles which make up everything.

Models of the Atom have Changed Over Time

1) Scientific models (p.1) change over time. This happens when new evidence is found that can't be explained by the current model.

2) This is what happened with the model of the atom.

3) You need to LEARN the history of the atom that's on page 83 for your physics exam. Make sure you can explain the experiments that led to changes in the model of the atom.

4) Based on current evidence scientists believe a nuclear model of the atom (see below) is the best description we have.

You need to Know the Current Model of the Atom

1) The nucleus is made up of particles called protons and neutrons.

2) Protons have a positive charge and neutrons have no charge.

3) So, the nucleus has an overall positive charge.

4) The radius of the nucleus is tiny compared to the that of the atom.

5) But, almost the whole mass of the atom is in the nucleus.

6) The rest of the atom is mostly empty space.

7) The negatively charged electrons whizz round the nucleus really quickly, in electron shells.

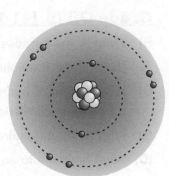

Atoms are Really, Really Tiny

Atoms are very small, so their sizes are usually written in standard form:

A is always a number between 1 and 10.

A × 10^n

n is the number of places the decimal point would move if you wrote the number out in decimal form. It's negative for numbers less than 1, and positive for numbers greater than 1.

For example, 5×10^{-3} is the same as 0.005. And 25 000 is the same as 2.5×10^4.

1) The radius of an atom is around 1×10^{-10} m (that's 0.0000000001 m).

2) Atoms can join together to form molecules.

3) The sizes of small molecules are also around 1×10^{-10} m.

I prefer the chocolate pudding model myself...

Scientists, eh? As soon as they've worked out one theory, they're off to find another. It's almost like they haven't thought about the people who have to revise this stuff at all.

Q1　In the current model of the atom is the nucleus positive, negative or neutral?　　　[1 mark]

Density

Time for some <u>maths</u> I'm afraid. But at least it comes with some fun experiments, so it's not all bad....

Density is Mass per Unit Volume

1) <u>Density</u> is a measure of how <u>compact</u> a substance is. You can calculate it using:

$$\text{Density (kg/m}^3) = \frac{\text{Mass (kg)}}{\text{Volume (m}^3)}$$

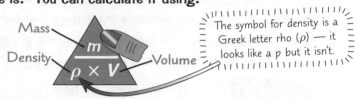

Mass — Density — Volume

$\frac{m}{\rho \times V}$

The symbol for density is a Greek letter rho (ρ) — it looks like a p but it isn't.

2) The density of an object depends on <u>what it's made of</u> and how its <u>particles</u> are <u>arranged</u>.

EXAMPLE: A 0.4 kg plank of wood has a volume of 0.8 m³. Calculate its density.

density = mass ÷ volume = 0.4 ÷ 0.8 = 0.5 kg/m³

You Need to be Able to Measure Density in Different Ways

PRACTICAL

Finding the density of a regularly-shaped object (e.g. a cuboid)

1) Use a <u>balance</u> to measure its <u>mass</u> (see p.218).
2) Measure its <u>length</u>, <u>width</u> and <u>height</u> with a <u>ruler</u>.
3) Then calculate its <u>volume</u> using the <u>formula</u> for that shape.
4) Use <u>density = mass ÷ volume</u> to find the density.

The volume of a cuboid is equal to length × width × height. The volume of any prism is equal to the area of the cross-section of the shape (A), multiplied by its height (h).

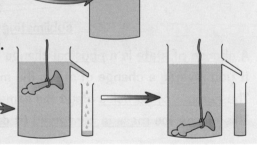

Finding the density of an irregularly-shaped object (e.g. an awards statue)

1) Use a <u>balance</u> to measure its <u>mass</u>.
2) <u>Fill</u> a <u>eureka can</u> (a can with a spout in its side) with water.
3) Place a <u>measuring cylinder</u> (p.218) under the spout.
4) Place your object <u>into the water</u> using a thread. This will <u>push</u> some of the water <u>out</u> through the spout.
5) <u>Measure the volume</u> of water that has collected in the measuring cylinder.
6) This is <u>equal to</u> the <u>volume</u> of the <u>object</u>.
7) Use the <u>formula</u> above to find the object's <u>density</u>.

Finding the density of a liquid

1) Place a <u>measuring cylinder</u> on a balance and <u>zero</u> the balance (p.218).
2) Pour <u>50 ml</u> of the liquid into the measuring cylinder.
3) Record the liquid's <u>mass</u> shown on the mass balance.
4) Use the <u>formula</u> above to find the <u>density</u>. The <u>volume</u> is <u>50 cm³</u>, or <u>0.00005 m³</u>.

For finding the volume of a liquid, you'll need to know that 1 ml = 1 cm³ and that 1 cm³ = 0.000001 m³.

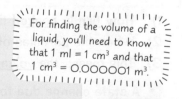

Learn this page. It is your density... I mean destiny...

Remember — density is all about how close together the particles in a substance are. Nice and simple really.

Q1   Describe a method you can use to calculate the density of an irregularly-shaped object.   [4 marks]

Q2   A cube has a volume of 0.05 m³. It has a density of 40 kg/m³. Calculate its mass.   [3 marks]

Particle Theory and States of Matter

According to particle theory, everything's made of tiny little balls. The table, this book, your Gran...

There are Three States of Matter

1) The three states of matter are solid (e.g. ice), liquid (e.g. water) and gas (e.g. water vapour).

2) The particle model explains the differences between the states of matter:
   - The particles of a certain material are always the same, no matter what state it is in.
   - But the particles have different amounts of energy and different arrangements in different states.

Solids

1) Particles are held close together by strong forces in a regular, fixed pattern.
2) The particles don't have much energy.
3) So they can only vibrate (jiggle about) around a fixed position.

Liquids

1) The particles are held close together in an irregular pattern.
2) The particles have more energy than the particles in a solid.
3) They can move past each other in random directions at low speeds.

Gases

1) The particles aren't held close together. There are almost no forces between them.
2) The particles have more energy than in liquids and solids.
3) The particles constantly move around in random directions at a range of speeds.

Mass Doesn't Change in a Change of State

1) A change of state can happen because of heating or cooling. The changes of state are:

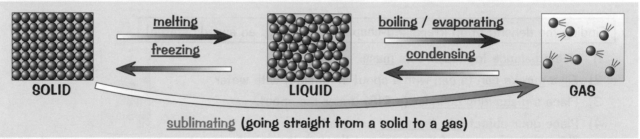

SOLID — melting / freezing → LIQUID — boiling / evaporating / condensing → GAS

sublimating (going straight from a solid to a gas)

2) A change of state is a physical change (not a chemical change — you don't end up with a new material).
3) If you reverse a change of state, the material will get back all the properties it had before the change.
4) The number of particles stays the same when the state changes. They just have a different arrangement.
5) This means the mass is conserved (it doesn't change).

Density Does Change in a Change of State

1) How tightly packed the particles are does change when the state changes.
2) When the particles of a substance move further apart, the substance takes up more space.
3) This means the volume of the substance increases.

- A state change due to heating means the volume increases.
- A state change due to cooling means the volume decreases.
- Since density = mass ÷ volume (see page 151), and mass is constant, then density must change too. Generally, substances are most dense when they're solids and least dense when they're gases.

Physics — it's really about state of mind...

The number of particles of a substance doesn't change in a change of state, so neither does its mass.

Q1 Describe the effects on a typical solid as it melts on its: a) density, b) mass, c) volume. [3 marks]

Topic P1 — Matter

Specific Heat Capacity

It takes <u>more energy</u> to <u>increase the temperature</u> of some materials than others.
That's where <u>specific heat capacity</u> comes in...

Heating Causes a Change in Temperature or a Change in State

1) <u>Heating</u> a substance increases its <u>internal energy</u> (the energy stored within it).
2) This can increase the energy in its <u>thermal store</u>, meaning a <u>change in temperature</u> (see below).
3) It can sometimes cause a <u>change of state</u> instead — see the next page.

Specific Heat Capacity Relates Temperature and Energy

1) The <u>specific heat capacity</u> of a substance is the <u>energy</u> needed to
raise the temperature of <u>1 kg</u> of that substance by <u>1 °C</u>.
2) You need to know how to use the <u>equation</u> relating temperature, energy, mass and specific heat capacity:

$$\text{Change in Thermal Energy (J)} = \text{Mass (kg)} \times \text{Specific Heat Capacity (J/kg°C)} \times \text{Change in Temperature (°C)}$$

EXAMPLE:

Water has a specific heat capacity of 4200 J/kg°C.
How much energy is needed to heat 2.00 kg of water from 10.0 °C to 100.0 °C?

1) First work out the <u>change in temperature</u>.
2) Then plug the numbers for <u>mass</u>, <u>specific heat capacity</u> and <u>change in temperature</u> into the equation.

change in temperature = 100.0 − 10.0 = 90 °C
change in thermal energy = 2.00 × 4200 × 90.0
= 756 000 J

You can Find the Specific Heat Capacity of a Substance

PRACTICAL

You can use the following experiment to find the specific heat capacity of a <u>liquid</u> or a <u>solid</u>:

1) Use a <u>mass balance</u> to measure the <u>mass</u> of your substance.
2) Set up the experiment shown below.

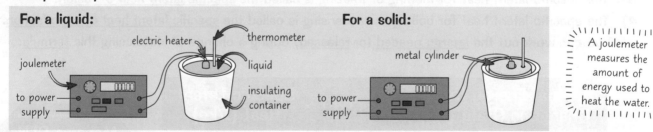

A joulemeter measures the amount of energy used to heat the water.

3) Before starting the experiment make sure the joulemeter reads <u>zero</u>.
4) Measure the <u>temperature</u> of the substance you're investigating, then turn on the power.
5) When the temperature has increased by a <u>set amount</u> (e.g. 10 °C), stop the experiment.
6) Record the <u>energy</u> on the <u>joulemeter</u> for that increase in temperature.
7) To calculate the <u>specific heat capacity</u> of your substance, <u>rearrange</u> the equation above and plug in your <u>measurements</u> and the <u>temperature change</u>.
8) <u>Repeat</u> the whole experiment at least three times.
9) Calculate the <u>mean</u> (see page 6) specific heat capacity of <u>your substance</u>.

I have a high capacity for holiday-specific heat.

I wish I had a high specific fact capacity...

Make sure you understand that equation and can rearrange it — it's a bit of a tricky one.

Q1 A 0.20 kg block of metal has a specific heat capacity of 400 J/kg°C.
Calculate the change in temperature for the metal block if 1600 J of energy is supplied to it. [3 marks]

Specific Latent Heat

Specific latent heat sounds like specific heat capacity but it's very different. It's all to do with changing state.

A Change of State means Internal Energy Changes but Not Temperature

1) Heating a material transfers energy to the material.
2) Instead of increasing the temperature of the material, it can change its state.
3) During a change of state, the temperature doesn't change. But the internal energy does.
4) The energy transferred is used to break bonds between particles. It's not used to raise the temperature.
5) When a material cools, energy is transferred away from it.
6) As a material condenses or freezes, bonds form between particles. This causes energy to be released.
7) So during the change of state, its internal energy decreases, but its temperature stays the same.
8) The flat spots on these graphs show that the temperature doesn't change during a change of state.

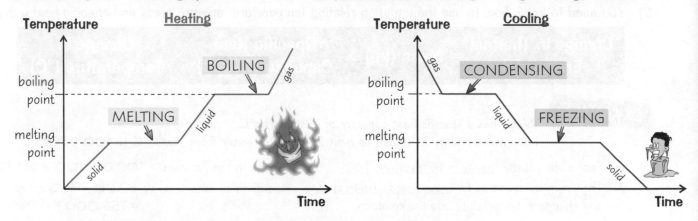

Specific Latent Heat is the Energy Needed to Change State

1) The specific latent heat of a substance is the amount of energy needed to change the state of 1 kg of the substance without changing its temperature.
2) Specific latent heat is different for different materials, and for different changes of state.
3) The specific latent heat for melting or freezing is called the specific latent heat of fusion.
4) The specific latent heat for boiling or condensing is called the specific latent heat of vaporisation.
5) You can work out the energy needed (or released) during a change of state using this formula:

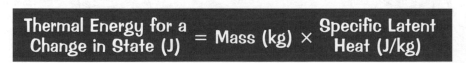

Thermal Energy for a Change in State (J) = Mass (kg) × Specific Latent Heat (J/kg)

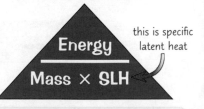

this is specific latent heat

$$\frac{\text{Energy}}{\text{Mass} \times \text{SLH}}$$

EXAMPLE:

The specific latent heat of vaporisation for water is 2 260 000 J/kg. How much energy is needed to completely boil 1.50 kg of water once it has reached its boiling point?

1) The mass and specific latent heat are in the right units, so just put them into the formula.
2) The units for the answer are joules because it's energy.

Energy = mass × specific latent heat
= 1.50 × 2 260 000
= 3 390 000 J

Changing state — like moving from Washington to Texas...

Remember, only use the specific latent heat equation if there's a change of state and no change in temperature. If the substance stays in the same state, and changes temperature, use the specific heat capacity equation (p.153).

Q1 The specific latent heat of fusion for a solid is 120 000 J/kg. How much energy is needed to melt 0.250 kg of the solid when it is already at its melting temperature? [2 marks]

Motion of Gas Particles

Gas particles fly around and bump into things, applying forces to them.
The particles in the air are doing this to you right now.

The Higher the Temperature of a Gas the Faster the Particles Move

1) If you increase the temperature of a gas you transfer energy to the kinetic energy stores of the particles.
2) The particles have more energy in their kinetic energy store so move around faster.
3) By cooling a gas down, energy is transferred away from the kinetic energy stores of the gas to those of the surroundings.
4) The particles now have less energy in their kinetic stores so move around more slowly.

Gas Particles Bump into Things and Create Pressure

1) In a gas, the particles are free to move around in completely random directions (p.152).
2) As gas particles move about, they randomly collide with each other. They also collide with anything that gets in the way, like the walls of their container.
3) Each time a gas particle hits something, it exerts a force on it.
4) All these collisions on the inside surface of the container cause an overall force on it.
5) The force applied over a given area is called pressure.
6) The more particles there are in a certain volume, the more collisions there will be with the walls of the container.
7) This means the pressure created by the gas will be higher.

Particles are randomly spread out and all move in random directions. Empty space between particles.

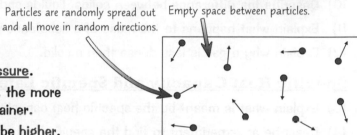

Changing the Temperature Changes the Pressure

If you increase the temperature of gas inside a sealed container of fixed volume, its pressure increases. Here's why:

1) Heating a gas transfers energy to the kinetic energy stores of the gas particles.
2) This means the gas particles move faster.
3) Faster moving particles will hit the walls of the container harder and more often.
4) This increases the force on the container walls.
5) A greater force on the walls means an increased pressure.

And, decreasing the temperature of a constant volume of gas inside a sealed container decreases its pressure:

1) Cooling a gas means the particles have less kinetic energy and move less quickly.
2) So the particles hit the walls with less force and less often, and the pressure decreases.

Gas particles need to watch where they're going...

Remember, the more gas particles there are, and the faster they travel, the higher the pressure. Simple...

Q1   Explain why a gas exerts pressure on its container.   [2 marks]

Q2   Explain what happens to the pressure of a fixed volume of gas
in a sealed container when its temperature decreases.   [3 marks]

Topic P1 — Matter

Revision Questions for Topic P1

Well, that wraps up <u>P1</u> — time to put yourself to the test and find out <u>how much you really know</u>.

- Try these questions and <u>tick off each one</u> when you <u>get it right</u>.
- When you've done <u>all the questions</u> under a heading and are <u>completely happy</u> with it, tick it off.

The Structure of the Atom (p.150) ☑

1) Name the model of the atom which was replaced by the nuclear model. ☑
2) What did Niels Bohr suggest about electrons in an atom? ☑
3) What is the typical radius of an atom? ☑
4) What is the charge of a proton? ☑
5) What is the charge of a neutron? ☑
6) Where is the majority of mass found in an atom? ☑

Density and States of Matter (p.151-152) ☑

7) What is density? ☑
8) What equation can be used to calculate an object's density if you know its volume and mass? ☑
9) Describe an experiment to find the density of a liquid. ☑
10) Describe the difference between solids, liquids and gases in terms of the movements of their particles. ☑
11) Explain what happens to the mass of a substance when it melts. ☑
12) Explain why a gas is less dense than a solid. ☑

Specific Heat Capacity and Specific Latent Heat (p.153-154) ☐

13) Explain what is meant by the specific heat capacity of a substance. ☑
14) Describe an experiment to find the specific heat capacity of a liquid. ☑
15) Explain why the temperature of a substance doesn't change during a change of state. ☑
16) What is meant by:
    a) the specific latent heat of fusion?
    b) the specific latent heat of vaporisation? ☑

Motion of Gas Particles (p.155) ☐

17) The temperature of a fixed volume of gas is increased.
    Explain what happens to the motion of the particles. ☑
18) What happens to the pressure of a gas in a sealed container of fixed volume when it is heated? ☑

Speed and Velocity

This page will set you up for the rest of the topic. <u>Learn it</u>, don't forget it, and <u>do the questions</u> at the end.

Distance and Speed are Scalars, Displacement and Velocity are Vectors

1) <u>Distance</u> is just <u>how far</u> an object has moved.

2) <u>Displacement</u> is the distance and direction in a <u>straight line</u> from an object's <u>starting point</u> to its <u>finishing point</u>.

I'm like a boy band — I only ever move in one direction.

3) For example, if you walk 15 m <u>north</u>, then 5 m <u>south</u>:
   - your <u>displacement</u> is <u>10 m</u>,
   - but the <u>distance</u> travelled is <u>20 m</u>.

4) The <u>speed</u> of an object is <u>how fast</u> it's going — the <u>direction</u> is <u>not important</u>. E.g. <u>speed = 30 mph</u>.

5) <u>Velocity</u> describes both the <u>speed and direction</u>. E.g. <u>velocity = 30 mph due north</u>.

6) Quantities like <u>speed</u> and <u>distance</u>, that have <u>size but not direction</u>, are called <u>scalar</u> quantities.

   <u>Scalar quantities</u>: speed, distance, mass, time, etc.

7) Quantities like <u>velocity</u> and <u>displacement</u>, that have a <u>direction as well as size</u>, are <u>vector</u> quantities.

   <u>Vector quantities</u>: velocity, displacement, force, acceleration, etc.

Speed, Distance and Time — the Equation

Make sure you learn this <u>equation</u>, it pops up a lot...

distance travelled (m) = speed (m/s) × time (s)

EXAMPLE: A cat walks at a constant speed of 0.4 m/s. Find how long it takes to walk 32 m.

1) <u>Rearrange</u> the equation above for time.   time = distance travelled ÷ speed

2) <u>Substitute</u> in the values for speed and distance travelled and calculate the <u>time</u>.   time = 32 ÷ 0.4 = 80 s

You Can Use the Equation to Find the Average Speed

1) In most real-life situations, an object's <u>speed</u> will be <u>changing</u> all the time.

2) You can find the <u>average speed</u> by using the <u>total distance travelled</u> and the <u>total time taken</u>.

EXAMPLE: A car travels 20 m in 1 s. It then travels 40 m in 3 s. Calculate the car's average speed for the whole journey.

1) Find the total <u>distance travelled</u> and the total <u>time taken</u>.   total distance = 20 + 40 = 60 m
   total time taken = 1 + 3 = 4 s

2) <u>Rearrange</u> the equation above for speed.   speed = distance travelled ÷ time

3) Substitute in the values for total distance and total time taken to find the <u>average speed</u>.   average speed = 60 ÷ 4
   = 15 m/s

Time to get this section going — wait, whose cat is this?

Know the difference between vectors and scalars — scalars have a size, vectors have a size AND a direction.

Q1   Find the distance travelled in 24 s by a car with a constant speed of 15 m/s.   [2 marks]

Q2   Calculate the average speed of a cyclist if they cycle 660 m in 120 s.   [2 marks]

Measurements of Motion

When investigating motion, you have to deal with a lot of measurements. And once you've taken those measurements, you need to get them in the right units. Thankfully, we've got you covered.

You can use Different Equipment to Measure Distance and Time

1) Generally, you measure speed by measuring distance and time, and then doing a calculation.

2) The equipment you use for measuring distance and time depends on what you're investigating.

3) If possible, your measuring instrument should be longer than the distance you're measuring.

4) For example, you should use a metre stick to measure something that's 45 cm long, not a 30 cm ruler.

5) If you're measuring something with a length of many metres, you'll need a long tape measure, or a trundle wheel (one of those clicky wheel things).

6) To measure time intervals longer than about 5 seconds, you can use a stopwatch.

7) To measure short intervals, it's best to use light gates connected to a computer (see p.224).

You Need to be Able to Convert Between Units

1) When using any equation, it's important to have your quantities in the right units.

2) For example, in the speed equation on the last page:
   - the speed is in m/s (metres per second),
   - the distance is in m (metres),
   - the time is in s (seconds).

3) You may need to convert (change) the units of a quantity.

4) Here are some examples of conversions you need to be able to do:

> To convert 16 km (kilometres) into m: multiply by 1000 — 16 × 1000 = 16 000 m
>
> To convert 22 ms (milliseconds) into s: divide by 1000 — 22 ÷ 1000 = 0.022 s
>
> To convert 36 cm (centimetres) into m: divide by 100 — 36 ÷ 100 = 0.36 m
>
> To convert 19 mm (milimetres) into m: divide by 1000 — 19 ÷ 1000 = 0.019 m

5) Getting hours and minutes into seconds is a little trickier. For example:

> To convert 8 hr (hours) into s:
> Multiply 8 by 60 to find the number of minutes — 8 × 60 = 480 minutes
> Then multiply 480 minutes by 60 to find the number of seconds — 480 × 60 = 28 800 s

EXAMPLE: A snail travels 0.36 km in 10 hours. Calculate the average speed of the snail in m/s.

1) Convert the distance from km to m.

0.36 km = 0.36 × 1000 = 360 m

2) Convert the time from hours to s.

10 hours = 10 × 60 = 600 minutes

3) Rearrange the equation on page 157 for speed.

600 minutes = 600 × 60 = 36 000 s

4) Substitute in the values, and calculate the speed.

speed = distance travelled ÷ time

average speed = 360 ÷ 36 000

= 0.01 m/s

6) As well as m/s, you might see speed shown in different units, e.g. km/h (kilometres per hour).

7) The speed in km/h is found from distance in km ÷ time in hours, see p.209.

We are the distance invaders, take us to your ruler...

Make sure you convert your values to the correct units before you do any calculations.

Q1 a) Convert 1.5 km to metres.   [1 mark]
     b) Calculate the number of seconds in 1 day.   [2 marks]

Acceleration

If an object is <u>accelerating</u>, its <u>velocity</u> is <u>changing</u>.

Acceleration is the Rate of Change of Velocity

1) Acceleration is the <u>change in velocity</u> in a certain amount of <u>time</u>.

2) <u>Learn</u> this equation for <u>calculating acceleration</u>:

$$\text{acceleration (m/s}^2) = \frac{\text{change in velocity (m/s)}}{\text{time (s)}}$$

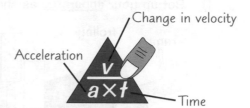

Change in velocity

Acceleration

$\dfrac{v}{a \times t}$

Time

3) To calculate the <u>change in velocity</u>, you find <u>final velocity – initial velocity</u>.

'From rest' means the cyclist starts at 0 m/s.

EXAMPLE: A cyclist accelerates from rest to 7.0 m/s in 25 s. Calculate her acceleration.

1) First find the <u>change in velocity</u>.   change in velocity = final velocity – initial velocity = 7.0 – 0 = 7.0 m/s

2) Then <u>substitute</u> this into the equation for acceleration.

acceleration = change in velocity ÷ time
= 7.0 ÷ 25 = 0.28 m/s²

4) If an object is <u>slowing down</u> (decelerating), it has a <u>negative acceleration</u>.

EXAMPLE: A motorcycle travelling at 30 m/s brakes, and comes to a stop after 6 s. Calculate her acceleration.

1) First find the <u>change in velocity</u>.   change in velocity = final velocity – initial velocity = 0 – 30 = –30 m/s

2) Then <u>substitute</u> this into the acceleration equation.

acceleration = change in velocity ÷ time
= –30 ÷ 6 = –5 m/s²

You can Calculate Uniform Acceleration Using Distance Travelled

1) If an object has <u>uniform acceleration</u>, its acceleration is <u>constant</u>.

2) For an object with uniform acceleration, you can use this <u>equation</u> if you know <u>how far</u> it has travelled:

(final velocity)² – (initial velocity)² = 2 × acceleration × distance
(m/s)²   (m/s)²   (m/s²)   (m)

You'll be given this equation in the exam so you don't need to remember it.

It might be easier to use the equation as $v^2 - u^2 = 2 \times a \times d$.

EXAMPLE: A horse is running with a constant acceleration of 0.45 m/s². It has an initial velocity of 8.0 m/s and runs a distance of 180 m. What is the horse's final velocity? Give your answer to 2 s.f.

1) <u>Rearrange</u> the equation for v² or (final velocity)². $v^2 - u^2 = 2 \times a \times d$

2) <u>Substitute</u> in the values and work out v².

$v^2 = (2 \times a \times d) + u^2$
$= (2 \times 0.45 \times 180) + 8.0^2$
$= 226$

3) Take the <u>square root</u> of v² to get the <u>final velocity</u>, v.

$v = \text{final velocity} = \sqrt{226} = 15.03... = 15 \text{ m/s (to 2 s.f.)}$

Uniform problems — get a clip-on tie or use the equation above...

In the exam, you might not be told which equation to use. List the information you're given to help you decide.

Q1   A spaceship has an acceleration of 8.25 m/s². It accelerates from rest to its top speed of 33 m/s.
Calculate the distance covered during this acceleration.
[3 marks]

Investigating Motion

Here's a simple _experiment_ you can try out. It will let you investigate _speed_ and _acceleration_.

You can Investigate the Motion of a Trolley on a Ramp

1) Set up your _apparatus_ as shown in the diagram below.

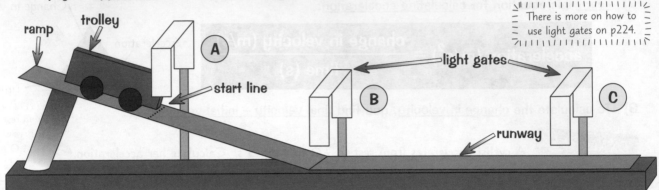

There is more on how to use light gates on p224.

2) Measure the _distances_ between light gates A and B, and B and C using a ruler.
3) Hold the trolley _still_ at the start line. Then, _let go_ of the trolley so that it starts to roll down the ramp.
4) As it rolls down the _ramp_, it will _accelerate_.
5) When the trolley reaches the _runway_, it will travel at a _constant speed_ (ignoring any friction).
6) Each _light gate_ will record the _time_ when the trolley passes through it.
7) You could measure the times using a _stopwatch_ instead of light gates, but this will be _less accurate_.
8) Another _advantage_ of using light gates is that the computer will calculate _speed_ and _acceleration_ at various points for you _automatically_. But you've _still_ got to know how you'd work them out _yourself_:

Calculating the Speed and Acceleration

1) The _time taken_ to travel between _gates A and B_ can be used to find the _average speed_ of the trolley as it moves down the ramp.
2) The _time taken_ to travel between _gates B and C_ can be used to find the _speed_ on the _runway_.
3) Use the equation _speed = distance ÷ time_ to find the speed on the ramp or runway.
4) Find the _acceleration_ of the trolley on the ramp using _acceleration = change in speed ÷ time_. You'll need to use the following values:
   - the _initial speed_ of the trolley (= 0 m/s),
   - the _final speed_ of the trolley, which equals the speed of the trolley on the _runway_ (ignoring _friction_),
   - the _time_ it takes the trolley to travel between light gates A and B.

You can Increase the Trolley's Acceleration and its Speed on the Runway

1) _Changing the set-up_ of your experiment will affect the _acceleration_ and _final speed_ of the trolley.
2) For example, you could _increase_ the _angle_ of the ramp.
3) This will _increase_ the trolley's _acceleration_ down the ramp and its _speed_ on the runway.
4) You could also move the _start line_ further up the ramp.
5) As the trolley has a _greater distance_ to accelerate over, its _speed_ on the runway will be higher.

If you want to investigate motion, it's best to invest in gates...

Know the ins and outs of this experiment — you could be asked about any part of it, or to describe the whole thing.

Q1 In the experiment above, state how increasing the angle of the ramp will affect:
   a) The acceleration of the trolley down the ramp. [1 mark]
   b) The time taken for the trolley to travel between light gates B and C. [1 mark]

Distance-Time Graphs

A <u>distance-time graph</u> can tell you all sorts of things — it can't tell you what to have for dinner though.

Distance-Time Graphs Tell You How Far Something has Travelled

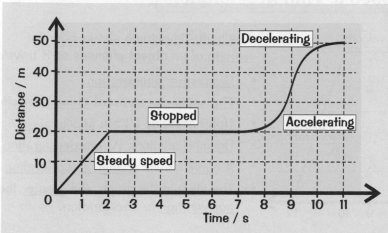

A distance-time graph tells you about the <u>motion</u> of an object:

- <u>Gradient</u> (slope) = <u>speed</u>.
- <u>Flat</u> sections are where it's <u>stopped</u>.
- <u>Straight</u> uphill (/) sections mean it is travelling at a <u>steady speed</u>.
- A <u>steeper</u> graph means it's going <u>faster</u>.
- <u>Curves</u> represent <u>acceleration</u>.
- A curve that is getting steeper means it's <u>speeding up</u> (accelerating).
- A <u>levelling off</u> curve means it's <u>slowing down</u> (decelerating).

The Speed of an Object can be Found From a Distance-Time Graph

1) The <u>gradient</u> (slope) of a distance-time graph at any point gives the <u>speed</u> of the object at that time.

2) For a <u>straight line part of a graph</u>:

$$\text{Gradient} = \frac{\text{change in the vertical}}{\text{change in the horizontal}}$$

EXAMPLE: Using the graph above, calculate the object's speed between 0 s and 2 s.

Find the <u>gradient</u> between 0 s and 2 s. This gives the <u>speed</u> during this time.

$$\text{Speed} = \text{gradient} = \frac{\text{change in the vertical}}{\text{change in the horizontal}} = \frac{20}{2} = 10 \text{ m/s}$$

3) You can also calculate the <u>average speed</u> of an object when it has <u>non-uniform motion</u> (i.e. it's <u>changing speed</u>).

4) Just divide the <u>total distance travelled</u> by the <u>time it takes</u> to travel that distance.

EXAMPLE:

The distance-time graph for a bike accelerating is shown on the right. The bike accelerates for 40 s and then travels at a steady speed for 10 s. Calculate the average speed for the bike for the first 50 s of travel.

To find the <u>average speed</u> of the bike find the <u>total distance travelled</u> from the graph and <u>divide</u> it by the <u>time taken</u>:

$$\text{average speed} = \frac{\text{total distance travelled}}{\text{time taken to travel}} = \frac{250 - 0}{50 - 0} = \frac{250}{50} = 5 \text{ m/s}$$

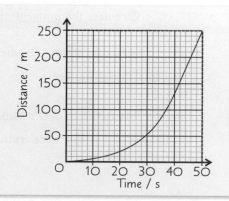

Tangent — a man who's just come back from holiday...

Try sketching distance-time graphs for different scenarios. Like cycling up a hill or running from a bear.

Q1   A stationary object initially accelerates. It then travels at a constant speed. It then decelerates to a stop. Sketch a distance-time graph for the object. [2 marks]

Velocity-Time Graphs

Huzzah, more graphs. And they're <u>velocity-time graphs</u> too, you lucky thing. Keep an eye out for those <u>negative gradients</u> — they're not too tricky really, it just means the object is <u>decelerating</u>.

Velocity-Time Graphs can Be Used to Find Acceleration

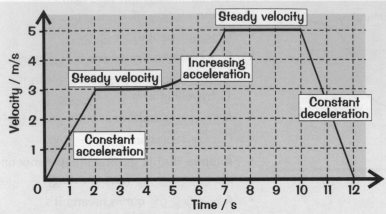

A <u>velocity-time</u> graph shows how the <u>velocity</u> of an object changes as it travels:

• <u>Gradient = acceleration</u>.

• <u>Flat</u> sections represent <u>steady</u> velocity.

• <u>Uphill</u> sections (/) are <u>acceleration</u>.

• <u>Downhill</u> sections (\) are <u>deceleration</u>.

• A <u>curve</u> means <u>changing acceleration</u>.

• The <u>steeper</u> the graph, the <u>greater</u> the <u>acceleration</u> or deceleration.

You can Find the Velocity and Acceleration from a Velocity-Time Graph

1) The <u>velocity</u> (or speed) at any time is simply found by <u>reading the value</u> off the <u>velocity axis</u>.

2) The acceleration at <u>any point</u> on a <u>straight uphill or downhill</u> section of a graph is found by calculating the <u>gradient</u> of that section.

EXAMPLE:

The graph shows the velocity-time graph of a runner.
Find:

a) the runner's velocity at 15 s

   Read the <u>velocity</u> off the graph when <u>time = 15 s</u>.

   Velocity at 15 s = 3 m/s

b) the runner's acceleration between 25 s and 35 s.

   Calculate the <u>gradient</u> of the graph <u>between 25 s and 35 s</u>.

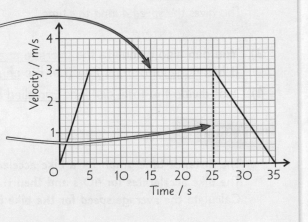

$$\text{Acceleration} = \text{gradient} = \frac{\text{change in the vertical}}{\text{change in the horizontal}}$$

$$= \frac{3-0}{35-25} = \frac{3}{10} = 0.3 \text{ m/s}^2$$

   The runner is <u>decelerating</u>, so the acceleration is <u>negative</u>.

   So, acceleration = −0.3 m/s

Understanding these graphs can be an uphill battle...

Remember — on a velocity-time graph, the gradient gives the acceleration.

Q1   A car initially travels at a steady speed. It then decelerates at a constant rate.
It is then stationary for a short time before accelerating with increasing acceleration.
Sketch a velocity-time graph for the car.
          [3 marks]

Forces and Free Body Force Diagrams

Forces are acting everywhere, so it only makes sense that you should learn about them. Read on...

Forces Can be Contact or Non-Contact

I should have chosen a non-contact sport...

1) A force is a push or a pull that acts on an object.

2) Forces are caused by objects interacting with each other.

3) When two objects interact a force acts on each object (see p.165)

4) All forces are either contact or non-contact forces.

5) When two objects have to be touching for a force to act, the force is a contact force.

Contact force examples:
friction, air resistance, tension, normal contact force

When an object exerts a force on a second object, the second object pushes back. This is the normal contact force.

6) If the objects do not need to be touching for the force to act, the force is a non-contact force.

Non-contact force examples:
magnetic force, gravitational force, electrostatic force

Free Body Force Diagrams Show All the Forces Acting on a Body

1) Forces are vectors (see page 157) so they have a size and direction.

2) An arrow can be used to show the direction of a force. The arrow's length shows the size of the force.

3) A free body force diagram is a diagram of an object with arrows representing the forces acting on it. E.g.:

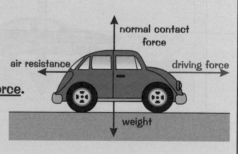

- This diagram shows the forces acting on a car as it moves along a road.
- The car's weight acts downwards.
- The normal contact force acts upwards.
- The arrows for weight and the normal contact force are the same length. This means these forces are the same size.
- Air resistance (drag) acts in the opposite direction to the driving force.
- The arrow for the driving force is longer than the arrow for air resistance. This means the driving force is bigger than the air resistance.

normal contact force

air resistance   driving force

weight

A Resultant Force is the Overall Force on a Point or Object

1) If a number of forces act at a single point, you can replace them with a single force.

2) This single force is called the resultant force.

3) It has the same effect as all the original forces added together.

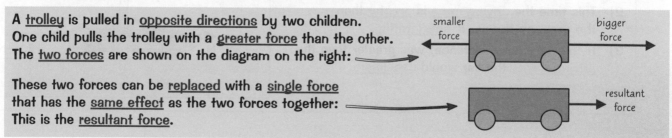

A trolley is pulled in opposite directions by two children.
One child pulls the trolley with a greater force than the other.
The two forces are shown on the diagram on the right:

smaller force   bigger force

These two forces can be replaced with a single force
that has the same effect as the two forces together:
This is the resultant force.

resultant force

Force yourself to do some work and learn this page...

Remember, on a free body force diagram, the longer the arrow, the bigger the force.

Q1   Draw a free body diagram for: a) a book on a table.   [2 marks]
                                                         b) a falling ball with a downwards resultant force.   [2 marks]

Topic P2 — Forces

Newton's First Law of Motion

Clever chap <u>Isaac Newton</u> — he came up with <u>three</u> handy laws about motion. This page covers the first one.

A Force is Needed to Change Motion

1) <u>Newton's First Law</u> says that a resultant force (p.163) is needed to make something <u>start moving</u>, <u>speed up</u> or <u>slow down</u>:

> If the resultant force on a <u>stationary</u> object is <u>zero</u>, the object will <u>remain stationary</u>. If the resultant force on a <u>moving object</u> is <u>zero</u>, it'll just carry on moving at the <u>same velocity</u> (the same speed <u>and</u> direction).

2) So, when a train, a car, a bus or anything else is <u>moving</u> at a <u>constant velocity</u>, the <u>driving</u> and <u>resistive</u> forces on it must be <u>balanced</u>.

3) Its velocity will <u>only</u> change if there's a <u>non-zero</u> resultant force acting on it.

4) A non-zero <u>resultant force</u> will always produce <u>acceleration</u> (or deceleration) in the <u>direction of the force</u>.

A Resultant Force of Zero Means all the Forces are Balanced

An object with a <u>zero resultant force</u> will either be moving at a <u>steady speed</u> or be <u>stationary</u>.

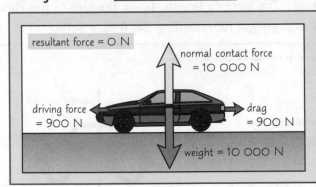

1) This diagram shows a <u>car</u> driving along a road.

2) The <u>driving force</u> is the <u>same as</u> the <u>drag</u>, so the car is <u>moving at a constant velocity</u>.

3) The <u>normal contact force</u> and the <u>weight</u> acting on the car also <u>balance</u> each other (otherwise the car would go <u>flying off</u> or <u>sink through the road</u>).

4) When all forces are <u>balanced</u>, i.e a zero resultant force, the object is said to be in <u>equilbrium</u>.

A Non-Zero Resultant Force Means the Forces are Unbalanced

If there's a <u>non-zero resultant force</u> on an object, then it will either <u>accelerate</u> or <u>decelerate</u>.

1) The diagram shows the same <u>car</u> driving along.

2) This time the <u>driving force</u> is <u>greater</u> than the <u>drag</u>, so the car is <u>accelerating</u>.

3) If the <u>drag</u> (air resistance) was greater than the <u>driving force</u>, the car would <u>decelerate</u>.

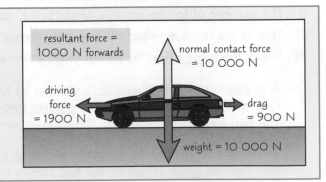

Force yourself to revise this... oh wait, I've already done that pun...

Newton's First Law means that an object at a steady speed doesn't need a resultant force to keep moving.

Q1   A car moving along a road has a forward force acting on it of 200 N and a backwards force of 150 N.
Is the car accelerating or moving with a constant velocity?   [1 mark]

Newton's Second and Third Laws of Motion

More laws eh? Isaac probably wasn't thinking about anyone having to revise them back in the 17th century.

Acceleration is Proportional to the Resultant Force

1) The larger the resultant force acting on an object, the more the object accelerates.

2) For a given force, an object with a larger mass will accelerate less than one with a smaller mass.

3) These two rules are what Newton's Second Law is about. There's an equation for this Law:

> force (N) = mass (kg) × acceleration (m/s²)   or $F = ma$

4) Remember that the force, F, is always the resultant force acting on the object.

> **EXAMPLE:**   A van with a mass of 3200 kg accelerates at 2.5 m/s².
> Calculate the resultant force acting on this vehicle.
>
> Substitute the values for mass and $F = ma$
> acceleration into the $F = ma$ equation. $= 3200 × 2.5 = 8000$ N

Newton's Third Law — Reaction Forces are Equal and Opposite

1) Newton's Third Law says that:

> When two objects interact, the forces they exert on each other are equal and opposite.

2) That means if you push something, the object will push back against you, just as hard.

3) And as soon as you stop pushing, so does the object.

4) But if the forces are always equal, how does anything ever go anywhere?

5) The important thing to remember is that the two forces are acting on different objects.

Push — Normal contact force

Skater A   Skater B

- When skater A pushes on skater B, she feels an equal and opposite force from skater B's hand.
- Both skaters feel the same sized force, in opposite directions, and so accelerate away from each other.

6) It's a bit more complicated for an object in equilibrium (see page 164). Imagine a book sat on a table:

> 1) The weight of the book pulls it down, and the normal contact force from the table pushes it up.
>
> 2) This is NOT Newton's Third Law.
>
> 3) These forces are different types and they're both acting on the book.
>
> The pairs of forces due to Newton's Third Law in this case are:
>
> - The book being pulled down by gravity towards the Earth (W_B) and the Earth being pulled up by the book (W_E).
> - The normal contact force from the table pushing up on the book (R_B) and the normal contact force from the book pushing down on the table (R_T).

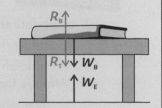

Newton's fourth law — revision must be done with cake...

Yum, cake. A couple of tricky concepts here — Newton's Second AND Third Laws. You can't say I don't spoil you.

Q1   Calculate the resultant force acting on a 26 000 kg lorry with an acceleration of 1.5 m/s².   [2 marks]

Mass, Weight and Gravity

Gravity attracts everything with <u>mass</u>, but you only notice it when one of the masses is <u>huge</u>, like a <u>planet</u>.

Gravity is the Force of Attraction Between All Masses

1) <u>Everything</u> that is made of <u>matter</u> has a <u>gravitational field</u> around it.
2) An object's gravitational field <u>attracts</u> other masses.
3) The bigger <u>the object</u> is, the <u>greater the strength</u> of its gravitational field.
4) <u>Earth</u> has a gravitational field that <u>pulls</u> us and everything else <u>towards it</u>.
5) Even <u>you</u> have a gravitational field, but it's so <u>teeny tiny</u> that it doesn't have any noticeable effect.

The Force due to Gravity is Called Weight

1) A planet's <u>gravitational field</u> makes things <u>accelerate</u> towards the <u>planet's surface</u>.
2) All objects have the <u>same acceleration</u> when <u>falling freely</u> under a planet's gravity.
3) The <u>acceleration due to gravity</u> is g. It is also known as the <u>gravitational field strength</u>.
4) g has a value of about <u>10 N/kg</u> (or 10 m/s^2) near the Earth's surface.
5) The value of g is <u>different</u> on <u>other planets</u>, so an object in free fall on another planet will have a <u>different acceleration</u>.
6) The <u>force acting</u> on an object when it's in a <u>gravitational field</u> is called the <u>weight</u>, or <u>gravity force</u>. It's measured in <u>newtons</u> (N).
7) It can be measured using a <u>calibrated spring balance</u> (or <u>newtonmeter</u>).
8) When a <u>mass</u> is put on the hook, the <u>spring</u> in the newton meter <u>extends</u>.
9) The <u>weight</u> can then be <u>read</u> from the meter.

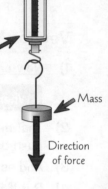

Mass

Direction of force

Weight and Mass are Not the Same Thing

1) Mass is just the <u>amount of 'stuff'</u> in an object.
2) A given object will have the same mass <u>anywhere</u> in the Universe.
3) The <u>more mass</u> an object has, the <u>larger its weight</u>.
4) A <u>higher gravitational field strength</u> means an object will <u>weigh more</u> for the same mass.
5) You can calculate the <u>weight</u> (or <u>gravity force</u>) of an object if you know its <u>mass</u> and the <u>strength</u> of the <u>gravitational field</u> that it is in (g):

$$\text{gravity force (N)} \atop \text{(weight)} = {\text{mass} \atop \text{(kg)}} \times {\text{gravitational field strength, } g \atop \text{(N/kg)}}$$

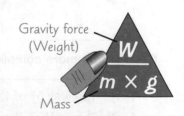

Gravity force (Weight)

$$\frac{W}{m \times g}$$

Mass

EXAMPLE: A chicken has a mass of 2.0 kg.

a) Calculate the weight, in newtons, of the chicken on Earth (g = 10 N/kg).
   <u>Substitute</u> the values for mass and g into the equation.   weight = $m \times g$ = 2.0 × 10 = **20 N**

b) The chicken has a weight of 34 N on a mystery planet.
   What is the gravitational field strength of the planet?
   1) <u>Rearrange</u> the equation for g. $g = W \div m$
   2) <u>Substitute</u> in the values for weight and mass.   = 34 ÷ 2.0 = **17 N/kg**

I'm always attracted to a shop with a sale on...

A common mistake is thinking that mass and weight are the same thing. They are not. Learn the difference.

Q1   A person has a weight of 820 N on Earth. Calculate their mass.   [2 marks]

Mechanical Energy Stores

Take a sneaky peek at page 202 for more about <u>energy stores</u>. This page covers two types of energy stores and how to calculate <u>how much</u> energy is in them.

An Object at a Height has Energy in its Gravitational Potential Energy Store

1) When an object is at any <u>height</u> above the Earth's surface, it has <u>energy</u> in its <u>gravitational potential energy store</u>.

2) You can <u>calculate</u> the <u>amount</u> of <u>energy</u> in an object's gravitational potential energy store using:

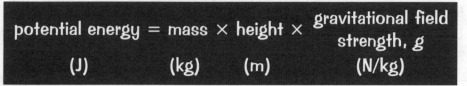

potential energy = mass × height × gravitational field strength, g

(J)　　　(kg)　　(m)　　　(N/kg)

or

$$PE = m \times h \times g$$

EXAMPLE:

Calculate the energy in the gravitational potential energy store of a 1.2 kg book when it is 4.25 m above the ground.

potential energy = mass × height × g
= 1.2 × 4.25 × 10
= 51 J

Don't forget, on Earth, g = 10 N/kg.

A Moving Object has Energy in its Kinetic Energy Store

1) When an object is <u>moving</u>, it has <u>energy</u> in its <u>kinetic energy store</u>.

2) This <u>energy</u> depends on both the object's <u>mass</u> and <u>velocity</u>.

3) The <u>greater its mass</u> and the <u>faster it's going</u>, the <u>more</u> energy it has in its kinetic energy store.

4) For example, a <u>high-speed train</u> will have <u>a lot more energy</u> in its kinetic energy store than you running.

5) You can use this <u>formula</u> to calculate the <u>kinetic energy</u> of a moving object:

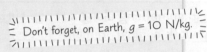

kinetic energy = 0.5 × mass × (speed)²

(J)　　　　　(kg)　　(m/s)²

or

$$KE = \tfrac{1}{2} \times m \times v^2$$

EXAMPLE:

A car of mass 1450 kg is travelling at 28 m/s.
Calculate the energy in its kinetic energy store, giving your answer to 2 s.f.

kinetic energy = 0.5 × mass × (speed)²
= 0.5 × 1450 × 28²
= 568 400 = 570 000 J (to 2 s.f.)

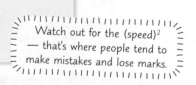

Watch out for the (speed)² — that's where people tend to make mistakes and lose marks.

There's potential for a joke here somewhere...

More equations to learn here. These ones are really useful, so make sure you know them.

Q1　A 0.80 kg ball is 1.5 m above the Earth's surface.
　　Calculate the energy in the ball's gravitational potential energy store. [2 marks]

Q2　An otter is swimming with a speed of 2.0 m/s. It has a mass of 4.9 kg.
　　Calculate the energy in the otter's kinetic energy store. [2 marks]

Work Done

I'm sure you already think physics is a lot of <u>work</u>, but this page is all about <u>work done</u>, or <u>energy transfer</u>.

If a Force Moves an Object, Work is Done

> When a <u>force</u> moves an object through a <u>distance</u>,
> <u>ENERGY IS TRANSFERRED</u> and <u>WORK IS DONE</u> on the object.

1) To make an object move, a force <u>must</u> act on it.

2) The force does '<u>work</u>' to move the object.

3) This causes <u>energy</u> to be <u>transferred to</u> the object's kinetic energy store.

4) The force usually <u>does work</u> against frictional forces too.

5) Doing work against frictional forces causes energy to be transferred to the <u>thermal energy store</u> of the object.

6) This causes the <u>temperature</u> of the object to <u>increase</u>.

'Work done' and 'energy transferred' are the same thing. You need to be able to <u>describe</u> the energy transfer when work is done. Look at p.203 for more on this.

- When you <u>push</u> something along a <u>rough surface</u> (like a <u>carpet</u>), you are doing work <u>against frictional forces</u>.
- Some energy is <u>transferred</u> to the <u>kinetic energy store</u> of the <u>object</u> because it starts <u>moving</u>.
- Some is also transferred to <u>thermal energy stores</u> due to the work done against friction.
- This causes the overall <u>temperature</u> of the object to <u>increase</u>.

7) If there's no friction, when <u>work</u> is done on an object <u>all</u> the energy is transferred to the <u>kinetic energy store</u> of the object.

8) <u>Work done</u> on an object can also be transferred to <u>other energy stores</u>.

9) For example, the work done on <u>lifting</u> an object off the ground will be equal to the energy <u>transferred</u> to its <u>gravitational potential energy store</u>.

There's a Formula Linking Work Done, Force and Distance

1) You can find out <u>how much work</u> has been done using this equation:

$$\text{Work (J)} = \text{Force (N)} \times \text{Distance (m)}$$

2) Or you may see it <u>shown</u> like this:

$$W = Fs$$

Work done

Force

Distance (moved along the line of action of the force)

The line of action of the force is the direction of the force.

3) <u>One joule of work</u> is done when a <u>force of one newton</u> causes an object to move a <u>distance of one metre</u> in the direction of the force.

4) You need to be able to <u>convert</u> joules to newton metres: <u>1 J = 1 Nm</u>.

Pay attention, there's a lot of work to be done on this page...

Remember, work done is just the same thing as energy transferred. It can be measured in J or Nm.

Q1 A force of 20 N pushes an object 20 cm in the direction of the force.
Calculate the work done on the object.

[3 marks]

Power

Whenever I think of power, I have to stop myself from plotting world domination whilst stroking a cat.

Power is the 'Rate of Doing Work' — i.e. How Much per Second

1) Power is a measure of how quickly work is being done.

2) As work done = energy transferred, you can define power like this:

> Power is the rate at which energy is transferred.

3) So, the power of a machine is the rate at which it transfers energy.

4) For example, if an electric drill has a power of 700 W, it transfers 700 J of energy every second.

---

1) Cars A and B are identical in every way apart from the power of their engines.

2) Car A's engine has a higher power than car B's engine.

3) Both cars race the same distance along a straight race track to a finish line.

4) This requires the same amount of energy to be transferred by each car.

5) Car A reaches the finish line faster than car B, because it transfers the energy over less time.

There's a Formula Linking Work Done, Time and Power

1) You can calculate power using this equation:

$$\text{power (W)} = \frac{\text{work done (J)}}{\text{time (s)}}$$

or

$$P = \frac{W}{t}$$

2) The unit of power is the watt (W).

3) 1 W = 1 J of energy transferred per second (J/s).

EXAMPLE: A motor transfers 4800 J of useful energy in 120 s. Find its power output.

Work done is the same as energy transferred.
So just substitute the values into the power equation.

$$\text{power} = \frac{\text{work done}}{\text{time}} = \frac{4800}{120} = 40 \text{ W}$$

EXAMPLE: An electric oven has an operating power of 0.790 kW. Calculate the amount of energy transferred by the oven when it is switched on for 3.50 hours.

1) First, convert kilowatts to watts by multiplying by 1000. Convert hours to minutes by multiplying by 60, then multiply by 60 again to convert to seconds.

power = 0.790 × 1000 = 790 W
time = 3.50 × 60 = 210 mins
= 210 × 60 = 12 600 s

2) Next, rearrange the power equation so work done is by itself.

$$\text{power} = \frac{\text{work done}}{\text{time}}, \text{ so}$$
work done = power × time

3) Since work done is the same as energy transferred, just substitute the values into the equation.

energy transferred = power × time
= 790 × 12 600
= 9 954 000 J

Watt's power? Power's watts...

Power crops up a lot (you'll see it again on page 182) but don't panic. Just remember it's the rate of energy transfer.

Q1   A bulb has a power of 12.0 W. Calculate the amount of time it would take for the bulb to transfer 1440 J of energy. Give your answer in minutes.   [3 marks]

Forces and Elasticity

Elasticity involves lots of physics and pinging elastic bands at people. OK, maybe not that last one.

A Deformation can be Elastic or Plastic

1) When you apply forces to an object, the object can be stretched, compressed or bent — this is deformation.

2) To deform an object, you need at least two forces.

3) Think of a spring — you need a pulling force at each end to stretch it. If you just pull one end, it'll just move along.

4) To compress a spring you also need two forces. The forces need to push from opposite ends of the spring to make it compress.

5) If an object returns to its original shape after the forces are removed, it's an elastic deformation.

6) If the object doesn't return to its original shape when you remove the forces, it's a plastic deformation.

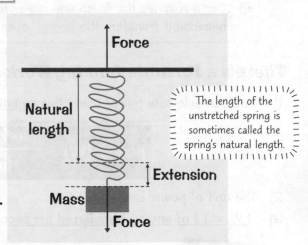

Extension is Directly Proportional to Force

1) When forces stretch a spring, it extends.

2) This extension is the difference in length between the stretched and unstretched spring.

3) Up to a given force, the extension is directly proportional to force.

4) How much an object stretches for a given force depends on its spring constant.

5) The spring constant depends on the material you're stretching.

6) The stiffer the material, the larger the spring constant.

7) The relationship between the extension of a spring and the force is called Hooke's law:

Force

Natural length

The length of the unstretched spring is sometimes called the spring's natural length.

Extension

Mass

Force

$$\text{force exerted by a spring} = \text{extension} \times \text{spring constant}$$
$$\text{(N)} \qquad\qquad \text{(m)} \qquad\qquad \text{(N/m)}$$

or $F = x \times k$

This equation can be applied to any object deforming elastically, not just springs.

EXAMPLE: A force is applied to a spring, with spring constant of 20 N/m. The spring extends by 2.5 cm. Given that the spring is obeying Hooke's Law, calculate the force applied to the spring.

1) First, convert the extension to m.

2) Then substitute the values into Hooke's Law and calculate the force.

extension = 2.5 ÷ 100 = 0.025 m

force = extension × spring constant
= 0.025 × 2
= 0.5 N

I hope this stuff isn't stretching you too much...

Hooke's Law is a fairly simple equation, but make sure you use it correctly. It only works for elastic deformations.

Q1   A spring has a natural length of 0.16 m. When a force of 3.0 N is applied to the spring, its length becomes 0.20 m. Calculate the spring constant of the spring.   [3 marks]

Forces, Elasticity and Work Done

When you <u>stretch</u> a spring, you <u>transfer energy</u>. But stretching it too much can cause problems...

Hooke's Law Stops Working when the Force is Great Enough

1) You can plot a <u>graph</u> of the <u>force</u> applied to an object and the <u>extension</u> caused.

2) Where the graph is a <u>straight line</u>, there is a <u>linear relationship</u> between force and extension.

3) This means they are <u>directly proportional</u> (i.e. if the force <u>doubles</u>, the extension does too, and so on).

4) The object is obeying <u>Hooke's Law</u> over this part of the graph.

5) The <u>gradient</u> of the <u>straight line</u> is equal to k, the <u>spring constant</u>. The <u>larger</u> the spring constant, the <u>steeper</u> the gradient.

6) <u>Beyond</u> point P, the object <u>no longer</u> obeys Hooke's law.

7) The relationship between <u>force</u> and <u>extension</u> is now <u>non-linear</u> (i.e. the graph <u>curves</u>).

8) Most objects <u>carry on</u> deforming elastically for a little bit <u>past point P</u>.

9) But if you <u>continue to increase</u> the deforming force, the object starts to deform <u>plastically</u>.

10) This means that the object <u>won't</u> spring back to its <u>original shape</u> after the stretching force has been <u>removed</u>.

11) When this happens the object has reached its <u>elastic limit</u>.

12) Some objects, <u>never</u> deform elastically, only plastically. These are called <u>plastic materials</u>.

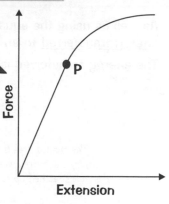

Work is Done to Deform an Object

1) When <u>forces</u> stretch an object, <u>work</u> is done.

2) If the deformation is <u>elastic</u>, energy is transferred to the object's <u>elastic potential energy store</u>.

3) The <u>work done</u> is equal to the <u>energy transferred</u>.

4) The <u>equation</u> for the <u>energy transferred</u> to an object's elastic potential energy store is:

> energy transferred in stretching = 0.5 × spring constant × (extension)²
> (J)   (N/m)   (m)²

5) You can also write this in <u>symbols</u>: $E = 0.5 \times k \times x^2$

6) You can only use this equation if the object is obeying <u>Hooke's law</u>.

EXAMPLE: A spring has a spring constant of 32 N/m and obeys Hooke's law.
Calculate the work done on the spring if it is stretched from 0.40 m to 0.45 m.

1) Calculate the <u>extension</u> of the spring.   extension = new length − original length = 0.45 − 0.40 = 0.05 m

2) <u>Substitute</u> the values into the equation.   energy transferred in stretching = 0.5 × spring constant × (extension)²
= 0.5 × 32 × 0.05² = **0.04 J**

You can also also find the energy transferred for a spring from a graph of force against extension (see p.172).

I hope you are full of the joys of spring...

More energy transfers — you'd better get used to them, there's more of them coming up later on in the book.

Q1   A 1.2 m long spring (k = 54 N/m) obeys Hooke's law and extends to 1.3 m.
Calculate the work done.   [3 marks]

Using Force-Extension Graphs

You can get a lot of <u>information</u> from <u>force-extension graphs</u>, including the <u>energy transferred</u>.

You Can Find the Work Done using a Force-Extension Graph

1) As well as using the equation on the previous page, you can also find the <u>energy transferred</u> to an object from its <u>force-extension graph</u>.

2) The energy transferred is equal to the <u>area under the graph</u>, up to its current extension.

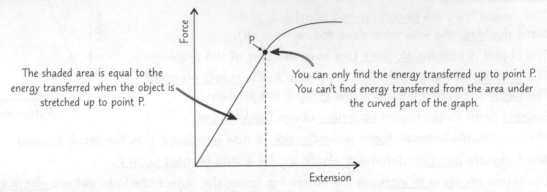

The shaded area is equal to the energy transferred when the object is stretched up to point P.

You can only find the energy transferred up to point P. You can't find energy transferred from the area under the curved part of the graph.

3) You can find the area using the <u>area of a triangle formula</u> or by <u>counting squares</u> under the graph.

4) It's really important that the <u>extension</u> is in <u>metres</u> before you find the area. You might have to <u>convert</u> your <u>units</u> (see p.158).

EXAMPLE:

The figure on the right shows the force-extension graph of a spring.
Calculate the energy transferred to the spring when it is extended up to point P.

1) The energy transferred when the spring is extended to point P is equal to the <u>area under the graph</u> up to that point.

2) This area is <u>highlighted</u> in orange.

3) Use the <u>area of a triangle</u> formula to find it.

4) Remember, the extension needs to be in <u>metres</u>.

   area of a triangle = 0.5 × base × height
   base = 4 cm = 0.04 m
   height = 10 N
   area of triangle under graph = 0.5 × 0.04 × 10 = 0.2 J
   So energy transferred = 0.2 J

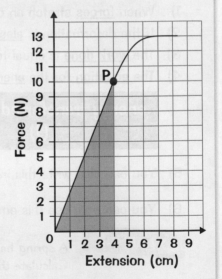

I could make a joke, but I don't want to stretch myself...

When calculating the energy transferred using a force-extension graph, make sure you're looking at a region below the linear part of the graph. Past that point, these calculations won't give you the right answer.

Q1 This question is about the spring in the example above.
   a) What is the extension of the spring for a force of 6 N? [1 mark]
   b) How much energy has been transferred to the spring when a force of 6 N has been applied? [3 marks]

Investigating Hooke's Law

<u>More springs</u> here, but now you actually get to do some <u>experiments</u> with them. Hip hip hooray.

You Can Investigate the Link Between Force and Extension

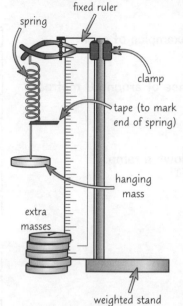

1) Set up the apparatus as shown in the diagram.
2) Measure the <u>mass</u> of one of the masses.
3) Calculate its <u>weight</u> (the <u>force</u> it will apply to the spring) using $W = mg$ (p.166).
4) Remove the hanging mass from the spring and measure the <u>original (natural) length</u> of the spring. Make sure you're looking at the tape at <u>eye level</u>.
5) <u>Replace</u> the hanging mass and allow the spring to come to <u>rest</u>.
6) Measure the new <u>length</u> of the spring.
7) Find and record the <u>extension</u>.

> extension = new length – original length

8) Add the extra <u>masses</u>, one at a time. Find the <u>extension</u> after each one.
9) <u>Plot a graph</u> of <u>force</u> (the total weight of the masses) against <u>extension</u>.

10) Draw a <u>line of best fit</u>. If you added enough masses, your graph will start to <u>curve</u>.
11) The <u>straight</u> part of the line of best fit is where the spring obeys <u>Hooke's law</u>.
12) For the straight line part of the graph, <u>gradient = spring constant</u> (see p.171).

The ruler needs to be exactly vertical.

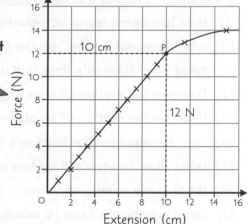

EXAMPLE:

A student carries out an investigation into the extension of a spring.
She produces the graph shown above.
Use the graph to calculate the spring constant of the spring.

1) The <u>spring constant</u>, is equal to the <u>gradient</u> of the force-extension graph up to P.

$$\text{gradient} = \frac{\text{change in y}}{\text{change in x}} = \frac{\text{change in force}}{\text{change in extension}}$$

2) <u>Calculate</u> the spring constant.

$$\text{gradient} = \frac{12}{10} = 1.2 \text{ N/cm}$$

so the **spring constant is 1.2 N/cm**

As the extension is in cm, the gradient gives you the spring constant in N/cm. However, you'll often see spring constants in N/m.

Make Sure you Carry Out your Experiment Safely

1) You should be <u>standing up</u> so you can get out of the way quickly if the masses fall.
2) You should also wear <u>safety goggles</u> to protect your eyes in case the spring snaps.

Time to spring into action with another experiment...

Remember to plot the extension of the spring, not just the new length after the spring is stretched.

Q1 Give one safety precaution you should take when carrying out the above experiment and explain why it is required.

[2 marks]

Revision Questions for Topic P2

Phew that was a lot of information — time to see what you've learnt and what needs revisiting.

- Try these questions and <u>tick off each one</u> when you <u>get it right</u>.
- When you've done <u>all the questions</u> under a heading and are <u>completely happy</u> with it, tick it off.

Motion (p.157-162) ☑

1) What is the difference between a scalar and a vector quantity? Give two examples of each. ☑
2) Write down the equation that links distance travelled, speed and time. ☑
3) Suggest a piece of equipment that would be suitable for measuring a distance of around 3 metres. ☑
4) Convert 22 ms into seconds. ☑
5) Define acceleration in terms of velocity. ☑
6) Describe an experiment to measure the acceleration of a trolley travelling down a ramp. ☑
7) How is the speed of an object found from its distance-time graph? ☑
8) What does a flat, horizontal section on a velocity-time graph represent? ☑

Forces, Newton's Laws and Work (p.163-169) ☑

9) Give two examples of non-contact forces. ☑
10) What is meant by the 'resultant force' acting on an object? ☑
11) What does Newton's First Law of motion state? ☑
12) Describe the motion of a moving object that has zero resultant force acting on it. ☑
13) Describe the motion of an object that has a non-zero resultant force acting on it. ☑
14) Give the equation for Newton's Second Law. ☑
15) What does Newton's Third Law of motion state? ☑
16) What is the difference between mass and weight? ☑
17) What equation is used to calculate the weight of an object from its mass? ☑

Energy and Elasticity (p.170-173) ☑

18) Give the equation for the energy in an object's gravitational potential energy store. ☑
19) Give the equation for the energy in the kinetic energy store of a moving object. ☑
20) Give the equation for the work done on an object when it's moved a certain distance by a force. ☑
21) What is the rate of energy transfer known as? ☑
22) How many joules per second is 1 watt equal to? ☑
23) What is the minimum number of forces needed to stretch, compress or bend an object? ☑
24) What is the difference between an elastic deformation and a plastic deformation? ☑
25) Give the equation that is known as Hooke's law. ☑
26) What constant can be found from calculating the gradient of a force-extension graph for a material obeying Hooke's law? ☑
27) Give the equation for calculating the energy transferred to a spring when it's stretched. ☑
28) Describe a simple experiment to investigate Hooke's law. ☑

Static Electricity

Electrons are transferred when insulators are rubbed together. This causes static electricity to build up.

All Matter Contains Charge

1) Atoms contain positive protons and negative electrons.
2) However most objects have the same number of protons and electrons.
3) The positive and negative charges cancel out so the substance has zero net charge. It is neutral.

Transferring Electrons causes Static Electricity

1) When two objects are rubbed together, electrons are scraped off one and dumped on the other.
2) If the objects are electrical conductors, the electrons will flow back into or out of them.
3) This means they stay neutral.
4) Insulators don't let electricity (charged particles) flow through them.
5) So the electrons can't move and charge builds up.
6) This build-up of charge is static electricity.
7) The object that lost electrons has a positive charge.
8) The object that gained electrons has a negative charge.
9) If enough charge builds up, it can suddenly move, causing sparks.

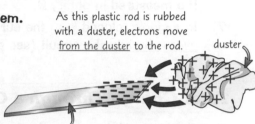

As this plastic rod is rubbed with a duster, electrons move from the duster to the rod.

duster

plastic rod

Like Charges Repel, Opposite Charges Attract

1) Electrically charged objects exert a force on one another.
2) It's a non-contact force — the objects don't need to touch.
3) Things with the same electric charge repel each other.
   Things with opposite electric charges attract each other.
4) You can show this using a hanging charged rod. If you put an object with the same charge near the rod, the rod moves away.
5) An oppositely-charged object attracts the rod towards it.

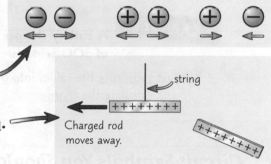

string

Charged rod moves away.

Electrically Charged Objects Attract Neutral Objects

1) You can show an object is charged by placing it near small, neutral scraps of paper.
2) The scraps of paper will 'jump' towards a charged rod.
3) This happens because the charged rod induces (causes) a charge in the paper.
4) If the rod is negatively charged it repels the electrons in the paper.
5) This gives the surface of the paper near the rod a positive charge. This is the opposite charge to the rod, so the rod and the paper are attracted together.
6) If the rod is positively charged, it attracts the electrons in the paper towards it and again the rod and paper are attracted together.

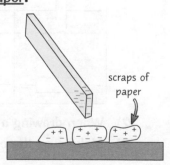

scraps of paper

Come on, think positive...

An insulating object becomes charged when it either gains or loses electrons to other objects.

Q1   Describe one way of demonstrating that an insulating object is carrying a static charge.   [2 marks]

Current and Circuit Diagrams

If the word <u>current</u> makes you think of delicious cakes instead of physics, that's all about to change.

A Potential Difference Pushes Charge Through a Resistance

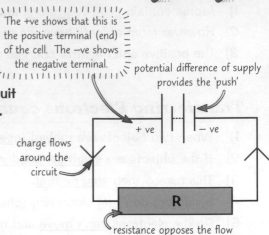

The +ve shows that this is the positive terminal (end) of the cell. The −ve shows the negative terminal.

1) <u>Electric current</u> is a rate of flow of <u>electrical charge</u>. This means how fast charge (<u>electrons</u>) is flowing.

2) Current is measured in <u>amperes</u>, A.

3) Charge is measured in <u>coulombs</u>, C.

4) Electrical charge will <u>only flow</u> round a complete (closed) circuit if something is providing a <u>potential difference</u>, e.g. a battery.

5) The <u>potential difference</u> is the '<u>driving force</u>' that pushes charge around the circuit. It's measured in <u>volts</u>, V.

6) <u>Resistance</u> is anything that <u>slows down</u> the flow of charge. It's measured in <u>ohms</u>, Ω.

7) In a <u>single</u>, closed <u>loop</u> the current is the same <u>everywhere</u> in the circuit (see p.180).

potential difference of supply provides the 'push'

charge flows around the circuit

R

resistance opposes the flow

Total Charge Through a Circuit Depends on Current and Time

1) The <u>bigger</u> the current, the <u>faster</u> the charge is flowing around the circuit.

2) <u>Charge flow</u>, <u>current</u> and <u>time</u> are related by this handy <u>equation</u>:

$$\text{charge flow (C)} = \text{current (A)} \times \text{time (s)}$$

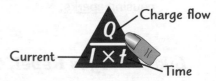

Charge flow — $\dfrac{Q}{I \times t}$ — Current, Time

EXAMPLE:

A battery charger passes a current of 2 A through a cell over a period of 300 seconds. How much charge is transferred to the cell?

Just <u>substitute</u> the values into the equation above and <u>calculate</u> the <u>charge</u>.

charge flow = current × time = 2 × 300
= 600 C

Circuit Symbols You Should Know

There's more about a.c. and d.c. on p.214.

1) You need to know these symbols to <u>understand</u> and <u>draw circuit diagrams</u>.

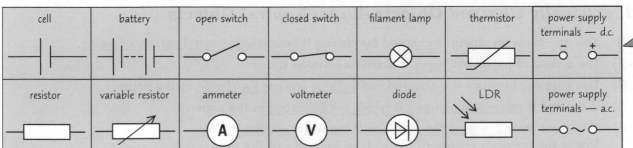

cell	battery	open switch	closed switch	filament lamp	thermistor	power supply terminals — d.c.
resistor	variable resistor	ammeter	voltmeter	diode	LDR	power supply terminals — a.c.

2) When drawing a circuit diagram, make sure all the <u>wires</u> in your circuit are <u>straight lines</u>.

3) Make sure the circuit you draw is <u>closed</u>. This means that it's a <u>complete loop</u>.

I think it's about time you took charge...

Current can be tricky to get your head around, but it's a key part of electricity. Remember, there needs to be a potential difference for current to flow, and current is the same at every point in a single closed loop.

Q1   Calculate how long it takes a current of 2.5 A to transfer a charge of 120 C.   [2 marks]

Potential Difference

On the previous page, you learnt that <u>potential difference</u> is the <u>driving force</u> that pushes the charge around a circuit. Unfortunately, you need to know about it in a bit more detail...

Energy is Transferred To and From Charges

1) Energy is transferred to a flowing charge from the <u>power supply</u> (e.g. cells, batteries).

2) The <u>amount of energy</u> transferred to each <u>coulomb</u> of charge depends on the <u>potential difference</u> of the power supply.

3) A <u>bigger potential difference</u> means <u>more energy</u> is supplied to each <u>coulomb</u> of charge.

4) The flowing charge <u>transfers the energy</u> to the <u>components</u> of the circuit.

The components in a circuit with the biggest resistances have the biggest potential differences across them.

5) The <u>energy transferred</u> to a component depends on the <u>potential difference</u> across the component and the <u>charge flowing</u> through it.

6) Here's the <u>equation</u> for the <u>energy transferred</u> to a component:

> **energy transferred (J) = charge (C) × potential difference (V)**
>
> joules   coulombs   volts

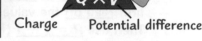

Energy transferred

$$\frac{E}{Q \times V}$$

Charge   Potential difference

7) So, | The <u>potential difference</u> (p.d.) across a component is the <u>amount of energy</u> transferred to that component per <u>unit charge passed</u>.

Potential difference is sometimes called voltage. They're the same thing.

8) One <u>volt</u> is one <u>joule per coulomb</u>.

9) For example, an <u>electric motor</u> with a potential difference across it of 9 V transfers <u>9 J of energy per coulomb of charge</u> that passes through it.

There's a Formula Linking Potential Difference and Current

1) The <u>current</u> flowing through a component depends on the <u>potential difference</u> across it and the <u>resistance</u> of the component.

Resistance measures how much the current is slowed down.

2) The formula linking <u>potential difference (pd)</u>, <u>current</u> and <u>resistance</u> is:

> **potential difference (V) = current (A) × resistance (Ω)**
>
> volts   amps   ohms

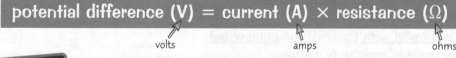

Potential difference

$$\frac{V}{I \times R}$$

Current   Resistance

 **EXAMPLE:** A 4.0 Ω resistor in a circuit has a potential difference of 6.0 V across it. What is the current through the resistor?

1) <u>Cover</u> the I in the <u>formula triangle</u> to find that $I = V \div R$. $I = V \div R$

2) <u>Substitute</u> in the values you have, and work out the current. $I = 6.0 \div 4.0 = 1.5$ A

Learn this page, and reach your full potential...

The equations on this page link together lots of quantities to do with electric circuits. They're pretty important, so make sure you know them well. You won't be given the equations in the exam, but you're bound to need them.

Q1   A current flowing through a resistor transfers 360 J of energy when 75 C of charge is passed through it. Calculate the potential difference across the resistor.   [2 marks]

Q2   A potential difference of 4.25 V is applied across a resistor, causing a current of 0.25 A to flow. Calculate the resistance, in ohms, of the resistor.   [2 marks]

I-V Characteristics

Yep. There's <u>plenty</u> of theory to learn in this topic. But there is a <u>practical</u> on this page too. Whoopie.

Linear Circuit Elements Have a Constant Resistance

1) Some components have a <u>fixed resistance</u> at a constant temperature, e.g. fixed resistors and wires.

2) These are known as <u>linear circuit elements</u>. Their resistance <u>doesn't</u> change with <u>current</u>.

3) However, the resistance of some components <u>changes</u> as the current changes.

4) These are known as <u>non-linear circuit elements</u>.

5) <u>Filament lamps</u> and <u>diodes</u> are examples of non-linear circuit elements.

I-V Characteristics Describe How Current Changes With P.d.

1) An '<u>I-V characteristic</u>' is a <u>graph</u> showing how the <u>current</u> (*I*) flowing through a component changes as the <u>potential difference</u> (*V*) across it changes.

2) <u>Linear circuit elements</u> have <u>straight line</u> *I-V* characteristics. E.g.

I-V characteristic for a fixed resistor at a constant temperature.

3) <u>Non-linear circuit elements</u> have <u>curved</u> *I-V* characteristics. E.g.

4) To find the <u>resistance</u> at any <u>point</u> on an *I-V* characteristic, first <u>read off</u> the values of *I* and *V* at that point. Then use <u>*R* = *V* ÷ *I*</u> (from *V* = *IR* on page 177) to calculate *R*.

I-V characteristic for a filament lamp.

There's more about these on the next page.

You Can Investigate I-V Characteristics `PRACTICAL`

Here's how to find the *I-V* characteristic of a <u>component</u>:

1) Set up the <u>test circuit</u> shown on the right.

- The <u>AMMETER</u> measures the <u>current</u> (in amps) flowing through the component.
- It must be placed <u>in series</u> (in line with) the component.
- It can be put <u>anywhere</u> in series in the <u>main circuit</u>.

- The <u>VOLTMETER</u> measures the <u>potential difference</u> across the component.
- It must be placed <u>in parallel with</u> (around) the <u>component</u> under test, <u>NOT</u> the variable resistor or battery.

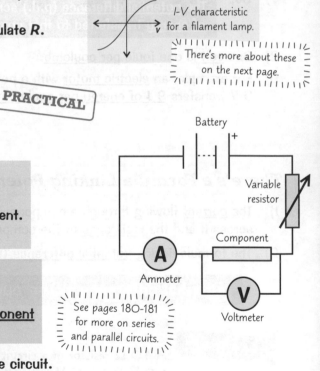

See pages 180-181 for more on series and parallel circuits.

2) The <u>variable resistor</u> is used to <u>change</u> the <u>current</u> in the circuit. This changes the <u>potential difference</u> across the <u>component</u>.

3) Record <u>sets</u> of <u>current</u> and <u>potential difference</u> readings by setting the variable resistor to <u>different values</u>.

4) The current readings in all these sets will either all be <u>positive</u> or all be <u>negative</u>. But you need to get readings with the <u>opposite sign</u> too. Do this by <u>swapping</u> over the wires connected to the battery to reverse the <u>direction</u> of the <u>current</u>. The ammeter should now display <u>readings</u> with the <u>opposite sign</u>.

5) Plot a <u>graph</u> with <u>current</u> on the *y*-axis and <u>potential difference</u> on the *x*-axis. Make sure you include your positive and negative values.

6) This is your <u>I-V characteristic</u>. Its shape depends on the <u>component you're investigating</u> (see p.179).

Circuit training — a lot less exhausting in Physics than in P.E....

So '*I-V* characteristic' is just a fancy name for a graph of current against voltage. Brilliant stuff.

Q1   Draw a circuit you could use to create an *I-V* characteristic for a thermistor.   [2 marks]

Circuit Devices

With your current and your potential difference measured, you can now make some sweet graphs...

Three Important I-V Characteristics

Here are three I-V characteristics, plotted from experiments like the one on the previous page:

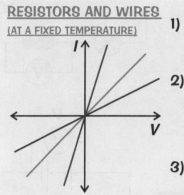

RESISTORS AND WIRES
(AT A FIXED TEMPERATURE)

1) Fixed resistors or wires at fixed temperatures have constant resistances.

2) Since V = IR (see p.177), current is directly proportional to potential difference at a certain resistance. (This means that if one is doubled the other is doubled too, etc.)

3) Their I-V characteristics are straight lines which go through the origin.

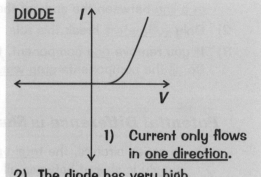

DIODE

1) Current only flows in one direction.

2) The diode has very high resistance in the reverse direction.

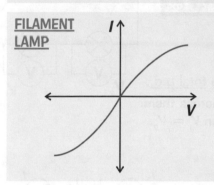

FILAMENT LAMP

1) The filament in the lamp is designed to heat up and glow.

2) So the filament's temperature increases as current increases.

3) As the filament heats up, its particles start to vibrate more.

4) This makes it more difficult for the charge-carrying electrons to get through the resistor.

5) The resistance increases and the current can't flow as easily.

6) So the graph gets less steep.

LDR is Short for Light-Dependent Resistor

1) The resistance of an LDR changes as the intensity of light changes.

2) In bright light, the resistance is low. In darkness, the resistance is high.

3) The I-V graph for an LDR at a constant temperature is a straight line.

4) LDRs can be used to turn on lighting automatically when it gets dark.

5) They're also used in burglar detectors.

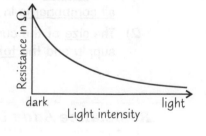

A Thermistor is a Temperature-Dependent Resistor

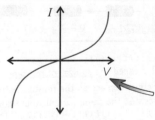

1) The resistance of a thermistor changes as the temperature changes.

2) In hot conditions, the resistance drops.

3) In cool conditions, the resistance goes up.

4) When the temperature of the surroundings is constant, their I-V graphs are curved.

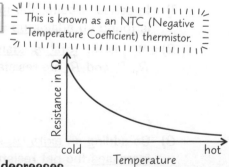

This is known as an NTC (Negative Temperature Coefficient) thermistor.

5) As the current increases, the thermistor warms up, so the resistance decreases.

6) Thermistors are used as temperature detectors, e.g. in car engines and central heating thermostats.

7) Thermostats turn the heating on when it's cool and off when it's warm.

In the end you'll have to learn this — resistance is futile...

Make sure you understand why these graphs have the shape they do, and you'll be ready for anything.

Q1   A fixed resistor has a constant resistance at a certain temperature.
      Describe its I-V characteristic. Explain why it has this type of I-V characteristic.   [2 marks]

Series Circuits

Series and parallel circuits are two <u>important types</u> that you need to know about. First up, <u>series circuits</u>.

Series Circuits — All or Nothing

1) In <u>series circuits</u>, the components are all connected <u>in a line</u> between the ends of the power supply.

2) Only <u>voltmeters</u> break this rule. They're <u>always</u> in <u>parallel</u> (see p.178).

3) If you remove <u>one</u> component, the circuit is <u>broken</u>. So <u>all</u> the components <u>stop working</u>.

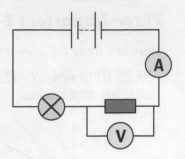

Potential Difference is Shared

1) In series circuits, the <u>total potential difference</u> (<u>p.d.</u>) of the <u>supply</u> is <u>shared</u> between all of the <u>components</u>.

2) If you <u>add up</u> the p.d. across <u>each component</u>, you get the <u>p.d. of the power supply</u>: $\longrightarrow$ $\boxed{V = V_1 + V_2}$

3) This is because energy is <u>transferred</u> to each charge by the <u>power supply</u>. The <u>same amount</u> of energy is then transferred from the charge by the <u>components</u>.

4) The <u>bigger</u> a component's <u>resistance</u>, the bigger its <u>share</u> of the <u>total p.d.</u>.

5) Components with the <u>same resistance</u> will have the <u>same p.d.</u> across them. So if the <u>two bulbs</u> in the circuit on the right were <u>identical</u>, then $V_1 = V_2$.

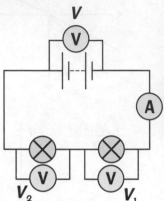

Current is the Same Everywhere

1) The <u>current</u> is the <u>same</u> through <u>all components</u> in a series circuit. $\longrightarrow$ $\boxed{I_1 = I_2 = I_3}$

2) The <u>size</u> of the current depends on the <u>total p.d.</u> of the power supply and the <u>total resistance</u> of the circuit, i.e. $I = V/R$.

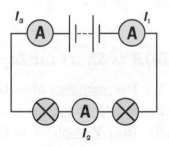

Resistance Adds Up

1) In series circuits, the <u>total (net) resistance</u> of components is found by <u>adding up</u> their resistances.

2) R_{total} is the <u>total resistance</u> of the circuit. R_1, R_2 and R_3 are resistances of the <u>components</u>:

$$R_{total} = R_1 + R_2 + R_3$$

3) So adding an <u>extra resistor</u> in a <u>series circuit</u> always <u>increases</u> the net resistance.

4) This is because the <u>battery</u> has to <u>push each charge</u> through them <u>all</u>.

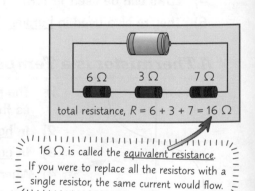

total resistance, $R = 6 + 3 + 7 = 16\ \Omega$

16 Ω is called the <u>equivalent resistance</u>. If you were to replace all the resistors with a single resistor, the same current would flow.

I like series circuits so much I bought the box set...

Series circuits are simple to make, but a real pain — if one of the bulbs in the diagrams above blew, it'd break the circuit, so they'd all go out. That's one of the reasons they're not as useful as parallel circuits (see the next page).

Q1   Three identical filament bulbs are connected in series to a power supply of 3.6 V.
      Calculate the p.d. across each bulb.
      [1 mark]

Series and Parallel Circuits

Time for a bit more on <u>series circuits</u>, and some fun old <u>parallel circuits</u>. It's like Christmas come early.

Parallel Circuits — Every Component Connected Separately

1) In <u>parallel circuits</u>, each component is <u>separately</u> connected to the ends of the power supply.

2) Only <u>ammeters</u> break this rule, they're <u>always in series</u> (see p.178).

3) If you take out <u>one</u> of the loops in a parallel circuit, the things in the <u>other</u> loops <u>won't</u> be affected.

4) So, things <u>in parallel</u> can be switched on and off <u>without affecting</u> each other.

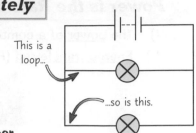

This is a loop...

...so is this.

Current is Shared, p.d is the Same Everywhere, Resistance is Tricky

1) In parallel circuits <u>all</u> branches get the <u>full source potential difference (p.d.)</u>.

2) So the p.d. is the <u>same</u> across all branches. Here, $V = V_1 = V_2$.

3) This is because <u>each charge</u> can only pass down <u>one branch</u> of the circuit, so it must <u>transfer all the energy</u> supplied to it by the <u>source p.d.</u> to whatever's on that branch.

4) In parallel circuits, there are <u>junctions</u> where the current splits or rejoins.

5) The total current going <u>into</u> a junction equals the total current <u>leaving</u>.

6) The <u>total resistance</u> of a parallel circuit is <u>less</u> than that of the branch with the <u>smallest</u> resistance.

7) The resistance is <u>lower</u> because the charge has <u>more than one</u> branch to take.

8) So adding a parallel branch to a circuit <u>increases</u> the <u>total current</u> (as $V = IR$ — see p.177).

You Can Investigate Circuits using Bulbs

1) The <u>brightness</u> of a <u>filament bulb</u> depends on how much <u>energy</u> is being transferred to it.

2) This depends on the <u>p.d.</u> across it and the <u>amount of charge</u> flowing through it, ($E = QV$, see p.177).

3) As current is the <u>rate of flow of charge</u>, energy transferred depends on <u>current</u> too.

4) You can explain <u>bulb brightness</u> in <u>series</u> and <u>parallel</u> circuits using rules from the last two pages.

SERIES
- Set up a circuit consisting of a <u>power supply</u> and a <u>bulb</u>.
- Add a <u>second bulb</u> in <u>series</u> with the first. The bulbs should both look <u>dimmer</u>.
- Add a <u>third bulb</u> in <u>series</u> with the first two. All three will look <u>even dimmer</u>.
- Each time you <u>add a bulb</u>, the <u>p.d.</u> across each bulb <u>falls</u> because its <u>shared</u>.
- The <u>current</u> also <u>falls</u>, because you're <u>increasing</u> the <u>resistance</u> of the circuit.
- So the <u>energy transferred</u> to each bulb <u>falls</u>, since $E = QV$.

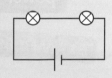

PARALLEL
- Repeat the experiment, this time adding each bulb in <u>parallel</u> on a new <u>branch</u>.
- The bulbs <u>shouldn't get dimmer</u> as you add more to the circuit.
- Adding bulbs <u>doesn't change</u> the <u>p.d.</u> across each bulb. It stays the <u>same</u> as the <u>supply p.d.</u>.
- The <u>current</u> on each branch <u>doesn't change</u> either because the <u>p.d.</u> and <u>resistance</u> is the same.
- So the <u>energy transferred</u> to each bulb <u>doesn't change</u>, since $E = QV$.

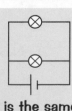

Sharing a current is tricky — they're so tiny to cut...

Remember, in parallel circuits, each branch has the same p.d., but the total current is shared between branches.

Q1 Three identical bulbs are connected in parallel to a 3.5 V battery. State the p.d. across each bulb. [1 mark]

Energy and Power in Circuits

Energy is transferred between stores (see page 202) by electrical appliances.

Power is the Rate of Energy Transfer

1) The power of a component tells you how much energy it transfers per second.

2) Energy transferred (E) and power (P) are related by the formula:

$$\text{energy transferred (J)} = \text{power (W)} \times \text{time (s)}$$

Energy transferred

$$\frac{E}{P \times t}$$

Power — Time

3) So a higher powered device transfers more energy between stores in a given time.

> **EXAMPLE:** A 600 W microwave is used for 5 minutes. How much energy does it transfer?
>
> 1) Convert the time into seconds. $t = 5 \times 60 = 300$ s
> 2) Substitute the numbers into $E = Pt$ $E = Pt = 600 \times 300$
>   to find the energy transferred. $= 180\ 000$ J

4) Energy is usually given in joules, but you may also see it given in kilowatt-hours.

5) A kilowatt-hour (kWh) is the amount of energy a device with a power of 1 kW (1000 W) transfers in 1 hour of use.

6) To calculate the energy transferred in kWh, you need power in kilowatts (kW) and the time in hours (h).

Calculate Power from Current and Potential Difference

1) The power of an appliance depends on the potential difference across it and the current flowing through it.

2) You can find it using this equation:

$$\text{power (W)} = \text{potential difference (V)} \times \text{current (A)}$$

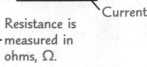

Power

Potential difference

$$\frac{P}{V \times I}$$

Current

3) You can also find the power if you don't know the potential difference, using:

$$\text{power} = \text{current}^2 \times \text{resistance}$$

or, in symbols: $P = I^2R$

Resistance is measured in ohms, Ω.

> **EXAMPLE:** A motor with a power rating of 1250 W has a resistance of 50 Ω. Calculate the current flowing through the motor.
>
> *Your calculator should have a '$\sqrt{\ }$' (square root) button to help with these calculations.*
>
> 1) First rearrange the formula $P = I^2R$ to make I the subject.
>   - Divide both sides by R. $P \div R = I^2$ so $I^2 = P \div R$
>   - Find the square root of both sides. $I = \sqrt{P \div R}$
>
> 2) Now just plug in the numbers. $I = \sqrt{1250 \div 50} = \sqrt{25}$
> $= 5$ A

You'll have the power — if you use these formulas wisely...

I'm afraid the best way to learn all of this is to just practise using those equations again and again. Sorry.

Q1   A p.d. of 2.5 V is applied across a resistor with a power rating of 8.5 W.
      Calculate the current flowing through the resistor.   [2 marks]

Magnets and Magnetic Fields

I think magnetism is an <u>attractive</u> subject, but don't get <u>repelled</u> by the exam — <u>revise</u>.

Forces Exist Between Magnets

1) All magnets have a <u>north pole</u> (N) and a <u>south pole</u> (S).
2) When two magnets are close, there is a <u>force</u> between them.
3) Two magnetic poles that are the <u>same</u> (<u>like poles</u>) <u>repel</u> each other.
4) Two <u>different</u> (<u>unlike</u>) magnetic poles <u>attract</u> each other.

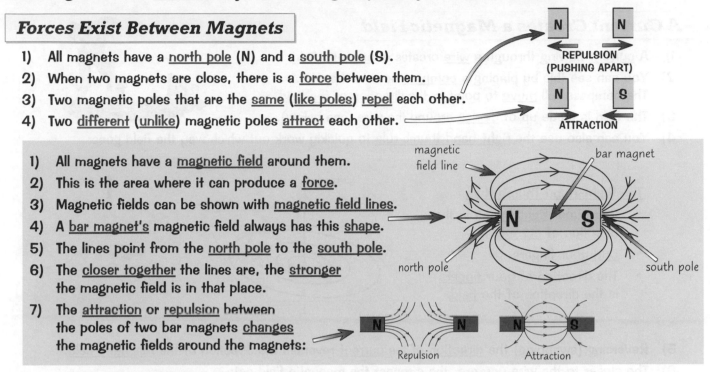

1) All magnets have a <u>magnetic field</u> around them.
2) This is the area where it can produce a <u>force</u>.
3) Magnetic fields can be shown with <u>magnetic field lines</u>.
4) A <u>bar magnet's</u> magnetic field always has this <u>shape</u>.
5) The lines point from the <u>north pole</u> to the <u>south pole</u>.
6) The <u>closer together</u> the lines are, the <u>stronger</u> the magnetic field is in that place.
7) The <u>attraction</u> or <u>repulsion</u> between the poles of two bar magnets <u>changes</u> the magnetic fields around the magnets:

There Are Different Ways to See Magnetic Field Patterns

1) You can use <u>iron filings</u> to see the <u>magnetic field</u> of a magnet. Just put the magnet under a <u>piece of paper</u> and <u>scatter</u> the iron filings on top. The iron filings will <u>align</u> themselves with the field lines.
2) The <u>needle</u> of a <u>compass</u> is a tiny <u>bar magnet</u>. It <u>points</u> in the <u>direction</u> of any <u>magnetic field</u> that it's in.
3) So you can use a <u>compass</u> to plot magnetic field patterns:

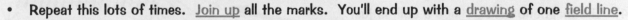

- <u>Draw around</u> a magnet on a <u>piece of paper</u>.
- Put a <u>compass</u> by the magnet and <u>mark</u> the <u>direction</u> the needle points in by drawing <u>a dot at each end</u> of it.
- <u>Move</u> the compass so that the <u>tail end</u> of the needle is where the <u>tip</u> of the needle was before.
- Repeat this lots of times. <u>Join up</u> all the marks. You'll end up with a <u>drawing</u> of one <u>field line</u>.
- Do this from <u>several different starting positions</u> around the magnet and you'll see the <u>field pattern</u>.

4) When a compass is <u>not near</u> a magnet it <u>always points north</u>.
5) So there must be a <u>magnetic field</u> around the Earth.
6) This provides evidence for the <u>core</u> (<u>inside</u>) of the Earth being <u>magnetic</u>.

Magnets Can be Permanent or Induced

1) <u>Permanent</u> magnets (e.g. bar magnets) create their <u>own</u> magnetic field <u>all the time</u>.
2) Some <u>magnetic materials</u>, such as <u>iron</u>, <u>steel</u>, <u>nickel</u> or <u>cobalt</u>, only produce a magnetic field while they're in another magnetic field. When this happens, they are known as <u>induced magnets</u>.
3) When you <u>take away</u> the magnetic field, induced magnets quickly <u>stop being magnets</u>.
4) Permanent magnets and induced magnets <u>always attract</u> each other.

Magnets are like farmers — surrounded by fields...

Lots of fun diagrams here, so get arty and practise drawing field lines around and between magnets.

Q1   Describe how to plot the magnetic field lines of a bar magnet with a compass.   [4 marks]

Electromagnetism

It would be really handy if you could turn a magnetic field on and off. Enter — electromagnetism.

A Current Creates a Magnetic Field

1) A current flowing through a wire creates a magnetic field.
2) You can see this by placing a compass near to the wire.
   The compass will move to point in the direction of the field..
3) The field is made up of circles around the wire (see below).
4) You can also use the right-hand thumb rule to quickly work out which way the field goes:

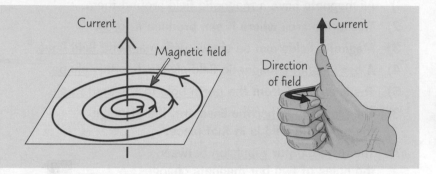

The Right-Hand Thumb Rule
- Point your right thumb in the direction of current.
- Curl your fingers.
- The direction of your fingers is the direction of the field.

5) Reversing (swapping) the direction of the current reverses the direction of the magnetic field.
6) The closer to the wire you are, the stronger the magnetic field gets.
7) And the larger the current through the wire is, the stronger the field is.

A Solenoid is a Coil of Wire

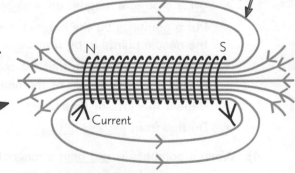

1) If you wrap a wire into a coil it's called a solenoid.
2) The magnetic field inside a solenoid is strong and uniform.
3) Uniform means the field has the same strength and direction everywhere.
4) The magnetic field outside a coil, is just like the one around a bar magnet.
5) Wrapping a wire into a solenoid increases the strength of the magnetic field produced by the current in the wire.

- This is because the field lines around each loop of wire line up with each other.
- So lots of field lines end up close to each other and pointing in the same direction.
- The closer together field lines are, the stronger the field is.

6) You can increase the field strength even more by putting a block of iron in the coil.

Give me one good raisin why I should make the currant joke...

Practise using the right-hand thumb rule. At least you shouldn't forget which hand to use — it's in the name.

Q1   Draw the magnetic field for a current-carrying wire.
Show the direction of the current and of the magnetic field.   [2 marks]

Revision Questions for Topic P3

Topic P3 — it was a tough ride but we got through it. Now let's see how much of it stuck...

- Try these questions and <u>tick off each one</u> when you <u>get it right</u>.
- When you've done <u>all the questions</u> under a heading and are <u>completely happy</u> with it, tick it off.

Static Electricity (p.175) ☐

1) Explain how static electricity can build up on a rod made of an insulating material when it's rubbed with a duster. ☑

2) Explain why a charged rod will attract small pieces of paper. ☑

Electricity and Circuits (p.176-179) ☑

3) What conditions are needed for charge to flow in a circuit? ☑

4) What are the units of: a) current,   b) charge,   c) potential difference? ☑

5) What is the equation linking current, charge flow and time? ☑

6) Draw the circuit symbols for: a) a battery,   b) a filament lamp,   c) a thermistor,   d) an LDR ☑

7) What is the equation linking potential difference, current and resistance? ☑

8) What does the *I-V* characteristic of a component show? ☑

9) Sketch the *I-V* characteristic of: a) a filament lamp, b) a wire, c) a diode. ☑

10) Describe how the resistance of an LDR changes with light-level. ☑

Series and Parallel Circuits (p.180-181) ☐

11) True or false? In a series circuit the sum of the p.d. across all the components is equal to the supply p.d. ☑

12) True or false? The current in a series circuit is different across different components. ☑

13) How would you find the equivalent resistance of two resistors in a series circuit? ☑

14) True or false? The total current going into a junction has to equal the total current leaving. ☑

15) How does the overall resistance of a circuit change when a resistor is added in parallel? ☑

Energy and Power in Circuits (p.182) ☑

16) Explain what is meant by the power of a circuit component? ☑

17) Give the equation that relates power, energy transferred and time. ☑

18) Explain what a kilowatt-hour is. ☑

19) Write the equation linking power to: a) potential difference and current,   b) current and resistance. ☑

Magnets and Magnetic Fields (p.183-184) ☑

20) True or false? The force between a north pole and a south pole is attractive. ☑

21) Sketch the field lines around a bar magnet. Show their directions too. ☑

22) What is the difference between a permanent magnet and an induced magnet? ☑

23) Describe what happens to magnetic field strength as you get further from a current-carrying wire. ☑

24) Sketch the shape of the magnetic field around a solenoid. Show the direction of the field lines. ☑

25) How can you increase the strength of a solenoid's magnetic field? ☑

Wave Basics

Waves <u>transfer</u> (carry) energy from one place to another without transferring any <u>matter</u> (stuff).

Waves Transfer Energy but not Matter

1) When waves travel through a <u>medium</u>, the <u>particles</u> of the medium <u>vibrate</u>.

2) A <u>medium</u> is just a fancy word for whatever the wave is <u>travelling through</u> (e.g. water, air).

3) The particles <u>transfer energy</u> between <u>each other</u> as they vibrate.

4) But overall, the particles stay in the <u>same place</u> — <u>only energy</u> is transferred.

5) For example, if you drop a twig into a calm pool of water, <u>ripples</u> spread out. The ripples don't <u>carry the water</u> (or the twig) <u>away</u> with them though.

6) And if you strum a <u>guitar string</u> the sound waves don't <u>carry the air away</u>. If they did, you'd feel a <u>wind</u> whenever there was a sound.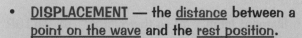

7) We can use these <u>four key words</u> to describe a wave:

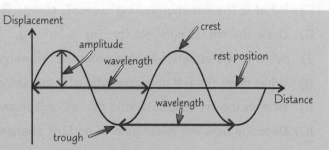

- **DISPLACEMENT** — the <u>distance</u> between a <u>point on the wave</u> and the <u>rest position</u>.
- **AMPLITUDE** — the <u>displacement</u> of a wave from the <u>rest position</u> to a <u>crest</u> or <u>trough</u>.
- **WAVELENGTH** — the is the <u>distance</u> from <u>one point</u> on a wave to the <u>same point</u> on the <u>next wave</u>, e.g. from crest to crest.
- **FREQUENCY** — the <u>number of complete waves</u> passing a certain point <u>each second</u>. Frequency is measured in <u>hertz</u> (<u>Hz</u>). 1 Hz is <u>1 wave per second</u>.
- **PERIOD** — the <u>time</u> it takes for <u>one complete wave</u> to pass a certain point. <u>Period = 1 ÷ frequency</u>.

Transverse Waves Have Sideways Vibrations

1) In <u>transverse waves</u>, the vibrations are <u>perpendicular</u> (at right angles) to the <u>direction the wave travels</u>.

2) <u>Ripples</u> on the <u>surface</u> of the <u>water</u> are transverse waves.

3) <u>Transverse waves</u> can travel on the <u>surface</u> of a <u>liquid</u>. But they <u>can't travel through liquids</u>.

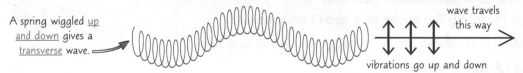

A spring wiggled <u>up and down</u> gives a <u>transverse</u> wave.

wave travels this way

vibrations go up and down

Longitudinal Waves Have Vibrations in the Direction of Travel

1) In <u>longitudinal waves</u>, the vibrations are in the <u>same direction</u> as the direction the <u>wave travels</u>.

2) <u>Sound waves</u> are a good example of longitudinal waves.

3) Longitudinal waves <u>squash up</u> and <u>stretch out</u> the arrangement of particles in the medium.

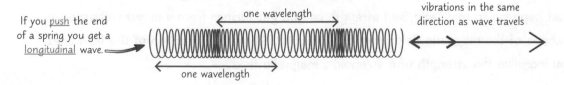

If you <u>push</u> the end of a spring you get a <u>longitudinal</u> wave.

one wavelength

one wavelength

vibrations in the same direction as wave travels

What about Mexican waves...

You won't get far unless you understand these wave basics. Try a question to test your knowledge.

Q1   It takes 40 seconds for 20 waves to pass a point. What is the period of the wave?   [2 marks]

Wave Speed

If you know the <u>frequency</u> and <u>wavelength</u> of a wave, you can work out its <u>speed</u> as well. How neat is that?

Learn the Wave Speed Equation

Wave speed is just how <u>fast</u> the wave is <u>moving</u>. You can find it using this <u>equation</u>:

$$\text{wave speed (m/s)} = \text{frequency (Hz)} \times \text{wavelength (m)}$$

Or:

Wave speed

Frequency

$$\frac{v}{f \times \lambda}$$

Wavelength

Tom had a freakishly
long wavelength.

EXAMPLE:

A wave has a frequency of 600 Hz and a wavelength of 0.2 m.
Calculate the wave speed.

Put the values into the wave speed equation.

$$v = f \times \lambda$$
$$= 600 \times 0.2$$
$$= 120 \text{ m/s}$$

Use an Oscilloscope to Find the Speed of Sound

1) Connect a signal generator to a <u>speaker</u>. This will let you generate sounds with a set <u>frequency</u>.

2) Connect <u>two microphones</u> to an <u>oscilloscope</u> (which shows waves on a screen).

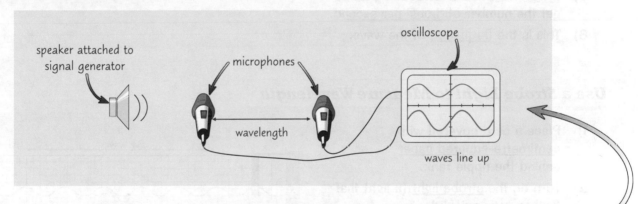

speaker attached to
signal generator

microphones

oscilloscope

wavelength

waves line up

3) Set up the oscilloscope so the <u>waves</u> reaching each microphone are shown as <u>separate waves</u>.

4) Start with <u>both microphones</u> next to the speaker. The waves should line up.

5) Slowly <u>move one microphone away</u> until the two waves are <u>lined up</u> again
   on the display. The microphones are now <u>exactly one wavelength apart</u>.

6) Measure the <u>distance between the microphones</u> with a ruler to find one <u>wavelength</u> (λ).

7) Use the formula $v = f\lambda$ to find the <u>speed</u> (v) of the <u>sound waves</u> passing through the <u>air</u>.

8) The frequency (f) is whatever you set the <u>signal generator</u> to.

I wish this topic would speed up...

You need to be able to describe how you would measure the speed of sound. Cover the page and try writing out
the method and drawing the diagram. It could get you some easy marks.

Q1   A sound wave has a speed of 340 m/s and a wavelength of 0.5 m. Calculate its frequency.   [2 marks]

Measuring Waves

PRACTICAL

Hey, look at that, more <u>experiments</u>. And people say physics is just fancy maths...

Find the Speed of Water Ripples with a Ripple Tank

1) You can generate <u>waves</u> in a <u>ripple tank</u> using a <u>motor</u> attached to a <u>dipper</u>.

2) The motor moves the dipper <u>up and down</u> to create water waves at a <u>fixed frequency</u>.

3) You find the <u>speed</u> of the water waves by measuring their <u>frequency</u> and <u>wavelength</u> and using the <u>wave speed equation</u> (see previous page).

4) For the experiments below, you should do at least <u>three repeats</u> for each measurement and take an <u>average</u>.

5) Of course, you must do all the usual things to make sure your experiments are <u>fair tests</u>:
   - keep the <u>equipment</u> the <u>same</u>.
   - keep all the <u>variables</u> the <u>same</u> every time, e.g. the <u>position</u> of the dipper, the <u>amplitude</u> of the waves, the <u>depth</u> of the water.

You'll Need a Cork and a Stopwatch to Measure Frequency

1) <u>Float</u> the cork in the ripple tank.

2) It should <u>bob up and down</u> as the waves pass it.

3) When the cork is at the <u>top</u> of a 'bob', <u>start the stopwatch</u>.

4) <u>Count</u> how many times the cork <u>bobs</u> in 20 seconds.

5) <u>Divide</u> the number of bobs by 20 to get the number of <u>'bobs' per second</u>.

6) This is the <u>frequency</u> of the wave.

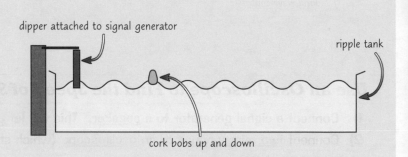

dipper attached to signal generator

ripple tank

cork bobs up and down

Use a Strobe Light to Measure Wavelength

1) Place a card covered with <u>centimetre-squared paper</u> behind the ripple tank.

2) Turn on the <u>strobe light</u> (a light that flashes very quickly).

3) <u>Adjust the frequency</u> of the strobe light until the waves appear to '<u>freeze</u>'.

4) The wavelength will be <u>small</u> and hard to measure <u>accurately</u>.

5) So, using the squared paper, measure the <u>distance</u> that, e.g. <u>five</u> waves cover.

6) <u>Divide</u> this distance by the <u>number of waves</u> to get the <u>wavelength</u>.

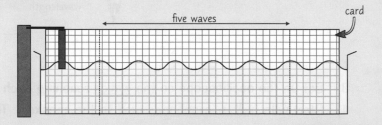

five waves

card

Disco time in the physics lab...

Practicals are like buses — you wait ages for one and then loads come at once. Typical.

Q1   Describe an experiment to measure the frequency of a water wave.   [3 marks]

Q2   A student is investigating the frequency of waves in a ripple tank.
      She counts how many times a cork bobs up due to the waves in the tank.
      She counts that the cork bobs 30 times in 20 seconds. What is the frequency of the waves?   [2 marks]

Reflection

Time to take a look in the mirror. No, really. This page is all about reflection.

Reflection is When Waves Bounce Back

1) When a wave meets a boundary between two materials, it may reflect (bounce back).

2) There's one rule for all reflected waves:

Angle of Incidence = Angle of Reflection

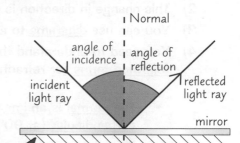

3) Each angle is measured from the normal.

4) The normal is an imaginary line at right angles to the boundary at the point the wave hits it (drawn with a dotty line).

5) Every wave always reflects at the same angle it hits the boundary at.

6) This diagram shows light rays being reflected from a mirror.

7) Rays are straight lines that point along the direction the wave is moving.

You Can Investigate Reflection Using a Ray Box and a Mirror   PRACTICAL

1) To investigate reflection, you'll need a light source (e.g. a ray box), a plane (flat) mirror and a piece of plain white paper.

2) Take the piece of paper and draw a straight solid line across it using a ruler.

3) Then draw a straight, dotted line at a right angle to the solid line. This dotted line is the normal.

4) Place the plane (flat) mirror so its shiny surface lines up with the solid line.

5) Using the ray box, shine a thin beam of light at the mirror. The light should hit the mirror where the normal meets the mirror. This is the incident light ray.

6) Your set-up should look something like this:

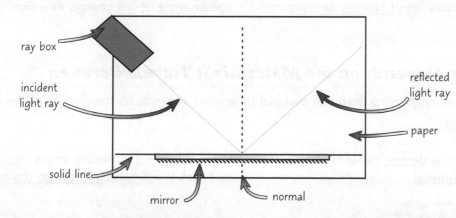

Do this experiment in a dark room so you can see the light beams clearly. Keep the light levels the same throughout your experiment.

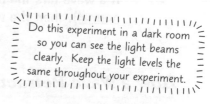

7) Trace the path that the light takes with a sharp pencil and a ruler.

8) Measure the angle of incidence (the angle between the incident ray and the normal) using a protractor.

9) Measure the angle of reflection (the angle between the reflected ray and the normal).

10) Repeat these three steps a few more times, changing the angle of incidence each time.

11) You'll find that no matter what its value is, the angle of incidence ALWAYS equals the angle of reflection.

12) Keep your test fair by keeping other variables the same. For example use the same mirror and keep the width and brightness of the beam the same every time.

Mirror mirror on the wall, make it the fairest test of all...

That's how to do an experiment with a mirror and a ray box. For my next trick, I'll pull a question out of my hat...

Q1   A student shines a beam of white light onto a plane mirror. The angle of incidence between the light beam and the normal is 27°. State what the angle of reflection will be.   [1 mark]

Refraction

Grab a glass of water and put a straw in it. The straw looks like it's <u>bending</u>. But it's not magic, it's <u>refraction</u>.

Refraction is When Waves Change Direction at a Boundary

1) When a wave travels <u>from one material into another</u>, it can <u>change direction</u>.

2) This change in direction is called <u>refraction</u>.

3) You can use <u>diagrams</u> to show refraction.

4) You need to understand the <u>following terms</u> for refraction:

- The <u>normal</u> is an <u>imaginary line</u> that's <u>perpendicular</u> (at 90°) to the boundary.
- The <u>angle of incidence</u> is the angle between the <u>incoming</u> (<u>incident</u>) <u>ray</u> and the <u>normal</u>.
- The <u>angle of refraction</u> is the angle between the <u>refracted ray</u> and the <u>normal</u>.

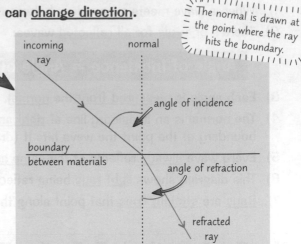

The normal is drawn at the point where the ray hits the boundary.

5) Whether a wave changes direction depends on the <u>angle</u> at which it hits the <u>boundary</u>.

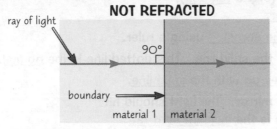

NOT REFRACTED

If a wave hits the boundary at <u>90°</u> (<u>along the normal</u>), then the wave <u>won't change direction</u>.

REFRACTED

If the wave hits the boundary at <u>any</u> other <u>angle</u>, it <u>will</u> change direction.

How a Wave Refracts Depends on the Materials it Travels Between

<u>How much</u> a wave <u>refracts</u> when passing from one material to another depends on the <u>density</u> of the materials. For example, for <u>light waves</u>:

If a <u>light wave</u> passes into a <u>denser</u> material, it will bend <u>towards the normal</u>.

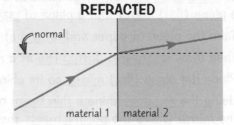

The <u>angle of incidence</u> is <u>larger</u> than the <u>angle of refraction</u>.

But if a <u>light wave</u> passes into a <u>less dense</u> material, it will bend <u>away from the normal</u>.

The <u>angle of incidence</u> is <u>smaller</u> than the <u>angle of refraction</u>.

Help, my wave isn't refracting! Well, that's perfectly normal...

Refraction has loads of uses (e.g. in glasses, cameras and telescopes). So make sure you really understand it.

Q1   State what is meant by refraction.   [1 mark]

Investigating Refraction [PRACTICAL]

Hurrah — it's time to whip out your ray box and get some refraction going on.

You Can Use Rectangular Glass Blocks to Investigate Refraction of Light

1) Before you get started, there are a couple of tips you should keep in mind.
2) This experiment uses a ray of light, so it's best to do it in a dim room.
3) That way you should be able to clearly see the ray.
4) The ray of light must be thin, so you can easily trace it and measure angles from it.
5) You can use a ray box to get a ray of light.

When You're Ready to Get Investigating...

1) Place a rectangular glass block on a piece of paper and trace around it.

2) Use a ray box to shine a ray of light at the middle of one side of the block.

3) Trace the ray as it enters and exits the block.

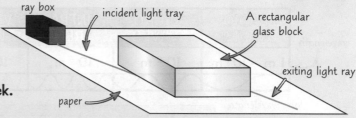

ray box   incident light tray   A rectangular glass block   exiting light ray   paper

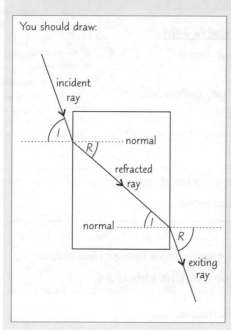

You should draw:

incident ray

I

R

normal

refracted ray

normal

I

R

exiting ray

4) Remove the block and join up the incident ray and the exiting ray with a straight line.

5) This shows the path of the refracted ray through the block.

6) Draw the normal at the point where the light ray entered the block.

7) Use a protractor to measure the angle of incidence, *I* (the angle between the incident ray and the normal).

8) Then measure the angle of refraction, *R* (the angle between the refracted ray and the normal).

9) Then draw the normal at the point where the light ray exited the block.

10) Measure the angle of incidence (in this case, this is between the ray that's travelling through the block and the normal).

11) Then measure the angle of refraction (here, it's the angle between the exiting ray and the normal).

12) Repeat steps 2-11, but keep changing the angle of incidence.

13) Record the angle of incidence and the angle of refraction each time.

You Should Notice a Few Things...

1) You should see that:
   - The ray of light bends towards the normal as it enters the glass block (see page 190).
   - The ray of light bends away from the normal as it leaves the glass block.
   - As you increase the angle of incidence, the angle of refraction increases too.

2) Light is an electromagnetic wave (p.192) — so this investigation shows one type of electromagnetic wave being refracted. In fact, all electromagnetic waves can be refracted.

Lights, camera, refraction...

This experiment isn't the easiest, but you still have to be able to describe how to do it and what it shows.

Q1   Describe an experiment you could do to investigate the refraction of light when it enters a glass block.   [3 marks]

Electromagnetic Waves

You've learned a lot about <u>light</u> so far, but light's just one <u>small part</u> of the <u>EM spectrum</u>...

There's a Spectrum of EM Waves

1) <u>Electromagnetic (EM) waves</u> are <u>transverse</u> waves (see page 186).
2) They can travel through <u>space</u>, where there are <u>no particles</u> (a <u>vacuum</u>).
3) They all travel at the <u>same speed</u> (300 000 000 m/s) through <u>air</u> or <u>space</u>.
4) EM waves vary in <u>wavelength</u> and <u>frequency</u>.
5) As they all travel at the same speed, those with <u>shorter wavelengths</u> have <u>higher frequencies</u> (from $v = f\lambda$).
6) There are EM waves of <u>every wavelength</u> in a certain range. This is known as a <u>continuous spectrum</u>.
7) The spectrum is split into <u>seven groups</u> based on <u>wavelength</u> and <u>frequency</u>.

RADIO WAVES	MICRO WAVES	INFRA RED	VISIBLE LIGHT	ULTRA VIOLET	X-RAYS	GAMMA RAYS
$1\text{ m} - 10^4\text{ m}$	10^{-2} m	10^{-5} m	10^{-7} m	10^{-8} m	10^{-10} m	10^{-15} m

wavelength

long wavelength, low frequency → short wavelength, high frequency

8) Our <u>eyes</u> can only detect a <u>small part</u> of the EM spectrum — <u>visible light</u>.
9) <u>Visible light</u> is made up of <u>different colours</u> of light. Each colour has a slightly different wavelength.
10) From <u>shortest to longest wavelength</u>, the colours are red, orange, yellow, green, blue, indigo and violet. They combine to make <u>white light</u>.

If you're struggling to remember the order of the colours in visible light, remember — Richard Of York Gave Battle In Vain.

EM Waves Transfer Energy

1) As well as being <u>reflected</u> or <u>refracted</u> by a material, waves can also be <u>absorbed</u>.
2) EM waves <u>transfer energy</u> from a <u>source</u> to an <u>absorber</u>. For example...

- An <u>electric heater</u> is a <u>source</u>.
- <u>Infra-red</u> waves transfer energy from the <u>thermal energy store</u> of the heater (the source).
- Energy is <u>transferred</u> to the <u>thermal energy store</u> of the object (the absorber).

3) The <u>higher the frequency</u> of the EM wave, the <u>more energy</u> it transfers.

Some EM Waves Can be Damaging

1) EM waves can be <u>absorbed</u> by body tissues.
2) If the EM wave transfers a lot of <u>energy</u>, this can cause <u>damage</u>.
3) When they enter living cells, they <u>collide</u> with <u>atoms</u> in molecules.
4) This may knock electrons off the atoms and cause <u>ionisation</u>.
5) Radiation that does this is known as <u>ionising radiation</u>.
6) Ionisation <u>damages cells</u> which may cause <u>genetic mutations</u> (changes in cells) and <u>cancer</u>, and can lead to <u>tissue damage</u> or <u>radiation sickness</u>.
7) <u>UV</u>, <u>X-rays</u> and <u>gamma rays</u> are all <u>ionising radiation</u>. <u>UV rays</u> are absorbed by the skin, but <u>X-rays</u> and <u>gamma rays</u> can pass through the skin and be absorbed by <u>deeper tissues</u>.

CGP — helping to shed light on EM Waves...

Here's one way to remember the order of EM waves — '<u>R</u>ock <u>M</u>usic <u>I</u>s <u>V</u>ery <u>U</u>seful for e<u>X</u>periments with <u>G</u>oats'.

Q1   Name three types of EM wave that can cause cancer.   [2 marks]

Uses of EM Waves

EM waves are used for all sorts of stuff — and <u>radio waves</u> are definitely the most fun. They make your car <u>radio</u> and your <u>TV</u> work. Life would be pretty quiet without them.

Radio Waves are Used Mainly for Communication

1) <u>Radio</u> and <u>TV</u> signals can be sent by radio waves.
2) <u>Very short wavelength</u> radio waves are used for FM radio and TV.
3) <u>Longer wavelength</u> radio waves can be used to send radio signals <u>around the world</u>.

Microwaves are Used for Satellites and Cooking

1) Communication with <u>satellites</u> uses microwaves, e.g. for <u>satellite TV</u> and <u>satellite phones</u>.
2) A signal is sent into <u>space</u> to a satellite dish <u>high</u> above the Earth.
3) The satellite <u>sends</u> the signal back to Earth in a different direction.
4) A <u>satellite dish</u> on the ground receives the signal.

1) <u>Microwave ovens</u> use microwaves to <u>cook food</u>.
2) The oven produces microwaves, which are <u>absorbed</u> by <u>water</u> in the food.
3) <u>Energy carried</u> by the microwaves is <u>transferred to</u> the water molecules, causing them to heat up.
4) This causes the rest of the <u>food</u> to heat up and quickly <u>cooks</u> it.

Infra-red Radiation Can be Used to Cook and Heat Things

1) <u>Infra-red</u> (IR) radiation is <u>given out</u> by all <u>objects</u>.
2) The <u>hotter</u> the object, the <u>more</u> infra-red radiation it gives out.
3) When an object <u>absorbs</u> infra-red radiation, <u>energy is transferred</u> to the object's <u>thermal energy store</u>. This makes it <u>warm up</u>.
4) Infra-red radiation can be <u>used</u> in many ways:

1) <u>Infra-red cameras</u> detect IR radiation and create a <u>picture</u>.
2) This is useful for seeing where a house is <u>losing energy</u>.
3) It can also allow you to see <u>hot objects</u> in the <u>dark</u>.

1) Infra-red radiation can also be used to <u>warm things</u>.
2) <u>Electric heaters</u> release lots of IR radiation to warm a room.
3) And <u>food</u> can be <u>cooked</u> using infra-red radiation.

The different colours mean different amounts of IR radiation are being detected from those areas. Here, the redder the colour, the more infra-red radiation is being detected from that area.

Surfers hate microwaves...

Microwaves are ace — without them I'd have nothing to eat and no one to talk to. Sad times.

Q1   State one use of radio waves.   [1 mark]

More Uses of EM Waves

Haven't had enough <u>uses of EM waves</u>? Good, because here's a few more. Get learning.

Visible Light is Used to Send Data Through Fibre Optic Cables

1) <u>Optical fibres</u> are thin <u>glass or plastic tubes</u> that can <u>carry data</u> over long distances.
2) They're often used to send information to <u>telephones</u> or <u>computers</u>.
3) Information is sent <u>as light rays</u> that bounce <u>back and forth</u> along the fibre.

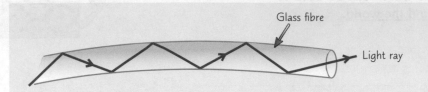

Glass fibre

Light ray

Ultraviolet Radiation Gives You a Suntan

1) <u>Ultraviolet radiation (UV)</u> is also produced by the Sun. It's what gives you a <u>suntan</u>.
2) <u>UV lamps</u> can be used to give people a <u>suntan</u> without the Sun (but this can be <u>dangerous</u> — see p.192).
3) When some materials <u>absorb UV light</u>, they <u>give off visible light</u>.
4) This can be pretty useful:

• <u>Energy-efficient lights</u> use <u>UV radiation</u> to produce <u>visible light</u>.
• <u>Security pens</u> can be used to <u>mark</u> property with your name (e.g. laptops).
• Under <u>UV light</u> the ink will <u>glow</u>, but it's <u>invisible</u> otherwise.
• This can help the police find out who <u>stolen property</u> belongs to.

X-rays and Gamma Rays are Used in Medicine

1) X-rays pass <u>easily through flesh</u> but not through <u>bones</u> or <u>metal</u>.
2) This can be used to create an <u>X-ray image</u> to check for <u>broken bones</u>.
3) <u>X-rays</u> can also treat people with <u>cancer</u>.
4) This is because they can <u>kill cells</u>. They are aimed at the <u>cancer cells</u> to kill them.

1) <u>Gamma rays</u> can also <u>kill cells</u>.
2) They can be used to <u>treat cancer</u> in the same way as X-rays.
3) They can also be used to <u>sterilise</u> (remove germs from) medical equipment.
    The equipment is <u>blasted</u> with <u>gamma rays</u> which <u>kill</u> any <u>living</u> things on it.
4) Gamma rays are also really good at <u>passing through</u> your body.
5) This is why <u>small</u> amounts of them are used in 'medical tracers'.
    How they <u>move around</u> the body can be tracked.
    This can tell doctors if <u>organs</u> are working as they should.

Don't lie to an X-ray — they can see right through you...

I hate to say it, but go back over the last few pages and read all of the uses for EM waves again to really learn 'em.

Q1   State two uses of X-rays.   [2 marks]

Atoms and Isotopes

Understanding what isotopes are is important for learning about radioactive decay. So let's get cracking.

Atoms are Made Up of Protons, Neutrons and Electrons

1) Atoms have a nucleus surrounded by electrons.
2) The nucleus is made up of protons and neutrons.
3) The atomic number is the number of protons in an atom.
4) The number of protons tells you what the element is (e.g. a carbon atom always has 6 protons).
5) Protons are positively charged and neutrons are neutral (have no charge).
6) So the nucleus of any element has an overall positive charge.
7) Electrons have a negative charge.
8) Atoms contain the same number of protons and electrons. So the positive and negative charges cancel out, and atoms have an overall neutral charge.
9) The atomic number (number of protons) is equal to the charge on the nucleus.
10) The mass number is the number of protons plus the number of neutrons in an atom — the mass of the nucleus.
11) You can represent atoms using this notation:

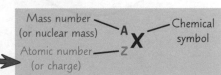

Mass number (or nuclear mass) → A — Chemical symbol
Atomic number (or charge) → Z ↘ X

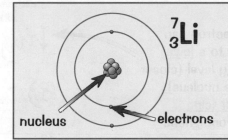

$^{7}_{3}\text{Li}$

nucleus — electrons

For example:
1) Lithium has the chemical symbol Li.
2) This lithium atom has three protons and four neutrons.
3) This gives it a mass number of seven.
4) So this atom can be represented by $^{7}_{3}\text{Li}$.

Isotopes are Different Forms of the Same Element

1) Isotopes are atoms of the same element.
2) They have the same number of protons but a different number of neutrons.
3) So isotopes have the same nuclear charge (atomic number) but a different nuclear mass (mass number).

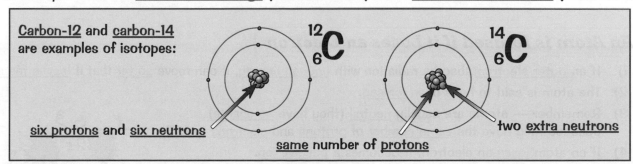

Carbon-12 and carbon-14 are examples of isotopes:

$^{12}_{6}\text{C}$ $^{14}_{6}\text{C}$

six protons and six neutrons   two extra neutrons

same number of protons

4) Most elements have different isotopes, but there are usually only one or two stable ones.
5) The other isotopes tend to be unstable and radioactive.
6) This means they give out radiation from the nucleus and may decay into other elements to become more stable (see p.197 for more on this).

Isotopes of an outfit — same dress, different accessories...

Make sure you can figure out how many protons and neutrons are in an atom from its symbol notation.

Q1   Give the number of protons and the number of neutrons in an atom of oxygen, $^{16}_{8}\text{O}$.   [2 marks]

Electron Energy Levels

If you need some motivation here, just think — you can tell everyone you've been doing <u>quantum physics</u> today.

Electrons Can be Excited to Higher Energy Levels

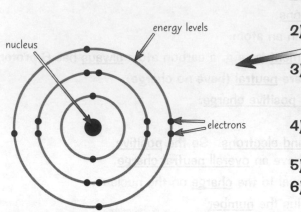

energy levels

nucleus

electrons

1) <u>Electrons</u> in an atom sit in <u>different</u> <u>energy levels</u> or shells.

2) Each <u>energy level</u> is a different distance from the <u>nucleus</u>.

3) The <u>further</u> an <u>energy level</u> is from the <u>nucleus</u>, the <u>more energy</u> an electron in that energy level has.

4) An electron can <u>move to a higher</u> energy level if it <u>absorbs electromagnetic (EM) radiation</u> (see p.192).

5) If this happens the electron is said to be '<u>excited</u>'.

6) The excited electron will then <u>fall back</u> to the original <u>energy level</u>.

7) It will emit EM radiation with the same amount of <u>energy</u> it <u>absorbed</u>.

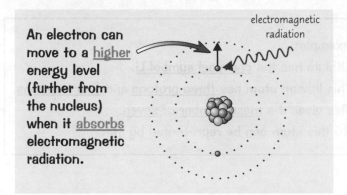

An electron can move to a <u>higher</u> energy level (further from the nucleus) when it <u>absorbs</u> electromagnetic radiation.

electromagnetic radiation

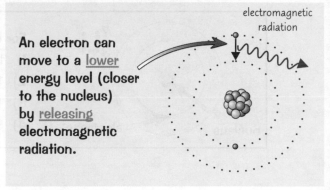

An electron can move to a <u>lower</u> energy level (closer to the nucleus) by <u>releasing</u> electromagnetic radiation.

electromagnetic radiation

8) The part of the <u>EM spectrum</u> the radiation is from depends on its <u>energy</u> (which depends on which <u>energy levels</u> the electron moves between).

9) A <u>higher energy</u> means a <u>higher frequency</u> of EM radiation.

10) So <u>changes</u> in <u>electron energy levels</u> can produce a wide <u>range of frequencies</u> of EM radiation.

An Atom is Ionised if it Loses an Electron

1) If an <u>outer electron</u> absorbs radiation with <u>enough energy</u>, it can move <u>so far</u> that it <u>leaves the atom</u>.

2) The atom is said to have been <u>ionised</u>.

3) Remember — atoms are usually <u>neutral</u> (they have <u>no charge</u>) because they have the <u>same number</u> of <u>protons</u> and <u>electrons</u> (p.195).

4) If an atom <u>loses</u> an electron, it becomes a <u>positive ion</u>.

5) It's <u>positive</u> because there are now <u>more protons</u> than <u>electrons</u>.

6) An atom can lose <u>more than one electron</u>.

7) The <u>more</u> electrons an atom loses, the <u>greater</u> its positive charge.

What's an atom's favourite chore? Ioning...

So, an electron absorbs EM radiation and moves up the energy levels, then falls back and emits EM radiation with the same amount of energy it absorbed. Simple...

Q1   What is a positive ion and how is one formed?   [2 marks]

Radioactive Decay

Prepare for the thrilling world of <u>radioactive decay</u>, where atoms turn into slightly different atoms.

There are Different Ways that Nuclei Can Decay

Nuclei is the plural of nucleus.

1) You saw on p.195 that <u>unstable</u> nuclei can <u>decay</u>.

2) If a nucleus decays, it <u>spits out</u> one or more of <u>four types</u> of radiation.

3) These four types of radiation are <u>alpha</u>, <u>beta</u>, <u>gamma</u> or <u>neutron</u>.

ALPHA PARTICLE (α)

- An <u>alpha</u> particle is <u>two neutrons</u> and <u>two protons</u> — the same as a <u>helium nucleus</u>.
- They have a <u>mass of 4</u> and a <u>charge of +2</u>.
- They are relatively <u>big</u>, <u>heavy</u> and <u>slow moving</u>.

BETA PARTICLE (β) ●

- A <u>beta</u> particle is just an <u>electron</u>. It has <u>virtually no mass</u> and a <u>charge of –1</u>.
- <u>Beta particles</u> are <u>small</u> and <u>fast moving</u>.

GAMMA RAY (γ) ⟋⟍⟋

- After spitting out an <u>alpha</u> or <u>beta</u> particle, the nucleus may need to get rid of some <u>energy</u>.
- It does this by emitting a <u>gamma ray</u> — a type of <u>electromagnetic wave</u>.
- Gamma rays have <u>no mass</u> and <u>no charge</u>.

NEUTRON ●

- If a nucleus contains <u>a lot</u> of <u>neutrons</u>, it may just <u>throw one out</u>.
- The <u>number of protons</u> stays the <u>same</u> but it now has a <u>different nuclear mass</u>.
- So it becomes an <u>isotope</u> of the <u>same element</u>.

Different Types of Radiation Can be Stopped by Different Materials

1) <u>Radiation</u> can only <u>penetrate</u> (travel) so far into a material before it's <u>absorbed</u>.

2) How far depends on the <u>type</u> of radiation and the <u>material</u> it's travelling through.

- <u>Alpha particles</u> have the <u>shortest</u> range in air.
- <u>Gamma radiation</u> travels a <u>long way</u> — it has the <u>longest</u> range in air.

3) Each type of nuclear radiation needs a different <u>materials</u> to stop it.

- <u>Alpha particles</u> are blocked by e.g. <u>paper</u>.
- <u>Beta particles</u> are blocked by e.g. <u>thin aluminium</u>.
- <u>Gamma rays</u> are blocked by e.g. <u>thick lead</u>.

The alpha and beta particles would also be blocked by the lead, and the alpha particles would also be blocked by the aluminium.

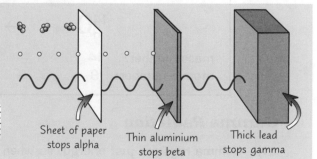

Sheet of paper stops alpha   Thin aluminium stops beta   Thick lead stops gamma

Try a question before your attention decays...

Make sure you learn the key facts each type of radiation. You'll need them on the next page.

Q1 Radiation is used to sterilise medical equipment sealed in foil packaging. The radiation needs to reach the equipment to sterilise it. Explain why alpha particles would be unsuitable for this use. [1 mark]

Topic P4 — Waves and Radioactivity

Decay Equations

Writing decay equations sound tricky, but it's really just adding and subtracting. Just remember the golden rule...

Nuclear Equations Must Be Balanced

1) When a nucleus decays, it will often change into a new element, as the nucleus changes its charge, its mass or both (see page 195).

2) You can write nuclear decays as nuclear equations.

3) They're written in the form: atom before decay → atom after decay + radiation emitted.

4) There is one golden rule to remember: the total mass and atomic numbers must be equal on both sides.

5) Mass number is the mass of the nucleus, and atomic number is the charge, so you can work out what happens to mass and charge as the nucleus decays.

Alpha Radiation

When a nucleus emits an alpha particle, it loses two protons and two neutrons, so:

- The mass number decreases by 4.
- The atomic number decreases by 2.

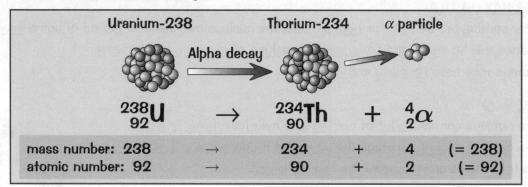

Uranium-238   Thorium-234 α particle

Alpha decay

$$^{238}_{92}U \quad \rightarrow \quad ^{234}_{90}Th \quad + \quad ^{4}_{2}\alpha$$

mass number: 238	→	234	+ 4	(= 238)
atomic number: 92	→	90	+ 2	(= 92)

Beta Radiation

In beta decay, a neutron changes into a proton and a beta particle (an electron) is emitted. So:

- The mass number doesn't change — as it has lost a neutron but gained a proton.
- The atomic number increases by 1 — because it has one more proton.

Carbon-14   Nitrogen-14 β particle

Beta decay

You can also write the beta particle as $^{0}_{-1}e$ in equations.

$$^{14}_{6}C \quad \rightarrow \quad ^{14}_{7}N \quad + \quad ^{0}_{-1}\beta$$

mass number: 14	→	14	+ 0	(= 14)
atomic number: 6	→	7	+ (−1)	(= 6)

Gamma Radiation

1) Gamma rays are just energy, so when a nucleus emits a gamma ray, the mass number and the atomic number don't change.

2) You might see gamma rays written as γ in balanced equations.

$$^{234}_{91}Pa \rightarrow {}^{234}_{91}Pa + \gamma$$

I think balancing equations is more fun than anything ever...

Right? Right?? *cough* I can't see your face, but I'm going to take a wild guess and say you don't believe me.

Q1   Complete this equation: $^{226}_{88}Ra \rightarrow {}^{-}_{-}Rn + {}^{4}_{2}\alpha$ [2 marks]

Activity and Half-Life

Radioactive decay is <u>random</u>, so how can we know when an isotope will decay? I give you, <u>half-lives</u>.

The Radioactivity of a Sample Always Decreases Over Time

1) <u>Radioactive isotopes</u> decay at <u>different rates</u>.
2) The <u>number of unstable nuclei</u> that <u>decay</u> in a given time is called the <u>activity</u>.
3) Activity is measured in <u>becquerels (Bq)</u> — the number of nuclei that decay each second.
4) So <u>one becquerel</u> is <u>one decay per second</u>.
5) As more <u>unstable nuclei</u> decay, the <u>activity</u> of the source as a whole <u>decreases</u>.

We Can Detect Radiation with a Geiger-Müller Tube

1) The <u>radiation</u> emitted from a radioactive isotope can be <u>detected</u> using a <u>Geiger-Müller tube</u>.
2) A <u>Geiger-Müller tube</u> lets you measure the <u>count rate</u>.
3) The count rate is the number of <u>radioactive particles</u> that reach the detector in a <u>given time</u>.
4) It's measured in <u>counts per minute</u> (or per second).
5) If the <u>activity</u> of a source <u>decreases</u>, the <u>count rate</u> (at a fixed distance) also <u>decreases</u>.

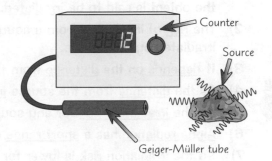

Counter

Source

Geiger-Müller tube

You Can't Predict when a Nucleus will Decay

1) <u>Radioactive decay</u> is a <u>random process</u>.
2) This means you <u>can't predict</u> when a particular nucleus is going to <u>decay</u>.
3) But you can make <u>predictions</u> about <u>how long</u> it will take for a <u>certain proportion of unstable nuclei</u> in a sample to <u>decay</u>.
4) You <u>can't predict</u> the activity as well when it's <u>low</u>.
5) This is because the <u>randomness</u> of radioactive decay becomes more <u>noticeable</u>.

Half-Life is a Measure of How Quickly Activity Decreases

> The half-life of a source is the average time taken for its activity (or count rate) to halve.

1) It's also the <u>average time taken</u> for <u>half</u> of the remaining <u>unstable nuclei</u> in a sample to <u>decay</u>.
2) A <u>short half-life</u> means the <u>activity falls quickly</u>, because <u>lots of</u> the nuclei decay in a <u>short time</u>.
3) A <u>long half-life</u> means the activity <u>falls more slowly</u> because <u>most</u> of the nuclei don't decay <u>for a long time</u>.

Half-life of a box of chocolates — about five minutes...

To measure half-life, you time how long it takes for the counts per minute (or second) to halve.

Q1   Explain what is meant by the activity of a source.   [1 mark]

Dangers of Radioactivity

All radioactive sources can cause <u>irradiation</u> and <u>contamination</u>. You need to know the differences between 'em.

Ionising Radiation Harms Living Cells

1) <u>Alpha, beta and gamma radiation</u> can <u>ionise atoms</u> (p.196).
2) They are known as <u>ionising radiation</u>.
3) As you've already seen, <u>ionising radiation</u> can enter and <u>damage living cells</u>.
4) It can cause <u>cancer</u> or <u>kill cells completely</u>.

Irradiation is Temporary

1) If the <u>radiation</u> from a <u>radioactive source</u> reaches an object, the object is said to be <u>irradiated</u>.
2) The <u>risk</u> of irradiation from a source is how <u>likely</u> it is that an object will be irradiated by the source.
3) It <u>depends</u> on the <u>distance</u> from the source and the <u>type of radiation</u> that the source emits.
4) As the <u>distance</u> from the source <u>increases</u>, the amount of radiation reaching that point decreases.
5) So the <u>irradiation risk</u> for any source is <u>lower</u> at <u>larger distances</u>.
6) <u>Alpha radiation</u> has a <u>short range</u> compared to <u>gamma radiation</u>.
7) So the <u>irradiation risk</u> is <u>lower</u> for a source that emits alpha radiation than for a source that emits gamma radiation (at a given distance).
8) <u>Irradiation</u> is <u>temporary</u> — if the source is <u>taken away</u>, any irradiation it's causing stops.

Contamination Lasts Longer

1) If any of a radioactive source ends up <u>on or in</u> an object, we say the object is <u>contaminated</u>.
2) For example, if you <u>touch</u> a radioactive source some atoms of it might <u>rub off onto your hand</u>, contaminating you.
3) The <u>contamination risk</u> is <u>how likely</u> it is that an object could get contaminated.
4) If a radioactive source is a <u>solid</u>, then there's <u>no contamination risk</u> for an object that <u>doesn't touch</u> the source.
5) But if the source is a <u>gas</u>, then it could <u>move</u> and come into contact with the object, <u>increasing</u> the <u>contamination risk</u>.
6) Gases are particularly dangerous for <u>people</u> as they can be <u>breathed in</u>, contaminating them from the <u>inside</u>.
7) If an object becomes <u>contaminated</u>, then the <u>irradiation risk</u> is <u>very high</u> as the <u>distance</u> between the source and the object is <u>so small</u>.
8) <u>Contamination lasts longer than irradiation</u> — if the <u>original source</u> is taken away, the atoms causing the contamination will be <u>left behind</u>.

Top tip number 364 — if something is radioactive, don't lick it...

If you're working with radioactive sources, read about the safety risks and make experiments as safe as possible.

Q1   Give two effects that ionising radiation can have on living cells.   [2 marks]

Q2   A scientist is carrying out an experiment which requires her to use a solid, alpha radiation source. She holds the source with tongs at arm's length at all times. Why is she unlikely to be irradiated by the source?   [2 marks]

Revision Questions for Topic P4

It's not quite time to wave goodbye to those pesky waves yet — have a go at these revision questions.

- Try these questions and <u>tick off each one</u> when you <u>get it right</u>.
- When you've done <u>all the questions</u> under a heading and are <u>completely happy</u> with it, tick it off.

Wave Basics (p.186-188) ☑

1) Sketch a diagram of a wave. Label the amplitude, wavelength, rest position, a crest and a trough. ☑
2) What is the difference between a transverse wave and a longitudinal wave?
   Give one example of each. ☑
3) Describe an experiment to measure the speed of sound. ☑
4) Describe an experiment to measure the wavelength of a water wave. ☑

Reflection and Refraction (p.189-191) ☑

5) Describe the relationship between the angle of incidence and the angle of reflection. ☑
6) In reflection, what is the normal? ☑
7) Why should you carry out experiments involving light beams in a dim room? ☑
8) True or false? A wave travelling from one material into another material will always change direction. ☑
9) Does a ray of light bend towards or away from the normal as it enters a glass block from air? ☑

EM Waves (p.192-194) ☑

10) What type of wave are EM waves — longitudinal or transverse? ☑
11) List the waves in the EM spectrum, in order of increasing wavelength. ☑
12) Explain why ultraviolet waves are dangerous. ☑
13) Give one use of each type of EM wave. ☑

Radiation (p.195-198) ☑

14) What is meant by the atomic number of an atom? What meant by is the mass number of an atom? ☑
15) What is meant by isotopes of an element? ☑
16) What does it mean for an electron to be 'excited'? What causes it? ☑
17) What happens to the charge of an atom when it becomes ionised? ☑
18) What causes nuclear radiation to be produced? ☑
19) What is an alpha particle? What is a beta particle? ☑
20) Which of alpha, beta and gamma radiation has the longest range in air? ☑
21) Which types of radiation are stopped by: a) paper,   b) thin aluminium,   c) thick lead? ☑
22) State what happens to the mass number and atomic number of a nucleus during alpha decay. ☑
23) State what happens to the mass number and atomic number of a nucleus during beta decay. ☑
24) Give the two different symbols you can use to represent a beta particle in equations. ☑

Half-life and Dangers of Radioactivity (p.199-200) ☑

25) What are the units of activity? ☑
26) What is meant by the count rate of a radioactive source? ☑
27) What equipment is used to measure count rate? ☑
28) Define the half-life of a radioactive source. ☑
29) What is irradiation? ☑
30) What is contamination? ☑

Energy and Energy Transfers

Energy is a tricky little beast. For one thing, it can be <u>stored</u> in lots of different ways.

Energy is Held in Energy Stores

Here are the energy stores you need to learn:

1) <u>KINETIC</u> — anything <u>moving</u> has energy in its <u>kinetic energy store</u>.
2) <u>THERMAL</u> — <u>all objects</u> have energy in this store. The <u>hotter</u> the object, the <u>more</u> energy in the store.
3) <u>CHEMICAL</u> — anything that can release energy by a <u>chemical reaction</u> has energy in this store, e.g. <u>food</u>.
4) <u>GRAVITATIONAL POTENTIAL</u> — any object <u>raised above ground level</u> has energy in this store.
5) <u>ELASTIC POTENTIAL</u> — anything <u>stretched</u> has energy in this store, like <u>springs</u> and <u>rubber bands</u>.
6) <u>ELECTROSTATIC</u> — e.g. two <u>charges</u> that attract or repel each other have energy in this store.
7) <u>MAGNETIC</u> — e.g. two <u>magnets</u> that attract or repel each other have energy in this store.
8) <u>NUCLEAR</u> — the <u>nucleus of an atom</u> releases energy from this store in <u>nuclear reactions</u> (p.197).

Energy can be Transferred Between Energy Stores

<u>Energy</u> can be transferred between <u>stores</u> in the following ways:

<u>BY HEATING</u>: energy is transferred from a <u>hotter</u> object to a <u>colder</u> object (e.g. heating a pan on a hob).

<u>MECHANICALLY</u>: a <u>force does work</u> (p.168) on an object (e.g. a force <u>pushing</u> an object along).

<u>ELECTRICALLY</u>: a <u>moving charge does work</u> (p.177) (e.g. a <u>current flowing</u> through a <u>light bulb</u>).

<u>BY RADIATION</u>: energy is transferred by e.g. <u>sound/light</u> (e.g. energy from the <u>Sun</u> reaching <u>Earth</u> by <u>light</u>).

When a System Changes, Energy is Transferred

1) A <u>system</u> is just the <u>single</u> object or a <u>group</u> of <u>objects</u> that you're interested in.
2) When a system <u>changes</u>, the way energy is <u>stored</u> changes in one of the ways above.
3) <u>Closed systems</u> are systems where <u>no matter</u> (stuff) or <u>energy</u> can <u>enter or leave</u>.
4) When a closed system changes, the <u>total energy</u> of the system stays the same (there is <u>no net change</u>).

For example...
- A <u>cold spoon</u> sealed in a flask of <u>hot soup</u> is a closed system.
- Energy is <u>transferred</u> from the thermal energy store of the <u>soup</u> to the thermal energy store of the <u>spoon</u> by heating.
- But <u>no energy</u> leaves the system. The total energy <u>stays the same</u>.

You Need to Know the Law of Conservation of Energy

Energy can be <u>transferred</u> usefully, <u>stored</u> or <u>dissipated</u>, but can <u>never</u> be <u>created</u> or <u>destroyed</u>.

> Dissipated is a fancy way of saying the energy is spread out into useless energy stores (so that it is unusable).

1) This means that whenever a system <u>changes</u>, energy is just <u>moved between stores</u>. It <u>never</u> disappears.
2) Even when energy is <u>dissipated</u> (or wasted), it <u>isn't</u> gone (see p.204).
3) It's just been transferred to an energy store that <u>we didn't want</u>.

Energy can't be created or destroyed — only talked about a lot...

Energy stores pop up everywhere in physics. Make sure you understand them before you read the next page.

Q1   A spring is stretched. How is the energy transferred to the elastic potential store of the spring?   [1 marks]

More Energy Transfers

Now for a closer look <u>two</u> types of <u>energy transfer</u> — <u>mechanical</u> transfer and transfer by <u>heating</u>.

Forces Can Cause Mechanical Energy Transfers

1) If a <u>force</u> moves an object, then <u>work is done</u>. Work done is <u>the same</u> as energy transferred.

2) Energy is transferred <u>mechanically</u> when a force moves an object and when forces <u>slow down</u> or <u>stop</u> an object.

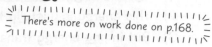 There's more on work done on p.168.

3) Here are a few <u>examples</u>:

<u>A ball projected up a slope</u>

1) Energy is transferred <u>mechanically</u> from the <u>kinetic energy store</u> of the ball to its <u>gravitational potential energy store</u>.

2) The ball <u>slows down</u> because the energy is being <u>transferred away</u> from its kinetic energy store.

<u>A ball falling from a height</u>

1) The ball is <u>accelerated</u> by the <u>constant force</u> of <u>gravity</u>.

2) Energy is <u>transferred</u> <u>mechanically</u> from the ball's <u>gravitational potential energy</u> store to its <u>kinetic energy</u> store.

<u>A car slowing down</u>

1) <u>Friction</u> acts between the car's <u>brakes</u> and its <u>wheels</u>.

2) Energy is transferred <u>mechanically</u> from the <u>wheels' kinetic energy</u> stores to the <u>thermal</u> energy stores of the <u>brakes</u> and <u>wheels</u>.

frictional forces cause a transfer of energy

<u>A car hitting a wall</u>

1) When the <u>car</u> and the <u>wall touch</u>, there is a <u>normal contact force</u> (p.163) on both of them.

2) Energy is transferred <u>mechanically</u> from the car's <u>kinetic</u> energy store to <u>lots</u> of other energy stores.

3) Some energy is transferred to the <u>elastic potential</u> and <u>thermal</u> energy stores of the <u>wall</u> and the <u>car</u>.

4) Some energy might also be <u>transferred away</u> by <u>sound</u> waves.

Energy is Transferred When You Heat Something Up

1) As an object is <u>heated</u>, energy is <u>transferred</u> to its <u>thermal</u> energy store.

2) This causes its <u>temperature to increase</u>.

3) For example, as <u>water</u> is heated in an <u>electric kettle</u>.

- Energy is transferred <u>electrically</u> to the <u>thermal</u> energy store of the kettle's heating element.
- Energy is then transferred <u>by heating</u> to the water's <u>thermal</u> energy store.
- So the <u>temperature</u> of the water <u>increases</u>.

---

4) <u>Different substances</u> need <u>different amounts</u> of energy for the <u>same</u> temperature change.

5) The amount of energy needed depends on their <u>specific heat capacity</u> and their mass. See p.153 for how to <u>calculate</u> the <u>energy transferred when heating</u>.

Transfer this information to your exam knowledge stores...

Bored of energy transfers yet? I hope not, as there are a few pages left. Keep transferring energy to your brain.

Q1   Describe the energy transfers that occur when a car slows down by braking.   [3 marks]

Efficiency

So energy is <u>transferred</u> between different <u>stores</u>. But not all of the energy is transferred to <u>useful</u> stores.

Energy is Always Wasted in any Energy Transfer

1) When energy is <u>transferred</u> between stores, some energy is transferred to the store you <u>want</u> it in.
2) This energy is <u>usefully</u> transferred.
3) But in <u>any</u> energy transfer, some energy is <u>always dissipated</u>.
4) This means the energy is transferred to <u>useless stores</u>.
5) These useless energy stores are usually <u>thermal energy stores</u>.
6) This energy is often described as 'wasted' energy.

> Remember — dissipated means spread out into useless stores.

- When you use a mobile phone, energy is transferred from the <u>chemical</u> energy store of the <u>battery</u>.
- Some energy is <u>usefully</u> transferred.
- But some is <u>dissipated</u> to the <u>thermal</u> energy store of the <u>phone</u>.

7) Wasted energy <u>still exists</u>, but is stored in <u>less useful</u> ways.

You can Calculate the Efficiency of an Energy Transfer

1) The <u>less energy</u> that's <u>wasted</u> by something, the <u>more efficient</u> it is.
2) You can work out the <u>efficiency</u> of an energy transfer using this equation:

$$\text{efficiency} = \frac{\text{useful output energy transfer (J)}}{\text{input energy transfer (J)}}$$

> This gives efficiency as a decimal, but you can turn it into a percentage — see below.

EXAMPLE: 36 000 J of energy is transferred to a television.
It transfers 28 800 J of this energy usefully.
Calculate the efficiency of the television. Give your answer as a percentage.

1) Put the numbers you're given <u>into the equation</u>.

$$\text{efficiency} = \frac{\text{useful output energy transfer}}{\text{total input energy transfer}}$$

$$= 28\ 800 \div 36\ 000$$
$$= 0.8$$

2) To change a <u>decimal</u> to a <u>percentage</u>, <u>multiply</u> your answer <u>by 100</u>.

$0.8 \times 100 = 80$, so efficiency = **80%**

3) All devices have an <u>efficiency</u> of less than 100%.
4) This is because <u>every device wastes some energy</u>.

Make sure your revising efficiency is high...

Make sure you know that equation for efficiency and how to use it.

Q1   An electrical device has an input energy of 500 J and a useful output energy of 80 J.
Calculate the efficiency of the device as a percentage.   [2 marks]

Reducing Unwanted Energy Transfers

There are a few ways you can <u>reduce</u> the amount of energy running off to a <u>completely useless</u> store.

Lubrication Reduces Frictional Forces

1) <u>Friction</u> acts between all objects that <u>rub together</u>.
2) This causes some energy in the system to be <u>dissipated</u>.
3) <u>Lubricants</u> can be used to <u>reduce the friction</u> between the objects.
4) For example, <u>oil</u> in <u>car engines</u> reduces friction between all of the moving parts.
5) This <u>reduces</u> the amount of <u>dissipated energy</u>.

Insulation Has a Low Thermal Conductivity

1) When part of a material is <u>heated</u>, that part of the material gains <u>energy</u>.
2) This energy is <u>transferred</u> across the material so that the rest of the material gets <u>warmer</u>.
3) For example, if you heated <u>one end</u> of a <u>metal rod</u>, the <u>other end</u> would <u>eventually</u> get warmer. This is known as <u>conduction</u>.
4) <u>Thermal conductivity</u> is a measure of how <u>quickly</u> energy is transferred by conduction through a material.
5) Materials with a <u>high thermal conductivity</u> transfer <u>lots</u> of energy in a <u>short time</u>.
6) Materials with a <u>low thermal conductivity</u> are called <u>thermal insulators</u>.
7) Thermal insulators can reduce unwanted transfers <u>by heating</u>, e.g. in the <u>home</u>.

Insulation is Important for Keeping Buildings Warm

You can keep your home cosy and <u>warm</u> by <u>reducing</u> the <u>rate of cooling</u>.
How <u>quickly</u> a building cools depends on:

1) How <u>thick</u> its <u>walls</u> are. The <u>thicker</u> the walls are, the <u>slower</u> a building will <u>cool</u>.

2) The <u>thermal conductivity</u> of its walls. Building walls from a material with a <u>low thermal conductivity</u> reduces the rate of cooling.

3) How much <u>thermal insulation</u> there is, e.g. <u>loft insulation</u> reduces energy losses through the roof.

A cat curled up on your lap — an excellent furmal insulator...

Did you know that Christmas jumpers are excellent insulators? Just another reason to wear them until March.

Q1 A builder is designing a house.
Give one way the builder could reduce the rate of cooling of the house. [1 mark]

Mechanical Energy Transfers & Calculations

Cast your mind back to p.168 — when a <u>force</u> is applied to an object, <u>work is done</u> and <u>energy is transferred</u>.

Falling Objects Transfer Energy Between Stores

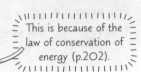

1) When an object <u>falls</u>, energy is transferred from its <u>gravitational potential energy</u> store to its <u>kinetic energy</u> store.

2) <u>Air resistance</u> means that a small amount of energy is also transferred to <u>thermal energy stores</u>.

3) Exam questions often tell you to <u>ignore</u> air resistance.

4) This means you can say:

> Energy transferred to <u>kinetic energy</u> store **=** Energy transferred from <u>gravitational potential energy</u> store

This is because of the law of conservation of energy (p.202).

5) If an object is <u>thrown upwards</u>, the reverse happens. Energy is transferred <u>from</u> the object's <u>kinetic energy</u> store <u>to</u> its <u>gravitational potential energy</u> store.

6) The <u>equation</u> for calculating the energy in the <u>kinetic energy store</u> of something is:

See page 167 for more on using these equations.

$$\text{kinetic energy} = \tfrac{1}{2} \times \text{mass} \times (\text{speed})^2 = \tfrac{1}{2} \times mv^2$$

7) The <u>equation</u> for calculating the energy in the <u>gravitational potential energy store</u> of an object is:

$$\text{gravitational potential energy} = \text{mass} \times \text{height} \times \text{gravitational field strength} = m \times h \times g$$

8) This equation gives the <u>change in gravitational potential energy</u> if an object moves. Just use the <u>change in height</u> of the object for *h*.

EXAMPLE:

The diagram shows a roller coaster car with mass 500 kg falling between points A and B. The height difference between A and B is 20 m. How much energy is transferred to the kinetic energy store of the car in moving from A to B? You can ignore air resistance and friction for this question.

You can assume that <u>all</u> of the energy transferred from the gravitational potential energy store of the car is <u>transferred</u> to its kinetic energy store.

So kinetic energy = gravitational potential energy
= $m \times h \times g$
= $500 \times 20 \times 10$
= 100 000 J

g = 10 N/kg on Earth (see p.166)

Elastic Objects Have Elastic Potential Energy Stores

1) <u>Springs</u> and other elastic objects, can be <u>stretched</u> by forces.

2) When this happens, <u>work is done</u> on the spring.

3) When work is done on the spring, energy is <u>transferred</u> to the spring's <u>kinetic energy store</u> (since the spring moves as it's being stretched) and then to its <u>elastic potential energy store</u>.

4) The <u>energy transferred</u> to the elastic potential energy store of a <u>stretched</u> spring is equal to <u>0.5 × spring constant × (extension)²</u> (see p.171).

You can also use this equation to calculate the energy stored when a spring is compressed.

Make the most of your potential — jump on your bed...

Make sure you learn the equation for kinetic energy and the one for gravitational potential energy too.

Q1 A 1.6 kg object is raised by a height of 5.0 m.
Calculate the energy gained in its gravitational potential energy store. *g* = 10 N/kg. **[2 marks]**

Electrical Energy Transfers & Calculations

Transferring energy <u>electrically</u> is really fun — it means you can play computer games...

Electrical Circuits Transfer Energy Electrically

1) When a device is <u>plugged</u> into a <u>socket</u> in the wall, it's connected to the <u>mains</u> (i.e. the <u>national grid</u>).
2) <u>Energy</u> is <u>transferred electrically</u> by alternating current (a.c. — see p.214) from the <u>mains</u> to the <u>device</u>.
3) <u>Batteries</u> also power devices. Energy in their <u>chemical energy stores</u> is <u>transferred electrically</u> to <u>devices</u>.
4) The <u>energy transferred</u> is equal to the <u>work done</u> by the current from the <u>battery</u> or <u>mains</u>.
5) Here are some <u>examples</u> of electrical devices and how they <u>usefully transfer</u> the energy <u>supplied</u>:

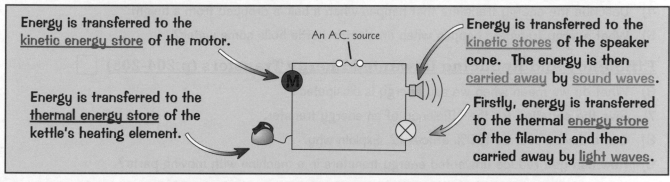

Energy is transferred to the <u>kinetic energy store</u> of the motor.

Energy is transferred to the <u>thermal energy store</u> of the kettle's heating element.

An A.C. source

Energy is transferred to the <u>kinetic stores</u> of the speaker cone. The energy is then <u>carried away</u> by <u>sound waves</u>.

Firstly, energy is transferred to the thermal <u>energy store</u> of the filament and then carried away by <u>light waves</u>.

6) Some energy from the mains or the battery is <u>wasted</u> before it gets to the device.
7) This happens because it's transferred to the <u>thermal energy stores</u> of the <u>wires</u> by <u>heating</u>.
8) Some energy is also <u>dissipated</u> (lost) <u>in the device</u> itself, for example:
   - In a <u>motor</u>, some energy is transferred to <u>thermal energy stores</u> (due to <u>friction</u>). Some is also carried away as <u>sound waves</u>.
   - In a <u>kettle</u>, some energy is transferred to the <u>thermal energy stores</u> of the kettle and <u>surroundings</u>.

Electrical Appliances Have Power Ratings

1) The <u>power rating</u> of electrical appliances (bulbs, kettles, hair dryers etc.) is often written on the appliance.
2) It tells you how much <u>energy</u> is <u>transferred</u> to the appliance <u>per second</u> (the <u>rate</u> of energy transfer):

> A <u>850 W microwave</u> will transfer <u>850 J</u> of energy from the <u>mains per second</u>.
> This <u>doesn't mean</u> 850 J of energy is transferred <u>to the food</u> by heating every second.
> This is because <u>no</u> device is <u>100%</u> efficient and some energy is <u>wasted</u> by the device (see above).

3) The <u>energy transferred</u> to a device is given by: <u>energy transferred = power × time</u> (see p.182).
4) Power is measured in <u>watts</u>, W, and energy transferred is usually measured in joules, J.
5) You also saw on p.182 that you can calculate power using the <u>potential difference</u> across a device and the <u>current</u> through it. The equation you need is: <u>power = current × potential difference</u>.

> Energy transferred can also be measured in kilowatt-hours, kWh. This is the amount of energy transferred to a 1000 W device in 1 hour. You calculate it using the same equation but with power in kW and time in hours.

EXAMPLE:

A kettle has a current of 12.0 A when a voltage of 230.0 V is applied across it. Calculate the power rating of the kettle.

power = current × potential difference = 12.0 × 230.0 = 2760 W

Go and put the kettle on, you deserve a brew...

...then once you have thought about all that energy you are transferring come back and have a go at this question.

Q1   A light bulb with a power rating of 35 W is connected to a battery for 2.0 minutes.
      Calculate the energy transferred to the bulb during this time.

[2 marks]

Revision Questions for Topic P5

Well, that wraps up <u>Topic P5</u> — but now to find out how much has sunk in, and how much is left to learn...

*   Try these questions and <u>tick off each one</u> when you <u>get it right</u>.
*   When you've done <u>all the questions</u> under a heading and are <u>completely happy</u> with it, tick it off.

<u>Energy Stores and Energy Transfers (p.202-203)</u> ☑

1) State the eight types of energy stores. ☑
2) State the four ways of transferring energy between energy stores. ☑
3) Give the law of conservation of energy. ☑
4) Describe the energy transfers that happen when a ball is dropped from a height. ☑
5) What energy transfers happen when an electric kettle boils some water? ☑

<u>Efficiency and Reducing Unwanted Energy Transfers (p.204-205)</u> ☑

6) What do we mean when we say energy is dissipated? ☑
7) Give the equation for the efficiency of an energy transfer. ☑
8) Can a device ever be 100% efficient? Explain why. ☑
9) How can you reduce unwanted energy transfers in a machine with moving parts? ☑
10) True or false? A high thermal conductivity means there is a high rate of energy transfer. ☑

<u>Mechanical and Electrical Energy Transfers (p.206-207)</u> ☑

11) Describe the energy transfers for an object thrown upwards, ignoring friction. ☑
12) Give the equation for the energy in the kinetic energy store of a moving object. ☑
13) Give the equation for the energy transferred to the gravitational potential energy store of an object lifted by a height, h. ☑
14) Give the equation for the energy in the elastic potential energy store of a stretched spring. ☑
15) Describe the useful energy transfer that occur when a motor is connected to a battery. ☑
16) Describe the useful energy transfers when a loudspeaker is connected to a battery. ☑
17) Give one way that energy is wasted in a motor. ☑
18) Give one way that energy is wasted in a heating device. ☑
19) What does the power rating of an electrical appliance tell you? ☑

Everyday Speeds and Accelerations

Are you ready for a super speedy page? Get set... gooooooooo!!

Speeds can be Given in Different Units

1) The unit for speed you'll mainly use in science is metres per second, m/s.

2) In the real world, speeds are often measured in miles per hour, mph or kilometres per hour, km/h.

3) Make sure you can convert between them:

Convert mph to km/h: There are about 1.6 kilometres to every mile. So multiply by 1.6. So 30 mph = 30 × 1.6 = 48 km/h.	**Convert km/h into m/s:** Divide by 3600 (i.e. 60 × 60) to turn hr into s, then multiply by 1000 to change from km to m. Or just divide by 3.6. So 48 km/h = 48 ÷ 3.6 = 13.33... ≈ 13 m/s (to 2 s.f.).

Learn these Typical Speeds

1) Walking — 1.4 m/s (5 km/h)
2) Running — 3 m/s (11 km/h)
3) Cycling — 5.5 m/s (20 km/h)
4) Cars in a built-up area — 13 m/s (47 km/h or 30 mph)
5) Cars on a motorway — 31 m/s (112 km/h or 70 mph)

6) Trains — up to 55 m/s (200 km/h)
7) A breeze — 5 m/s
8) A gale — 20 m/s
9) The speed of sound in air is 340 m/s

You Need to be Able to Estimate Acceleration

1) To estimate an acceleration, you may need to estimate the time a change in speed takes.

2) Then you can use the equation: acceleration = change in velocity ÷ time taken ($a = v \div t$, p.159).

> **EXAMPLE:** A car starts from rest and accelerates up to 50 km/hr as quickly as possible. Estimate its acceleration in m/s².
>
> First, change the speed to m/s: 50 km/hr = 50 ÷ 3.6 = 13.88... m/s
>
> This is a fairly typical speed for a car in town. You'd guess it takes a few seconds for most cars to get up to this speed — say it takes 2 seconds.
>
> Acceleration = change in velocity ÷ time taken = 13.88... ÷ 2 = 6.94... ≈ 7 m/s² (to 1 s.f.)

Give your answer to 1 s.f. for rough estimates like this.

Large Decelerations can be Dangerous

1) When things decelerate (slow down) too fast, e.g. in car crashes, the forces involved can cause injuries.

2) This is because a large deceleration requires a large force (as $F = ma$, from p.165).

3) Increasing the time taken to slow down reduces the deceleration (since $a = v \div t$).

4) Reducing the deceleration decreases the forces involved, reducing the risk of injury.

5) Safety features in cars and protective clothing (e.g. helmets and shin pads) are designed to increase collision times.

6) For example, seat belts stretch slightly and air bags slow you down gradually.

7) Bike helmets and shin pads slow down impacts with your body when they get squashed.

Remember, 'd' can mean acceleration or deceleration.

My acceleration towards the kettle is about 10 m/s²...

Have a go at converting the typical speeds above from m/s to km/hr, then check against the answers in the brackets.

Q1   Explain how increasing the time taken to slow down affects the forces involved in deceleration.   [2 marks]

Stopping Distances and Reaction Times

The <u>stopping distance</u> is the distance covered between the driver <u>spotting</u> a hazard and the vehicle <u>stopping</u>.

Stopping Distance = Thinking Distance + Braking Distance

1) The <u>further</u> it takes a driver to <u>stop</u> their car after seeing a hazard, the <u>higher</u> the risk of <u>crashing</u>.

2) The <u>stopping distance</u> is divided into the <u>thinking distance</u> and the <u>braking distance</u>:

The <u>thinking distance</u> is the distance the car travels in the driver's <u>reaction time</u>. It's affected by:

1) Your <u>reaction time</u> — this is affected by <u>tiredness</u>, <u>alcohol</u>, <u>drugs</u> and <u>distractions</u>.

2) Your <u>speed</u> — the <u>faster</u> you're going, the <u>further</u> you'll travel during your reaction time.

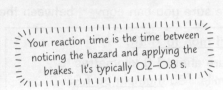
Your reaction time is the time between noticing the hazard and applying the brakes. It's typically 0.2–0.8 s.

The <u>braking distance</u> is the distance taken to stop <u>once the brakes have been applied</u>. It's affected by:

1) Your <u>speed</u> — the <u>faster</u> you're going, the <u>further</u> it takes to stop.

2) The <u>mass</u> of the car — a car full of <u>people</u> and <u>luggage</u> won't stop as quickly as an empty car.

3) The <u>brakes</u> — <u>worn</u> or <u>faulty</u> brakes won't be able to brake with <u>as much force</u>.

4) The <u>grip</u> of your tyres on the road — you're more likely to <u>skid</u> when the road is <u>dirty, icy or wet</u> and if the <u>tyres</u> are <u>bald</u>.

The Ruler Drop Experiment Measures Reaction Times

1) Get someone else to hold a ruler so it <u>hangs between</u> your thumb and forefinger.

2) Your forefinger should be lined up with <u>zero</u>.

3) Without any warning, the person holding the ruler <u>drops it</u>.

4) Close your thumb and finger to try to <u>catch the ruler as quickly as possible</u>.

5) Record the <u>distance</u> the ruler has dropped.

6) The <u>longer</u> the <u>distance</u>, the <u>longer</u> the <u>reaction time</u>.

7) A ruler will always fall at the <u>same rate</u>, so you can use a <u>ruler drop conversion table</u> to convert <u>distance caught</u> to <u>reaction time</u>.

8) For example, catching after <u>25 cm</u> is a reaction time of <u>0.23 s</u>.

9) Remember, reaction times are typically <u>0.2–0.8 s</u> so your results should be close to that range.

10) Make sure you do a lot of <u>repeats</u> to find the <u>mean distance</u> that the ruler fell.

11) Make sure it's a <u>fair test</u>, e.g. use the <u>same ruler</u> each time and catch it with the <u>same hand</u>.

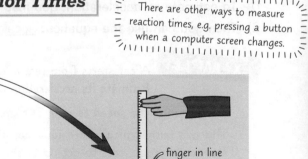
There are other ways to measure reaction times, e.g. pressing a button when a computer screen changes.

finger in line with zero

ruler is dropped without warning

distance fallen

Stop right there — and learn this page...

Bad visibility also causes crashes — if it's foggy, it's harder to notice a hazard, so there's less room to stop.

Q1   Explain why being tired can increase stopping distance.   [2 marks]

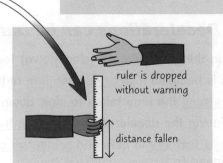

Non-Renewable Energy Sources

We use <u>A LOT</u> of electricity — I bet you're reading this in a room with an <u>electric light</u>, with your <u>phone</u> on in your pocket, and maybe the <u>radio</u> in the background. The energy to power it all has to come from <u>somewhere</u>.

Non-Renewable Energy Sources Will Run Out One Day

1) We get <u>most</u> of our energy from <u>non-renewable</u> sources.

2) These are sources that will <u>run out</u> one day.

3) The main non-renewables are the three <u>fossil fuels</u> (<u>coal</u>, <u>oil</u> and <u>natural gas</u>) and <u>nuclear fuels</u> (<u>uranium</u> and <u>plutonium</u>).

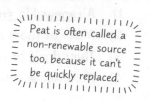
Peat is often called a non-renewable source too, because it can't be quickly replaced.

Most Power Stations Use Steam to Drive a Turbine

1) <u>Non-renewable power stations</u> usually <u>heat water</u> to produce <u>steam</u>.
   - <u>Fossil fuels</u> are <u>burnt</u> and the heat is used to make <u>steam</u>.
   - <u>Nuclear fuels</u> produce energy in a <u>nuclear reactor</u> which is used to make <u>steam</u>.

2) The steam causes a <u>turbine</u> to turn.

3) The turbine is attached to a <u>generator</u> which <u>produces electricity</u> as it turns.

They said turbine, Dave.

A <u>fossil fuel power station</u> looks like this:

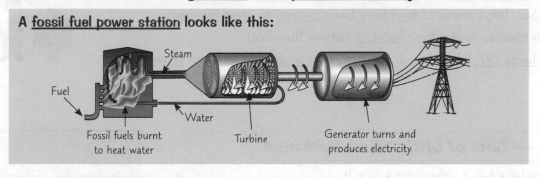
Steam
Fuel
Water
Fossil fuels burnt to heat water
Turbine
Generator turns and produces electricity

Non-Renewables are Reliable (For Now)

1) <u>Fossil fuels</u> and <u>nuclear energy</u> are <u>reliable</u>.

2) There are enough <u>fossil</u> and <u>nuclear fuels</u> to meet <u>current demand</u>.

3) We always have some in <u>stock</u> so power plants can respond <u>quickly</u> to <u>changes in demand</u>.

4) However, these fuels are <u>slowly running out</u>.

Non-Renewable Sources Cause Environmental Problems

1) All three <u>fossil fuels</u> (coal, oil and natural gas) release <u>carbon dioxide</u> (CO_2) when they burn.

2) This CO_2 contributes to <u>climate change</u> and <u>global warming</u>.

3) Burning coal and oil releases <u>sulfur dioxide</u>, which causes <u>acid rain</u>.

4) <u>Coal mining</u> makes a <u>mess</u> of the landscape.

5) <u>Oil spillages</u> cause <u>serious environmental problems</u>.

6) <u>Nuclear waste</u> (from nuclear power stations) is very <u>dangerous</u> and difficult to <u>dispose of</u>.

7) <u>Nuclear power</u> also carries the risk of a <u>major nuclear accident</u>.

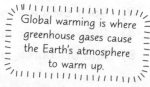
Global warming is where greenhouse gases cause the Earth's atmosphere to warm up.

It all boils down to steam...

Steam engines were invented as long ago as the 17th century, yet we're still using that idea to produce most of our electricity over 300 years later. Pretty impressive, eh?

Q1   State two environmental problems that result from the burning of coal.   [2 marks]

Renewable Energy Sources

Renewable energy sources, unlike non-renewables, <u>don't run out</u> (funny that).

Renewable Energy Sources Will Never Run Out

1) A <u>renewable energy source</u> is one that will <u>never run out</u>.
2) Most of them do some <u>damage to the environment</u>, but in <u>less nasty</u> ways than non-renewables.
3) They <u>don't</u> provide as much energy as <u>non-renewables</u> and the <u>weather-dependent</u> ones can be <u>unreliable</u>.
4) Renewable sources include <u>bio-fuels</u>, <u>wind</u> power, the <u>Sun</u>, <u>hydro-electricity</u> and the <u>tides</u>.

Bio-fuels are Made from Plant Products and Animal Dung

1) <u>Bio-fuels</u> can be burnt to produce <u>electricity</u> or used to run <u>cars</u> in the same way as <u>fossil fuels</u>.
2) <u>Extra bio-fuels</u> can made or grown throughout the year, and <u>stored</u> for when they're needed.
3) This means bio-fuels are fairly <u>reliable</u>.
4) One of their <u>disadvantages</u> is that they need <u>room to grow</u>.
5) In some places, large areas of <u>land</u> have been <u>cleared</u> to grow <u>bio-fuels</u>.
6) This leads to species losing their <u>habitats</u> (where they live).
7) They also <u>release CO$_2$</u> when burnt, but they also <u>absorb</u> some when <u>growing</u>.

Wind Power — Lots of Little Wind Turbines

1) Each wind turbine has a <u>generator</u> inside it.
2) The rotating <u>blades</u> turn the generator and produce <u>electricity</u>.
3) There's <u>no pollution</u> once they're built.
4) But some people think they <u>spoil the view</u>. And they can be <u>very noisy</u>.
5) They <u>only</u> work when it's <u>windy</u>, so you can't always <u>supply</u> electricity, or respond to <u>high demand</u>.

Solar Cells — Expensive but No Environmental Damage

1) Solar cells generate <u>electricity</u> from <u>sunlight</u>.
2) There's <u>no pollution</u> (although they do use quite a lot of energy to make).
3) Solar cells are mainly used to generate electricity on a <u>small scale</u>, e.g. in <u>homes</u>.
4) Solar power is most suitable for <u>sunny countries</u>, but it can be used in <u>cloudy countries</u>, such as Britain.
5) And of course, you <u>can't</u> make solar power at <u>night</u> or <u>make more</u> when there's extra demand.

Time to recharge.

Burning poo.... lovely...

Given our electricity-guzzling ways, it's pretty important we find ways to generate electricity without destroying the planet. Burning cow pats may not be the ultimate fix, but it's a start. See the next page for more ways.

Q1   State two renewable energy sources.   [2 marks]

Q2   State two disadvantages of using wind power to generate electricity.   [2 marks]

More On Energy Sources

Two more renewable energy sources to learn, then we'll look at trends in the crazy world of energy production.

Hydro-electricity — Building Dams and Flooding Valleys

1) Producing hydro-electricity usually involves flooding a valley by building a big dam.
2) Rainwater is caught and flows out through turbines.
3) Hydro-electric plants don't release any pollution once they're up and running.
4) But there is a big impact on the environment due to the flooding of the valley.
5) Plants rot and release greenhouse gases, which lead to global warming (see p.211).
6) Animals and plants also lose their habitats.
7) There's no problem with reliability in countries that get rain regularly.
8) And more water can easily be let through when there's extra demand for electricity.

Tidal Barrages — Using the Tides of the Sea

1) Tidal barrages are also big dams with turbines in them.
2) They're built across tidal rivers or estuaries (where rivers meet the sea).
3) Water passing through the turbines generates electricity.
4) There is no pollution but they alter the habitat for wildlife, e.g. wading birds and sea creatures, and affect boat access.
5) The amount of energy generated changes with the tides.
6) But tidal barrages are pretty reliable as we can predict the tides (we know what they're going to do).

None shall pass!

Renewables are Growing, but we Still Depend on Non-Renewables

1) In the 1900s, electricity use hugely increased.
2) This is because the population and the number of things that used electricity increased.
3) Most of this electricity was generated using non-renewable fuels.
4) But we've become more aware that these fuels will run out one day and that they cause environmental damage.
5) So we're investing time and money in developing renewable energy sources, but progress is slow.
6) In the UK, a lot of our electricity still comes from non-renewable energy sources.
7) This is partly because most renewables generate less electricity than non-renewables.
8) Also, many renewable energy sources are less reliable than non-renewables (e.g. they're weather-dependent).
9) Since around the year 2000, our total electricity use has been falling slowly.
10) This is because we're trying harder to make energy efficient appliances and save electricity.
11) We're also trying to cut down on the oil (diesel and petrol) we use to fuel our cars (e.g. using electric cars), and the gas we use to heat our homes.

Trends in energy use — light bulbs wearing sunglasses...

There are problems with every kind of electricity production, and no one wants any of them happening in their backyard. But if we want to carry on living the way we are, we're going to need to make some compromises.

Q1 Suggest a reason why the UK's electricity use has gone down since the year 2000. [1 mark]

Electricity and the National Grid

There are two types of current — <u>alternating</u> and <u>direct</u>. The <u>national grid</u> supplies alternating current.

Alternating Voltage Keeps Changing Direction

1) An <u>alternating current</u> (a.c.) is produced by an <u>alternating voltage</u> (or <u>alternating potential difference</u>, <u>p.d.</u>).

2) <u>Alternating</u> just means that the p.d. and current <u>constantly change direction</u>.

3) The <u>UK mains electricity</u> (in your home) is <u>a.c.</u> at <u>50 Hz</u> and around <u>230 V</u>.

4) <u>Direct current</u> (d.c.) is produced by a <u>direct voltage</u>. The current and the p.d. <u>don't change direction</u>.

5) You get <u>d.c.</u> from <u>batteries</u> and <u>cells</u>.

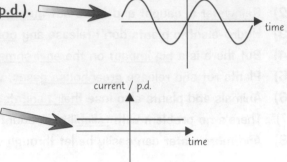

Electricity Gets Around via the National Grid...

1) The <u>national grid</u> is a network of <u>wires</u> and <u>transformers</u>.

2) It transfers energy from UK <u>power stations</u> to <u>homes</u> and the <u>industry</u>.

3) A <u>huge</u> amount of <u>power</u> needs to be transmitted across the country.

4) Since $P = IV$ (see p.182), you need either a <u>high p.d.</u> or a <u>high current</u> to get this huge power.

5) The <u>problem</u> with a <u>high current</u> is that you lose <u>loads of energy</u> as the wires <u>heat up</u>.

6) So instead, the <u>p.d. is boosted</u> up really high (to 400 000 V) to keep the <u>current very low</u>.

7) This <u>saves money</u> as less energy is <u>wasted</u> as heat.

8) This makes the national grid an <u>efficient</u> way of transferring energy.

...With a Little Help from Transformers

1) Transformers <u>change</u> the <u>p.d.</u> of an a.c. supply.

2) They have two coils, a <u>primary coil</u> (the voltage going in) and a <u>secondary coil</u> (the voltage going out).

3) The two coils are joined with an <u>iron core</u>.

4) The <u>change in p.d.</u> depends on the <u>number of turns</u> on one coil <u>compared</u> to the other.

5) In the national grid, the p.d. is <u>increased</u> using a <u>step-up transformer</u>. A step-up transformer has <u>more turns</u> on the <u>secondary</u> coil than the primary.

6) The p.d. is then <u>reduced</u> again at the consumer end using a <u>step-down transformer</u>. A step-down transformer has <u>more turns</u> on the <u>primary</u> than the secondary.

7) The <u>power</u> is the same in each coil.

8) Since <u>power = p.d. × current</u>, this means that:

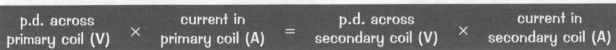

| p.d. across primary coil (V) | × | current in primary coil (A) | = | p.d. across secondary coil (V) | × | current in secondary coil (A) |

Transformers — there's more than meets the eye...

Fun fact — the step-down transformers on power lines get a bit warm, so birds love to nest on them.

Q1   The voltage across the primary coil of a step-down transformer is 40 V, with a current of 2 A. The voltage across the secondary coil is 10 V. What is the current in the secondary coil?   [3 marks]

Wiring in the Home

Now then, did you know... electricity is <u>dangerous</u>? It can kill you. Well just <u>watch out</u> for it, that's all.

Plugs Contain Three Wires

Appliances usually contain <u>three wires</u>:

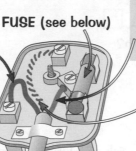

FUSE (see below)

<u>NEUTRAL WIRE</u> — blue

1) The neutral wire <u>completes</u> the circuit.
2) When the appliance is working normally, current flows through the <u>live</u> and <u>neutral</u> wires.
3) It is around <u>0 V</u>.

<u>LIVE WIRE</u> — brown

1) The live wire carries the <u>alternating voltage</u> (potential difference, p.d.).
2) It is at about <u>230 V</u>.

<u>EARTH WIRE</u> — green and yellow

1) The earth wire is for <u>safety</u>.
2) It carries the <u>current away</u> if something goes <u>wrong</u>.
3) It's also at <u>0 V</u>.

1) There is a <u>p.d.</u> between the <u>live wire</u> and your <u>body</u> (which is at 0 V).
2) Touching the live wire can cause a <u>current</u> to flow through your body.
3) This can give you a dangerous <u>electric shock</u>.
4) Even if a switch is turned <u>off</u> (the switch is <u>open</u>), touching the live wire is still <u>dangerous</u>. This is because it still has a p.d. of <u>230 V</u>.
5) <u>Any</u> connection between the <u>live</u> and <u>earth</u> wires can be <u>dangerous</u>.
6) The p.d. could cause a <u>huge current</u> to flow, which could result in a <u>fire</u>.

Earthing and Fuses Prevent Shocks

1) The diagram shows a <u>normal toaster</u>.
2) If a fault developed and the <u>live wire</u> touched the toaster's <u>metal casing</u>, it could become live, which could be <u>dangerous</u>.
3) So, all appliances with <u>metal cases</u> have an <u>earth wire</u> attached to the metal case.

4) If the <u>live wire</u> touches the <u>metal case</u>, a current will flow down the <u>earth wire</u>.
5) The earth wire is <u>very thick</u>, to give it a <u>low resistance</u>, which causes a <u>big current</u> to flow through it.

6) This large current <u>melts</u> the fuse, <u>cutting off</u> the live supply.
7) So it's <u>impossible</u> to get an <u>electric shock</u> from the case.

If the appliance has a <u>casing</u> that's <u>an insulator</u> (e.g. <u>plastic</u>, see p.175) then it's <u>double insulated</u>. Anything with double insulation <u>doesn't need an earth wire</u> as it can't become live.

Electricity rule number 1 — don't stick your fingers in the socket...

So wiring's fun isn't it? Unfortunately, it could be in your exams so you'd best get it learnt.

Q1   A metal kettle is plugged into the mains supply. State how you know it needs an earth wire.   [1 mark]

Revision Questions for Topic P6

Congratulations! That's it for the theory. There's just the practical stuff to go now. Oh, and these questions...

- Try these questions and tick off each one when you get it right.
- When you've done all the questions under a heading and are completely happy with it, tick it off.

Everyday Transport (p.209-210) ☑

1) How do you convert from mph to km/h?
2) State typical speeds for:
   a) walking,
   b) running,
   c) sound.
3) Explain how a bike helmet reduces the risk of injury in a crash.
4) What is meant by a driver's reaction time?
5) Give examples of two things that might affect a driver's reaction time.
6) List four things that will affect the braking distance of a car.
7) Describe an experiment that you could use to measure your reaction time.

Generating and Using Electricity (p.211-215) ☑

8) List four non-renewable energy sources.
9) Describe how electricity is generated from burning fossil fuels.
10) State two major problems with using nuclear fuels to generate energy.
11) What's the difference between renewable and non-renewable energy sources?
12) Describe how electricity is generated using wind power.
13) Give one disadvantage of generating electricity from the tides.
14) What is the voltage and frequency of the mains electricity supply in the UK?
15) What is the difference between direct voltage and alternating voltage?
    Sketch a graph of p.d. against time for each.
16) Why does the national grid carry electricity at high voltages?
17) Name the device that is used to increase the voltage
    between a power station and the cables of the national grid.
18) What are the three main wires in a plug?
19) Explain why touching the brown wire is dangerous.
20) What does it mean if an appliance is double insulated?

Safety and Ethics

- <u>Topic CS7</u> covers <u>practical skills</u> you'll need to know about for your course (including 15% of your exams).
- You need to do at least <u>16 practical activities</u> (experiments). These are covered during the biology, chemistry and physics topics earlier in the book. They're <u>marked up</u> with <u>practical stamps</u> like this one.
- This topic covers some <u>extra things</u> you need to know about practical work.

Make Sure You're Working Safely in the Lab

1) Wear <u>sensible clothing</u> (e.g. shoes that will protect your feet from spillages). Also:
   - Wear a <u>lab coat</u> to protect your <u>skin</u> and <u>clothing</u>.
   - If needed, wear <u>safety goggles</u> to protect your <u>eyes</u>, and <u>gloves</u> to protect your <u>hands</u>.
2) Be aware of <u>general safety</u> in the lab, for example don't touch any <u>hot equipment</u>.
3) Follow any <u>instructions</u> that your teacher gives you <u>carefully</u>.
4) <u>Chemicals</u> and <u>equipment</u> can be <u>hazardous</u> (dangerous). E.g. some chemicals are <u>flammable</u> (they <u>catch fire easily</u>) — this means you must be careful <u>not</u> to use a <u>Bunsen burner</u> near them.

Here are some <u>tips</u> for working with <u>chemicals</u> and <u>equipment</u> safely...

Working with chemicals

1) Make sure you're working in an area that's <u>well ventilated</u> (has a good flow of air).
2) If you're doing an experiment that produces nasty <u>gases</u> (such as chlorine), carry out the experiment in a <u>fume hood</u>. This means the gas <u>can't escape</u> into the room you're working in.
3) Never <u>touch</u> any chemicals (even if you're wearing gloves):
   - Use a <u>spatula</u> to transfer <u>solids</u> between containers.
   - Carefully <u>pour</u> liquids between containers using a <u>funnel</u>. This will help <u>prevent spillages</u>.
4) Take care when you're <u>mixing</u> chemicals. For example, if you're <u>diluting</u> a liquid, always add the <u>concentrated substance</u> to the <u>water</u>, not the other way round.

Working with equipment

1) Use <u>clamp stands</u> to stop masses and equipment falling.
2) Make sure <u>masses</u> are <u>not too heavy</u> (so they <u>don't break</u> the equipment they're used with).
3) Use <u>pulleys</u> that are <u>not too long</u> (so hanging masses <u>don't hit the floor</u> during the experiment).
4) Let hot things <u>cool</u> before moving them. Or wear <u>insulated gloves</u> while handling them.
5) If you're using an <u>immersion heater</u>, you should always let it <u>dry out</u> in air. This is just in case any liquid has <u>leaked</u> inside the heater.
6) When working with electronics, make sure you use a <u>low voltage</u> and <u>current</u>. This prevents the wires <u>overheating</u>. It also stops <u>damage to components</u>.
7) If you're using a <u>laser</u>, always wear <u>laser safety goggles</u>. Never <u>look directly into</u> the laser or shine it <u>towards another person</u>. Make sure you turn the laser <u>off</u> if it's not needed.

You Need to Think About Ethical Issues

Any <u>organisms</u> that you use in your experiments need to be treated <u>safely</u> and <u>ethically</u>. This means:

1) Animals should be <u>handled carefully</u>. Any captured <u>wild animals</u> should be <u>returned to their habitat</u> after the experiment. Animals <u>kept</u> in the <u>lab</u> should be <u>well cared for</u>, e.g. they should have <u>plenty of space</u>.
2) Other <u>people</u> that <u>take part</u> in any experiment should be <u>happy</u> to do so.

Safety first...

Have a good think about safety and ethics before you start any experimental work — it's all important stuff.

Apparatus and Techniques

Get your lab coats on, it's time to find out about the skills you'll need to <u>take measurements</u> and <u>record data</u>...

You can Measure Substances Using a Balance

1) To weigh a substance, start by putting the <u>container</u> you're weighing your substance <u>into</u> on the <u>balance</u>.

2) Set the balance to exactly <u>zero</u>. Then <u>add</u> your <u>substance</u> and read how much it <u>weighs</u>.

3) If you're weighing out a <u>solid</u>, you need to make sure you know <u>exactly how much</u> you've used. There are different ways you can do this. For example:

- If you're <u>dissolving</u> a solid in a solvent to make a <u>solution</u>, you could <u>wash</u> any remaining solid into the new container using the <u>solvent</u>.

- You could set the balance to zero <u>before</u> you put your <u>weighing container</u> on the balance. Then <u>reweigh</u> the weighing container <u>after</u> you've transferred the solid. Use the <u>difference in mass</u> to work out <u>exactly</u> how much solid you added to your experiment.

Three Ways to Measure Liquids

pipette filler

<u>Pipettes</u> are used to suck up an <u>accurate</u> volume of liquid and <u>transfer</u> it to another container. The <u>pipette filler</u> lets you <u>safely control</u> the amount of liquid you're drawing up.

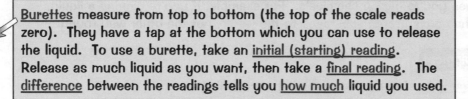

If you only want a couple of drops of liquid, and you don't need to measure it, you can use a <u>dropping pipette</u>. For example, this is how you'd add a couple of drops of indicator into a mixture.

dropping pipette

<u>Burettes</u> measure from top to bottom (the top of the scale reads zero). They have a tap at the bottom which you can use to release the liquid. To use a burette, take an <u>initial (starting) reading</u>. Release as much liquid as you want, then take a <u>final reading</u>. The <u>difference</u> between the readings tells you <u>how much</u> liquid you used.

tap

<u>Measuring cylinders</u> come in many different <u>sizes</u>. Choose one that's the right size for the measurement you want to make. It's no good using a huge 1000 cm³ cylinder to measure out 2 cm³ of a liquid — it'll be hard to tell where 2 cm³ is, and you'll end up with <u>big errors</u>.

Always measure the volume of a liquid by reading from the <u>bottom of the meniscus</u> (the curved upper surface of the liquid) when it's at <u>eye level</u>.

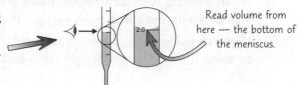

Read volume from here — the bottom of the meniscus.

You May Have to Measure the Time Taken for a Change

1) You should use a <u>stopwatch</u> to time experiments. Using a <u>stopwatch</u> that measures to the nearest <u>0.01</u> or <u>0.1 s</u> will make your results more <u>accurate</u>.

2) Always make sure you <u>start</u> and <u>stop</u> the stopwatch at exactly the right time. E.g. if you're investigating the rate of a reaction, you should start timing at the <u>exact moment</u> you mix the chemicals.

3) It's a good idea to get the <u>same person</u> to do the timing so the results are as <u>precise</u> as possible.

4) If you're carrying out experiments involving acceleration or speed, you could use a <u>light gate</u> (see p.224).

Apparatus and Techniques

Measure Temperature Accurately with a Thermometer

1) Put the <u>bulb</u> of your thermometer <u>fully</u> in the substance you're measuring.
2) Wait for the temperature to become <u>stable</u> before you take your reading.
3) Read your measurement off the <u>scale</u> at <u>eye level</u>.

bulb

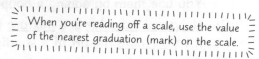
When you're reading off a scale, use the value of the nearest graduation (mark) on the scale.

Measure Most Lengths with a Ruler

1) In most cases you can use an ordinary <u>centimetre ruler</u> to measure <u>lengths</u>.

2) It does depend on what you're measuring though. <u>Metre rulers</u> or <u>long measuring tapes</u> are good for <u>large</u> distances. <u>Micrometers</u> are used for measuring tiny (e.g. the <u>diameter of a wire</u>).

3) Decide on the <u>appropriate units</u> for your measurements. For example, the length of a <u>leaf</u> would be better measured in <u>millimetres</u>, but the <u>distance you could run in 10 seconds</u> would be better measured in <u>metres</u>.

4) Make sure your ruler is <u>parallel to</u> the thing you want to measure.

parallel to ✓   not parallel to ✗

5) It may be <u>tricky</u> to measure just <u>one</u> of something accurately, e.g. waves in water. Instead, you can measure the length of <u>ten</u> of them together. Then <u>divide</u> by ten to find the <u>length of one</u>.

6) If you're taking <u>lots of measurements</u> of the <u>same</u> object, make sure you always measure from the <u>same point</u> on the object. It can help to put a <u>pointer</u> onto the object to line your ruler up against.

7) Make sure the ruler and the object are always at <u>eye level</u> when you take a reading.

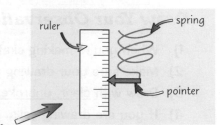
ruler   spring   pointer

Measuring the Area of Something in Biology

1) In biology, you might need to measure the <u>area</u> of something (e.g. part of a habitat, a living thing).

2) Living things are usually quite <u>tricky shapes</u>. You can make their area easier to work out by comparing them to a <u>simpler shape</u> and working out the area of that (e.g. <u>clear zones</u> where bacteria can't grow are roughly <u>circular</u> — see page 73).

3) To find the area of something:

- First, take <u>measurements</u> of its dimensions.

  To find the area of a <u>rectangular field</u>, you'd need to measure its <u>length</u> and <u>width</u> (e.g. using a <u>trundle wheel</u>).

- Then <u>calculate</u> its <u>area</u>.

  Area of a <u>rectangle</u> = <u>length</u> × <u>width</u>.
  So, if your field is 30 m by 55 m, the <u>area</u> would be 30 × 55 = <u>1650 m²</u>.

Don't forget the units of area are always something squared, e.g. mm².

4) Here are some other <u>area formulas</u> that may be useful:

- Area of a triangle = ½ × base × height
- Area of a circle = πr^2 (see page 74)

Apparatus and Techniques

There are Different Methods for Measuring pH

There are several ways to measure pH:

1) <u>Indicators</u> are dyes that <u>change colour</u> depending on whether they're in an <u>acid</u> or an <u>alkali</u>. You use them by adding a couple of drops of the indicator to your solution.

2) <u>Universal indicator</u> is a <u>mixture</u> of indicators. It changes colour <u>gradually</u> as pH changes. You can use it to <u>estimate</u> the pH of a solution based on the <u>colour</u> the solution goes when you add the indicator.

3) There are also <u>paper indicators</u>. These are <u>strips of paper</u> that contain indicator. If you put a <u>small amount</u> of solution onto indicator paper, the paper will <u>change colour</u>:

   • <u>Litmus paper</u> turns <u>red</u> in acidic conditions and <u>blue</u> in alkaline conditions.
   • <u>Universal indicator paper</u> can be used to <u>estimate</u> pH.

litmus paper

4) Indicator paper is <u>useful</u> when:

   • You <u>don't</u> want to change the colour of <u>all</u> of the substance.
   • The substance is <u>already</u> coloured (so it might <u>hide</u> the colour of the indicator).
   • You want to find the pH of a <u>gas</u> — hold a piece of <u>damp indicator paper</u> in a <u>gas sample</u>.

5) <u>pH probes</u> measure pH <u>electronically</u>. They are more <u>accurate</u> than indicators.

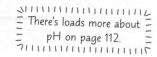
There's loads more about pH on page 112.

Draw Your Observations Neatly

1) When you're making sketches of what you can see under a <u>microscope</u>, use a <u>sharp pencil</u>.

2) Make sure your drawing takes up <u>at least half</u> of the space available.

3) Draw with <u>clear, unbroken lines</u>. <u>Don't</u> do any <u>colouring</u> or <u>shading</u>.

4) If you are drawing <u>cells</u>, draw the <u>sub-cellular structures</u> the right size <u>compared to</u> the rest of the cell.

5) Include a <u>title</u>. Also include the <u>magnification</u> that you used.

6) <u>Label</u> the <u>important features</u> using <u>straight lines</u>. Make sure the lines <u>don't cross over each other</u>.

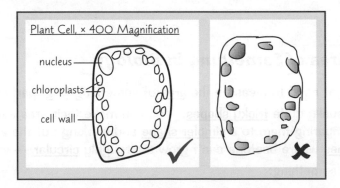

Plant Cell, × 400 Magnification
nucleus
chloroplasts
cell wall

Use a Protractor to Find Angles

1) Place the <u>middle</u> of the protractor on the <u>pointy bit</u> of the angle.

2) <u>Line up</u> the <u>base line</u> of the protractor with one line of the <u>angle</u>.

3) Measure the angle of the <u>other line</u> using the scale on the <u>protractor</u>.

4) If you need to draw lines at an angle use a <u>sharp pencil</u>. This helps to <u>reduce errors</u> when measuring the angles.

5) If the lines are <u>too short</u> to measure the angle easily, you may have to <u>make them longer</u>. Again, make sure you use a <u>sharp pencil</u> and a <u>ruler</u> to do this.

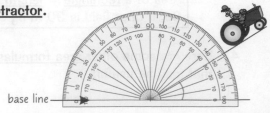
base line

Apparatus and Techniques

Organisms Should Be Sampled At Random Sites in an Area

1) It's usually <u>not possible</u> to count <u>every single organism</u> in an area. Instead, you can take <u>samples</u> of the population in the area you're interested in. This is useful if you're looking at the <u>distribution</u> of an organism in an area, or working out its <u>population size</u>.

2) You can use <u>quadrats</u> or <u>transects</u> to take population samples (see pages 58 and 61).

3) If you only take samples from <u>one part</u> of an area, your results will be <u>biased</u>. This means they won't accurately <u>represent</u> the <u>whole area</u>.

4) To make sure that your sampling isn't biased, it needs to be <u>random</u>. For example:

If you're looking at plant species in a field...
1) <u>Divide</u> the field into a <u>grid</u>.
2) <u>Label the grid</u> along the bottom and up the side with numbers.
3) Use a <u>random number generator</u> (e.g. on a computer or calculator) to pick coordinates, e.g. (2,4).
4) Take your samples at these coordinates.

Non-random sampling
Only looks at a small part of the field.

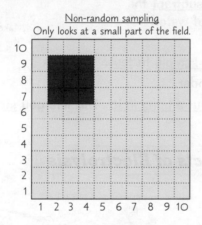

Random sampling
Randomly selects squares from all over the field.

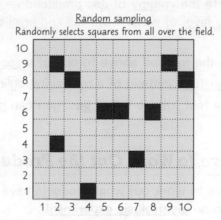

Colorimeters Measure the Intensity of Colour

Colorimeters are <u>machines</u> that measure <u>colour</u>. They work like this:

1) <u>Light</u> is passed through a solution.
2) Some of the light is <u>absorbed</u> by the solution.
3) The colorimeter gives an <u>absorbance value</u> — a measure of how much light has been absorbed by the solution. <u>Darker</u> solutions have a <u>higher</u> absorbance value.

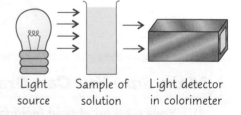

Light source — Sample of solution — Light detector in colorimeter

<u>Colorimeters</u> can be handy in experiments. For example:

1) <u>Amylase</u> breaks <u>starch</u> down into <u>maltose</u>. There's an experiment on page 17 that shows how you can use <u>iodine solution</u> to investigate the <u>rate</u> of this reaction — have a look back at it now.

2) At the start of the experiment, when there is starch present, the reaction mixture is <u>blue-black</u>. At the point when <u>all</u> of the starch has been <u>broken down</u>, it turns <u>browny-orange</u>.

3) You can use a <u>colorimeter</u> to find the moment that this change happens.

4) First, use the <u>colorimeter</u> to measure the <u>absorbance value</u> of a mixture of <u>iodine solution</u> and <u>maltose</u>. (This mixture should have a <u>browny-orange colour</u>.)

5) Take <u>samples</u> of the reaction mixture during the experiment and measure their <u>absorbance values</u>.

6) When one of the samples has the <u>same</u> absorbance value as the iodine water and maltose mixture, that's the point at which <u>all</u> the starch has been <u>broken down</u>.

Apparatus and Techniques

To Collect Gases, the System Needs to be Sealed

1) You might want to <u>collect</u> the gas produced by a reaction.

2) The most accurate way to measure the volume of gas is to collect it in a <u>gas syringe</u> (see page 128).

3) You could also collect it using an <u>upside down measuring cylinder</u>:

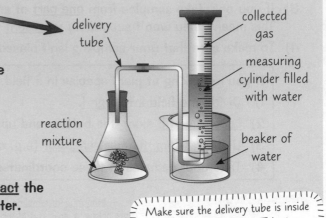

- <u>Set up</u> the <u>equipment</u> like in the <u>diagram</u>.
- Record the <u>starting level</u> of the water in the measuring cylinder.
- Any gas from the reaction will pass <u>through</u> the delivery tube and <u>into</u> the <u>measuring cylinder</u>.
- The gas will <u>push the water out</u> of the measuring cylinder.
- Record the <u>end level</u> of water in the measuring cylinder.
- Calculate the <u>volume</u> of gas produced — <u>subtract</u> the <u>starting level</u> of water from the <u>end level</u> of water.

Make sure the delivery tube is inside the measuring cylinder. This stops the gas escaping out into the air.

4) You can use the method above to collect a <u>gas sample</u> to <u>test</u>.
- Use a <u>test tube</u> instead of a measuring cylinder.
- When the test tube is full of gas, you can <u>put a bung in it</u>. This lets you <u>store</u> the gas for later.

You May Have to Work Out the Products of Electrolysis

There's more about electrolysis on pages 116-118.

1) You may have to work out what products have been made in an <u>electrolysis experiment</u>.

2) To do this, you need to be able to <u>collect</u> any gas that's produced. Then you can do a <u>test</u> to find out what gas you've collected (see page 119).

3) The easiest way to collect the gas is in a <u>test tube</u>.

4) Here's how to set up the equipment...

Make Sure You Can Draw Diagrams of Your Equipment

1) Your <u>method</u> should include a <u>labelled diagram</u> of how your equipment will be <u>set up</u>.

2) Use <u>scientific drawings</u> — each piece of equipment is drawn as if you're looking at it <u>from the side</u>.

3) For example:

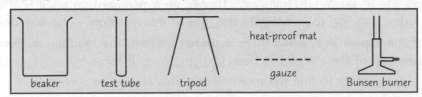

4) The <u>beaker</u> and <u>test tube</u> above <u>aren't sealed</u>. To show them <u>sealed</u>, draw a <u>bung</u> in the top.

Electrolysis still seems like magic to me...

...but wizardry won't help you here, unfortunately. It's best you just get your head down and learn this stuff.

Heating Substances

You need to be able to decide on the best and safest method for heating a substance...

Bunsen Burners Heat Things Quickly

Here's how to use a Bunsen burner...

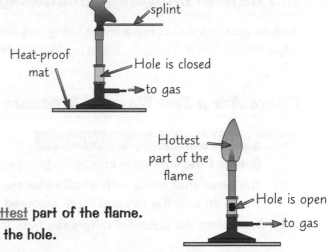

1) Connect the Bunsen burner to a gas tap.
   Check that the hole in the Bunsen burner is closed.

2) Place the Bunsen burner on a heat-proof mat.

3) Light a splint and hold it over the Bunsen burner.

4) Now, turn on the gas.
   The Bunsen burner should light with a yellow flame.

5) Open the hole to turn the flame blue.
   The more open the hole, the hotter the flame.

6) Heat things just above the blue cone — this is the hottest part of the flame.

7) When the Bunsen burner isn't heating anything, close the hole.
   This makes the flame yellow and easy to see.

8) If you're heating a container (with your substance in it) in the flame, hold it at the top with tongs.

9) If you're heating a container over the flame, put a tripod and gauze over the Bunsen burner before you light it. Then place the container on the gauze.

10) Remember, you shouldn't use a Bunsen burner to heat things that are flammable (catch fire easily).

Water Baths & Electric Heaters Have Set Temperatures

1) A water bath is a container filled with water. It can be heated to a specific temperature.

2) An electric water bath will check and change the temperature for you. Here's how you use one:

   - Set the temperature on the water bath.
   - Allow the water to heat up.
   - Place your container (with your substance in it) in the water bath using tongs.
   - The level of the water outside the container should be just above the level of the substance inside it.
   - The substance will be warmed to the same temperature as the water.

   A water bath
   rubber duck   reaction container
   temperature control

3) The substance in the container is surrounded by water, so the heating is very even.

4) Electric heaters often have a metal plate that can be heated to a specific temperature.

   - Place your container on top of the hot plate.
   - You can heat substances to higher temperatures than you can in a water bath.
     (You can't use a water bath to heat something higher than 100 °C.)
   - You have to stir the substance to make sure it's heated evenly.

A bath and an electric heater — how I spend my January nights...

My science teacher used to play power ballads when he lit a Bunsen burner. Then he'd sway like he was at a gig.

Working with Electronics

Electrical devices are used in loads of experiments, so make sure you know how to use them.

You Have to Interpret Circuit Diagrams

Before you can do an experiment using any electrical devices, you have to plan and build your circuit using a circuit diagram. Make sure you know all of the circuit symbols on p.176.

There Are a Few Ways to Measure Potential Difference and Current

Voltmeters Measure Potential Difference

1) Connect the voltmeter in parallel (see page 178) across the component you want to test.

2) The wires that come with a voltmeter are usually red (positive) and black (negative). These go into the red and black coloured ports on the voltmeter.

3) Then read the potential difference from the scale (or from the screen if the voltmeter is digital).

Ammeters Measure Current

1) Connect the ammeter in series (see page 178) with the component you want to test.

2) Ammeters usually have red and black ports to show you where to connect your wires.

3) Read off the current shown on the scale (or screen).

Turn your circuit off between readings. This stops wires overheating, which could affect your results.

Multimeters Measure Both

1) Multimeters measure a range of things — usually potential difference, current and resistance.

2) To find potential difference, connect the multimeter in parallel across the component you want to test. Plug the red wire into the port that has a 'V' (for volts).

3) To find the current, connect the multimeter in series with the component you want to test. Use the port labelled 'A' (for amps) or 'mA' (for milliamps).

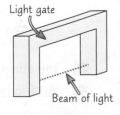

4) The dial on the multimeter should then be turned to the relevant section — for example, to measure the current in amps, turn the dial to 'A'.

5) The screen will display the value you're measuring.

Light Gates Measure Time, Speed and Acceleration

1) A light gate sends a beam of light from one side of the gate to a detector on the other side. When something passes through the gate, the light beam is interrupted.

2) The gate can measure when the beam was interrupted and how long it was interrupted for.

3) Light gates can be connected to a computer. To find the speed of an object, type the length of the object into the computer. The computer will then calculate the speed of the object as it passes through the beam.

4) To measure acceleration, use an object that interrupts the signal twice in a short period of time, e.g. a piece of card with a gap cut into the middle.

5) The light gate measures the speed for each section of the object. It uses this to calculate the object's acceleration. This can then be read from the computer screen.

See p.160 for an example of light gates being used.

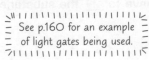

Light gate

Beam of light

Card interrupts the beam

A light gate is better than a heavy one...

After finishing this page, you should be able to take on any electrical experiment that they throw at you... ouch.

Answers

Topic B1 — Cell Level Systems

p.11 — Cells and Microscopy
Q1 It acts as a selective barrier, so it controls what goes in and out of the cell *[1 mark]*. It contains receptor molecules so that other molecules can communicate with the cell *[1 mark]*.

p.12 — Light Microscopy
Q1 Take a clean slide and use a pipette to put one drop of water in the middle of it *[1 mark]*. Use tweezers to place the onion skin on the slide and add a drop of stain *[1 mark]*. Carefully lower a cover slip onto the slide using a mounted needle *[1 mark]*.

p.13 — More on Light Microscopy
Q1 total magnification = eyepiece lens magnification × objective lens magnification
8 × 15 = 120
So the total magnification is ×120 *[1 mark]*.

p.14 — DNA
Q1 C *[1 mark]*
Q2 It's a large, complex molecule made up of nucleotides (monomers) joined together in a long chain *[1 mark]*.

p.15 — Enzymes
Q1 the active site *[1 mark]*

p.16 — More on Enzymes
Q1 If the pH is too high it affects the bonds holding the active site together *[1 mark]*. This changes the shape of the active site and denatures the enzyme *[1 mark]*.

p.17 — Investigating Enzyme Activity
Q1 33 ÷ 60 = 0.55 cm³/second *[1 mark]*

p.18 — Respiration
Q1 Because energy is released during the reaction *[1 mark]*.

p.19 — More on Respiration
Q1 ethanol *[1 mark]*
carbon dioxide *[1 mark]*.
Q2 E.g. aerobic respiration produces much more ATP than anaerobic respiration *[1 mark]*.

p.20 — Biological Molecules
Q1 a) (simple) sugars *[1 mark]*
b) amino acids *[1 mark]*

p.21 — Photosynthesis
Q1 Photosynthesis produces glucose *[1 mark]*, which is used to make larger, complex molecules that make up the mass of the plant's living material/the plant's biomass *[1 mark]*.

p.22 — Investigating Photosynthesis
Q1 Any two from: e.g. the light intensity. / The temperature. / The type of plant used *[1 mark for each correct answer]*.

Topic B2 — Scaling Up

p.23 — The Cell Cycle and Mitosis
Q1 The cell's DNA is replicated so that when it divides during mitosis, the two new cells will contain identical DNA *[1 mark]*.
Q2 Mitosis is when a cell reproduces itself by splitting to form two identical offspring *[1 mark]*.

p.24 — Cell Differentiation and Stem Cells
Q1 Differentiation is when a cell changes to become specialised for its job *[1 mark]*.

p.25 — Diffusion and Active Transport
Q1 a) Diffusion is the net movement of particles from an area of higher concentration to an area of lower concentration *[1 mark]*.
b) Active transport is the movement of particles across a membrane against a concentration gradient/from an area of lower to an area of higher concentration *[1 mark]*. It uses energy *[1 mark]*.

p.26 — Osmosis
Q1 Osmosis is the movement of water molecules across a partially permeable membrane from an area of higher water concentration to an area of lower water concentration. / Osmosis is the diffusion of water molecules across a partially permeable membrane down a water potential gradient (i.e. from an area of higher water potential to an area of lower water potential) *[1 mark]*.
Q2 Water will move out of the carrot cells *[1 mark]*. This is because water will move down the water potential gradient as a result of osmosis / water will move from a solution with a higher water concentration to a solution with a lower water concentration by osmosis *[1 mark]*.

p.27 — Exchange of Materials
Q1 surface area = 5 × 5 × 6
= 150 cm²
volume = 5 × 5 × 5
= 125 cm³
surface area : volume ratio
= 150 : 125 (= 6 : 5) *[1 mark]*

p.28 — Exchange Surfaces
Q1 A multicellular organism needs to supply its cells with the substances it needs to live and get rid of waste products *[1 mark]*. Diffusion across the outer membrane is too slow because some cells are deep inside the organism — it's a long way from them to the outside environment *[1 mark]*. Also, multicellular organisms have a low surface area to volume ratio *[1 mark]*. It's difficult to exchange enough substances to supply a large volume of organism through a small outer surface *[1 mark]*.

p.29 — The Circulatory System
Q1 the right ventricle *[1 mark]*

p.30 — The Blood Vessels
Q1 So that substances can diffuse in and out of them quickly *[1 mark]*.
Q2 They have a big lumen to help the blood flow even though it's at a low pressure *[1 mark]* and they have valves to keep the blood flowing in the right direction *[1 mark]*.

p.31 — The Blood
Q1 E.g. their biconcave disc shape gives them a large surface area for absorbing oxygen *[1 mark]*. They don't have a nucleus, which allows more room for carrying oxygen *[1 mark]*. They contain haemoglobin, which allows red blood cells to carry oxygen *[1 mark]*.

p.32 — Transport in Plants
Q1 They are made from living cells *[1 mark]*, with sieve plates/end walls between the cells *[1 mark]*. There are small holes in the sieve plates/end walls *[1 mark]*.

p.33 — Transpiration and Stomata
Q1 guard cells *[1 mark]*

p.34 — Investigating Transpiration
Q1 As it gets darker, the stomata close *[1 mark]*. This means that very little water can escape *[1 mark]*, so the rate of transpiration through the plant decreases *[1 mark]*.

Topic B3 — Organism Level Systems

p.36 — The Nervous System
Q1 brain *[1 mark]*
spinal cord *[1 mark]*

p.37 — Hormones
Q1 Endocrine glands release hormones *[1 mark]*. These travel in the bloodstream *[1 mark]* to target cells / organs *[1 mark]*. These have receptors so they can respond to the hormone *[1 mark]*.

p.38 — The Menstrual Cycle
Q1 FSH *[1 mark]*

p.39 — Contraception
Q1 E.g. oral contraceptives can have unpleasant side-effects *[1 mark]*. / She might find it difficult to take her pills at the right time *[1 mark]*.

p.40 — Controlling Blood Sugar Level
Q1 In type 1 diabetes, the person produces little or no insulin *[1 mark]*, whereas in type 2 diabetes, the person still produces insulin but they don't respond properly to it *[1 mark]*.

Topic B4 — Community Level Systems

p.41 — Ecosystems and Competition
Q1 an individual *[1 mark]*
Q2 Any two from, e.g. space / food / water / mates *[1 mark for each correct answer]*.

p.42 — Abiotic and Biotic Factors
Q1 Any two from, e.g. light intensity / moisture level / temperature / pH of the soil *[1 mark for each correct answer]*.

p.43 — Interactions Between Organisms
Q1 This is an example of mutualism *[1 mark]* because the relationship benefits both the cow and the bacteria *[1 mark]*.

p.44 — Recycling and the Water Cycle
Q1 Energy from the Sun makes water from the sea evaporate, turning it into water vapour *[1 mark]*. The warm water vapour is carried upwards *[1 mark]*. When it gets higher up, it cools and condenses to form clouds *[1 mark]*. Water then falls from the clouds as precipitation, usually as rain *[1 mark]*.

p.45 — The Carbon Cycle
Q1 Microorganisms in the carbon cycle are decomposers *[1 mark]*. They break down dead organisms and waste products *[1 mark]* and release CO_2 through respiration as they do so *[1 mark]*.

p.46 — The Nitrogen Cycle
Q1 Decomposers break down dead leaves and release ammonia *[1 mark]*. Then nitrifying bacteria turn the ammonia into nitrites and then into nitrates *[1 mark]*.

Answers

Topic B5 — Genes, Inheritance and Selection

p.48 — Genes and Variation
Q1 An organism's genotype means all of the genes and alleles that it has *[1 mark]*.

p.49 — More on Variation and Genetic Variants
Q1 A mutation is a change to the order of bases in DNA *[1 mark]*.

p.50 — Sexual Reproduction and Meiosis
Q1 24 *[1 mark]*

p.51 — Genetic Diagrams
Q1 aa *[1 mark]*

p.52 — More Genetic Diagrams & Sex Determination
Q1 XX *[1 mark]*

p.53 — Classification
Q1 An artificial classification system sorts organisms into groups depending on characteristics you can see *[1 mark]*. A natural classification system sorts organisms into groups based on how closely related they are *[1 mark]*.

p.54 — Evolution and Natural Selection
Q1 Some of the musk oxen may have had a genetic variant/allele which gave them thicker fur *[1 mark]*. Those musk oxen would have been more likely to survive and reproduce *[1 mark]* and so pass on the genetic variant/allele for thicker fur *[1 mark]*. Thicker fur may have become more common in the population over time *[1 mark]*.

p.55 — Evidence for Evolution
Q1 Fossils can show what organisms that lived a long time ago looked like *[1 mark]*. Arranging them in date order shows how organisms gradually changed/developed *[1 mark]*.

Topic B6 — Global Challenges

p.57 — Investigating Distribution and Abundance
Q1 E.g. the student could use a pitfall trap in each area of woodland *[1 mark]*. Each trap could be set up and left overnight *[1 mark]*. The next day, insects present in the traps could be counted and the student could compare what was found in the two traps *[1 mark]*.

p.58 — More on Investigating Distribution and Abundance
Q1 Sweep a pond net along the bottom of the pond *[1 mark]*. Empty the organisms that you have collected into a white tray with a bit of water in it *[1 mark]* and then count the insects in the tray *[1 mark]*.

p.59 — Population Size
Q1 Population size = (number in first sample × number in second sample) ÷ number in second sample previously marked
= (22 × 26) ÷ 4
= 143 crabs
[2 marks for correct answer, otherwise 1 mark for correct working]

p.60 — Using Keys and Factors Affecting Distribution
Q1 Any two from: e.g. air temperature / sand temperature / sand moisture level / sand pH *[1 mark for each correct answer]*.

p.61 — Using Transects
Q1 E.g. mark out a line/transect across the field using a tape measure *[1 mark]*. Place a quadrat at the start of the line and count and record the organisms you find in the quadrat *[1 mark]*. Then place your quadrat at the next sampling point on the transect and count and record the organisms you find in the quadrat *[1 mark]*. The second sampling point could be directly after the first quadrat or after a gap (e.g. after 2 metres) *[1 mark]*. Carry on sampling until you reach the end of the transect *[1 mark]*.

p.62 — Human Impacts on Ecosystems
Q1 E.g. the building of houses on a meadow would destroy the habitats provided by the meadow *[1 mark]*. This is likely to reduce the number of species that can live in the area, therefore reducing biodiversity *[1 mark]*.

p.63 — More Human Impacts on Ecosystems
Q1 In a protected area, development of the land would be limited *[1 mark]*. This would protect the frog species' habitat and therefore help to stop the frog species from becoming extinct *[1 mark]*.

p.64 — Maintaining Biodiversity
Q1 E.g. undiscovered plant species may contain new chemicals that we can use in medicines *[1 mark]*. If these plants become extinct we could miss out on new medicines *[1 mark]*.

p.65 — Selective Breeding
Q1 E.g. to produce animals with a high meat/milk yield *[1 mark]*. / To produce crops with disease resistance/larger fruit *[1 mark]*.

p.66 — Genetic Engineering
Q1 It can improve the yield of the crop *[1 mark]*, because herbicide-resistant crops can be sprayed with herbicides to kill weeds without the crop being damaged *[1 mark]*.

p.67 — Health and Disease
Q1 A non-communicable disease is one that cannot be passed from one organism to another *[1 mark]*.

p.68 — How Disease Spreads
Q1 It's spread when infected leaves rub against healthy leaves *[1 mark]*.

p.69 — More on How Disease Spreads
Q1 crown gall disease *[1 mark]*

p.70 — Reducing and Preventing the Spread of Disease
Q1 E.g. by getting rid of the mosquitoes you can prevent the disease from being passed on *[1 mark]*. This could be done by using insecticides/by destroying their habitat so they can no longer breed *[1 mark]*.

p.71 — The Human Immune System
Q1 When you damage a blood vessel, platelets clump together to form a blood clot *[1 mark]*. This stops microorganisms from entering the wound *[1 mark]*.

p.72 — Vaccinations and Medicines
Q1 antibodies *[1 mark]*

p.73 — Investigating Antimicrobials
Q1 To show that any difference in the size of the clear zone is only due to the effect of the antibiotic used *[1 mark]*.

p.74 — Comparing Antimicrobials
Q1 a) A *[1 mark]*
b) diameter = 13 mm
radius = 13 ÷ 2 = 6.5 mm *[1 mark]*
$\pi r^2 = \pi \times 6.5^2 = 132.7...$
= 133 mm² *[1 mark]*

p.75 — Developing New Medicines
Q1 The doctor knows whether the patient is getting the drug or the placebo in a blind trial but not in a double-blind trial *[1 mark]*.

p.76 — Non-Communicable Diseases
Q1 Exercise decreases the amount of stored body fat *[1 mark]*.

p.77 — More on Non-Communicable Diseases
Q1 Any two from: e.g. cirrhosis / cardiovascular disease / some cancers *[1 mark for each correct answer]*.

p.78 — Treating Cardiovascular Disease
Q1 E.g. they can cause side effects *[1 mark]*.

p.79 — Stem Cells in Medicine
Q1 The patient's immune system recognises the cells as foreign and attacks them *[1 mark]*.
Q2 E.g. some people feel that human embryos shouldn't be used for experiments since each is a potential human life *[1 mark]*.

p.80 — Using Genome Research in Medicine
Q1 If doctors know which genes make people more likely to get type 2 diabetes *[1 mark]*, they could provide individual advice on the best diet and lifestyle to reduce the risk of type 2 diabetes developing *[1 mark]*.

Topic C1 — Particles

p.82 — States of Matter
Q1 In a liquid, there are weak forces of attraction between the particles *[1 mark]*. The particles are free to move about/move about randomly, *[1 mark]* but they stay close together *[1 mark]*.

p.83 — The History of the Atom
Q1 The plum pudding model *[1 mark]*.
Q2 E.g. nucleus   shells

electrons

[1 mark for correct structure, 1 mark for correct labels]

Answers

p.84 — The Atom

Q1 a) +1

b) 0

c) −1

[1 mark for all three parts correct]

Q2 In the nucleus *[1 mark]*.

p.85 — Atomic Numbers and Mass Numbers

Q1 a) 16 − 8 = 8 neutrons *[1 mark]*

b) 40 − 20 = 20 neutrons *[1 mark]*

c) 27 − 13 = 14 neutrons *[1 mark]*

p.86 — Ions and Isotopes

Q1 a) Chlorine-35: 17 protons *[1 mark]*.

b) Chlorine-37: 17 protons *[1 mark]*.

Q2 35 + 1 = 36 electrons *[1 mark]*

Topic C2 — Elements, Compounds and Mixtures

p.87 — The Periodic Table

Q1 2 *[1 mark]*

Q2 Potassium and sodium will have similar chemical properties because they are both in Group 1 *[1 mark]*.

p.88 — Electron Shells

Q1 2.8.3

or

[1 mark]

p.89 — Simple Ions

Q1 1+ *[1 mark]*

p.90 — Ionic Bonding

Q1 KBr *[1 mark]*

p.91 — Ionic Compounds

Q1 When melted, the ions in an ionic compound are free to move, so an electric current can flow *[1 mark]*.

p.92 — Covalent Bonding

Q1

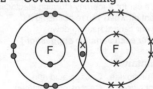

[1 mark]

Q2

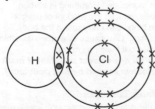

[1 mark]

p.93 — Simple Molecules

Q1 Simple molecules have weak intermolecular forces that are broken when they boil *[1 mark]*. As these forces are weak these molecules boil at low temperatures *[1 mark]*.

p.94 — Giant Covalent Structures and Fullerenes

Q1 Any two from, e.g. diamond is colourless, graphite is black / graphite conducts electricity, diamond doesn't / carbon atoms form four covalent bonds in diamond and three in graphite *[1 mark for each difference]*.

p.95 — Polymers and Properties of Materials

Q1 polymer B *[1 mark]*

p.96 — Metals

Q1 E.g. copper is a good electrical conductor *[1 mark]* because it contains electrons. These electrons are free to move, so an electric current can flow *[1 mark]*.

p.97 — States, Structure and Bonding

Q1 A — gas *[1 mark]*,

B — solid *[1 mark]*,

C — liquid *[1 mark]*.

p.98 — Purity

Q1 The impure sample would have a lower melting point than pure substance X *[1 mark]*. The impurities in the sample will cause its melting point to be lower *[1 mark]*.

p.99 — Simple Distillation

Q1 Pour the solution in a flask connected to a condenser *[1 mark]*. Heat the solution until the water evaporates *[1 mark]*. The water vapour will pass into the condenser where it will cool and condense *[1 mark]*. The pure water can be collected in a beaker (and the solid sodium carbonate will be left in the flask) *[1 mark]*.

Q2 The boiling points of propanol and water are similar, so you can't separate them using simple distillation *[1 mark]*.

p.100 — Fractional Distillation

Q1 liquid A *[1 mark]*

p.101 — Filtration and Crystallisation

Q1 crystallisation *[1 mark]*

p.102 — Chromatography

Q1 Pencil marks won't dissolve in the solvent / react with the solvent *[1 mark]*.

Q2 a sheet of chromatography paper/filter paper *[1 mark]*

p.103 — Interpreting Chromatograms

Q1 R_f of Y = $\dfrac{\text{distance travelled by Y}}{\text{distance travelled by solvent front}}$

= 3.6 cm ÷ 6.0 cm *[1 mark]*

= 0.60 *[1 mark]*

p.104 — Relative Masses

Q1 M_r of NaCl = 23.0 + 35.5

= 58.5 *[1 mark]*

Q2 M_r of $Mg(OH)_2$ = Mg + 2 × (O + H)

= 24.3 + (2 × (16.0 + 1.0)) *[1 mark]*

= 24.3 + (2 × 17.0)

= 24.3 + 34.0

= 58.3 *[1 mark]*

p.105 — Molecular and Empirical Formulas

Q1 2 and 2 both divide by 2.

2 ÷ 2 = 1, so the empirical formula of the compound is HO *[1 mark]*.

Topic C3 — Chemical Reactions

p.107 — Conservation of Mass

Q1 M_r(reactants) = 2 × A_r(Cu) + M_r(O_2).

= (2 × 63.5) + (16.0 + 16.0)

= 127.0 + 32.0

= 159.0 *[1 mark]*

M_r(products) = 2 × M_r(CuO)

= 2 × (63.5 + 16.0)

= 2 × 79.5

= 159.0 *[1 mark]*

M_r(products) = M_r(reactants), so the mass has been conserved *[1 mark]*.

p.108 — Chemical Formulas

Q1 a) Br^- *[1 mark]*

b) CO_3^{2-} *[1 mark]*

c) Li^+ *[1 mark]*

Q2 $Mg(OH)_2$ *[1 mark]*

p.109 — Chemical Equations

Q1 a) water → hydrogen + oxygen *[1 mark]*

b) gas *[1 mark]*

p.110 — Balancing Chemical Equations

Q1 $4Na + O_2 \rightarrow 2Na_2O$

[1 mark for a correctly balanced equation]

Q2 $2Fe + 3Cl_2 \rightarrow 2FeCl_3$

[1 mark for a correctly balanced equation]

p.111 — Endothermic and Exothermic Reactions

Q1 a) exothermic *[1 mark]*

b)

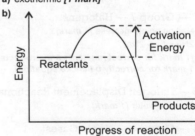

[1 mark for correct shape of reaction profile. 1 mark for correctly labelled axes. 1 mark for products, reactants and activation energy being correctly labelled.]

p.112 — Acids and Bases

Q1 a) Acidic *[1 mark]*

b) Yellow *[1 mark]*

p.113 — Reactions of Acids

Q1 Calcium chloride/$CaCl_2$ *[1 mark]*

p.114 — Neutralisation Reactions

Q1 $H_2SO_4 + 2KOH \rightarrow K_2SO_4 + 2H_2O$

[1 mark for formula of K_2SO_4 correct, 1 mark for correct balancing]

Answers

p.115 — Making Salts
Q1 E.g. warm the nitric acid and add the iron oxide to it *[1 mark]*. When all the acid has been neutralised, any excess iron oxide will sink to the bottom of the flask *[1 mark]*. Filter out the excess iron oxide using filter paper *[1 mark]*. Evaporate off some of the water from the solution, then leave it to cool and form crystals *[1 mark]*. Filter off the crystals and allow them to dry *[1 mark]*.

p.116 — Oxidation, Reduction and Electrolysis
Q1 Carbon/C is being oxidised *[1 mark]*. Copper oxide/CuO is being reduced *[1 mark]*.

p.117 — Electrolysis
Q1 Sodium/Na *[1 mark]*
Q2 Chlorine/Cl_2 *[1 mark]*

p.118 — Electrolysis of Copper Sulfate Solution
Q1 The mass of the cathode will increase *[1 mark]*, because at the cathode copper ions from the solution will turn into copper metal *[1 mark]*.

p.119 — Tests for Gases
Q1 Check to see if the gas will relight a glowing splint *[1 mark]*. If the splint will relight, then the gas is oxygen *[1 mark]*.
Q2 hydrogen *[1 mark]*

Topic C4 — Predicting and Identifying Reactions and Products

p.121 — Group 1 — Alkali Metals
Q1 lithium hydroxide *[1 mark]*
hydrogen gas *[1 mark]*

p.122 — Group 7 — Halogens
Q1 Melting points increase *[1 mark]*.
Q2 $2Na + I_2 \rightarrow 2NaI$
[1 mark for correct reactants and products, 1 mark for correctly balanced equation]

p.123 — Halogen Displacement Reactions
Q1 Bromine water *[1 mark]*.

p.124 — Group 0 — Noble Gases
Q1 Group 0 *[1 mark]*
Q2 xenon *[1 mark]*

p.125 — Predicting Properties of Elements
Q1 Any answer between −130 °C and −93 °C *[1 mark]*.

p.126 — Reactivity of Metals
Q1 a) Metal B, Metal C, Metal A *[1 mark]*
b) Metal A is copper.
Metal B is magnesium.
Metal C is zinc
[1 mark for all three correct].

p.127 — The Reactivity Series and Displacement
Q1 Tin would not displace zinc from zinc sulfate solution *[1 mark]*, since it is lower than zinc in the reactivity series/it is less reactive than zinc *[1 mark]*.

Topic C5 — Monitoring and Controlling Chemical Reactions

p.128 — Reaction Rates
Q1 E.g. mix the two solutions and place the reaction vessel over a sheet of paper with a mark on it *[1 mark]*. Time how long it takes for the mark to be covered up *[1 mark]*.

p.129 — Rate Experiments
Q1 Any two from: e.g. the volume of acid used / the mass of zinc used / the surface area of the zinc used / the temperature
[1 mark for each correct answer.]

p.130 — Calculating Rates
Q1 The rate of the reaction *[1 mark]*.

p.131 — Collision Theory
Q1 As the temperature increases, the particles move faster, so they collide more often *[1 mark]*. Increasing the temperature also increases the energy of the collisions *[1 mark]*. So at higher temperatures there are more successful collisions / more particles collide with enough energy to react *[1 mark]*.

p.132 — Collision Theory and Catalysts
Q1 The rate of reaction would be faster with powder than with pieces of ribbon *[1 mark]*. The powder has a larger surface area to volume ratio than the ribbon *[1 mark]*. This means that the frequency of collisions will be greater with the powder, so the rate will be faster *[1 mark]*.
Q2 A catalyst is a substance that increases the rate of a reaction *[1 mark]*, without being chemically changed or used up in the reaction *[1 mark]*.

p.133 — Identifying Catalysts
Q1 At the end of the reaction, the same amount of dark brown powder should still be visible at the bottom of the flask *[1 mark]*.

p.134 — Dynamic Equilibrium
Q1 A reversible reaction is one where the products can react with each other to produce the reactants *[1 mark]*.
Q2 None of the reactants or products can escape *[1 mark]*.

Topic C6 — Global Challenges

p.136 — Extracting Metals from Their Ores
Q1 Yes, because tin is below carbon in the reactivity series / tin is less reactive than carbon *[1 mark]*.

p.137 — Extracting Metals with Electrolysis
Q1 cathode / negative electrode *[1 mark]*.

p.138 — Life-Cycle Assessments
Q1 Making the material *[1 mark]*.
Making the product *[1 mark]*.
Using the product *[1 mark]*.
Disposing of the product *[1 mark]*.

p.139 — Using Life-Cycle Assessments
Q1 E.g. the energy required to extract the raw materials / whether the raw materials are renewable or not / whether any harmful gases are produced when the product is made / whether any waste products are harmful or not / how much carbon dioxide is produced by the car during use / how environmentally friendly the cars are to dispose of *[1 mark]*.

p.140 — Recycling Materials
Q1 Any two from: e.g. recycling saves the energy needed to extract materials from the Earth / conserves limited supplies of materials in the Earth / cuts down on the amount of waste going to landfill sites / causes less damage to the landscape through mining
[1 mark for each correct answer].

p.141 — Crude Oil
Q1 C_nH_{2n+2} *[1 mark]*
Q2 LPG/liquefied petroleum gas *[1 mark]*

p.142 — Hydrocarbons
Q1 Crude oil is not formed fast enough to replace the amount we are using *[1 mark]*.
Q2 $C_{50}H_{102}$ will have the higher boiling point *[1 mark]*. It has a longer hydrocarbon chain, so it has stronger intermolecular forces between the chains *[1 mark]*.

p.143 — Cracking
Q1 400 °C - 700 °C *[1 mark]*
70 atmospheres *[1 mark]*

p.144 — The Atmosphere
Q1 Green plants evolved over most of the Earth *[1 mark]*. As they photosynthesised they produced oxygen *[1 mark]*.

p.145 — The Greenhouse Effect
Q1 E.g. carbon dioxide, water vapour and methane *[1 mark for each]*
Q2 The Sun gives out electromagnetic radiation *[1 mark]*. This passes through the Earth's atmosphere and the shorter wavelengths are absorbed by the Earth *[1 mark]*. The Earth gives off some of the heat energy it absorbed as infrared radiation *[1 mark]*. Some of the infrared radiation is absorbed by greenhouse gases instead of escaping into space *[1 mark]*.

p.146 — Global Warming
Q1 Any two from: e.g. walking or cycling instead of using a car for a journey / turning electrical equipment off when you're not using it / turning your central heating down.
[1 mark for each sensible suggestion]

p.147 — Pollutants
Q1 E.g. Sulfur dioxide. Causes acid rain. / Oxides of nitrogen. Causes acid rain/can cause photochemical smog. / Carbon monoxide. Breathing in carbon monoxide reduces the amount of oxygen that the blood can carry round the body. / Particulates. Can cause or worsen breathing problems/coat buildings in soot.
[1 mark for any correct pollutant, 1 mark for a problem caused by that pollutant.]

p.148 — Water Treatment
Q1 The water is first passed through a wire mesh, which screens out large objects *[1 mark]*. Then it is passed through gravel and sand beds to filter out any other solid bits *[1 mark]*.

Answers

Topic P1 — Matter

p.150 — The History of the Atom and Atomic Structure
Q1 positive *[1 mark]*

p.151 — Density
Q1 E.g. use a mass balance to find the mass of the object *[1 mark]*. Fill a eureka can with water to just below the spout, then put the object in the water in the can and put a measuring cylinder below the spout *[1 mark]*. Measure the volume of water displaced by the object using a measuring cylinder *[1 mark]*. Then calculate the density of the object using density = mass ÷ volume *[1 mark]*.

Q2 density = mass ÷ volume, so
mass = density × volume *[1 mark]*
= 40 × 0.05 *[1 mark]*
= 2 kg *[1 mark]*

p.152 — Particle Theory and States of Matter
Q1 a) It will decrease *[1 mark]*.
b) It will stay the same *[1 mark]*.
c) It will increase *[1 mark]*.

p.153 — Specific Heat Capacity
Q1 change in thermal energy = mass × specific heat capacity × change in temperature, so change in temperature = change in thermal energy ÷ (mass × specific heat capacity) *[1 mark]*
= 1600 ÷ (0.20 × 400) *[1 mark]*
= 20 °C *[1 mark]*

p.154 — Specific Latent Heat
Q1 Energy = mass × specific latent heat
= 0.250 × 120 000 *[1 mark]*
= 30 000 J *[1 mark]*

p.155 — Motion of Gas Particles
Q1 When gas particles collide with the walls of their container they each cause a force on the wall *[1 mark]*. The overall force of all the particles on the wall in a given area is known as pressure *[1 mark]*

Q2 When the temperature of a gas decreases, the energy stored in the kinetic stores of the gas particles/their speed decreases *[1 mark]*. This means they hit the walls of the container less hard and less often *[1 mark]*. Therefore the pressure decreases *[1 mark]*.

Topic P2 — Forces

p.157 — Speed and Velocity
Q1 distance travelled = speed × time
= 15 × 24 *[1 mark]*
= 360 m *[1 mark]*

Q2 speed = $\dfrac{\text{distance travelled}}{\text{time}}$
= $\dfrac{660}{120}$ *[1 mark]*
= 5.5 m/s *[1 mark]*

p.158 — Measurements of Motion
Q1 a) To convert from km to m, multiply by 1000.
1.5 km = 1.5 × 1000
= 1500 m *[1 mark]*

b) Number of hours in 1 day = 24 *[1 mark]*
To convert from hours to seconds, multiply by 60, and then multiply by 60 again.
24 hours = 24 × 60 × 60
= 86 400 s *[1 mark]*

p.159 — Acceleration
Q1 $v^2 - u^2 = 2 \times a \times d$, so
$d = (v^2 - u^2) \div (2 \times a)$ *[1 mark]*
= $(33^2 - 0^2) \div (2 \times 8.25)$ *[1 mark]*
= 66 m *[1 mark]*

p.160 — Investigating Motion
Q1 a) It will increase *[1 mark]*.
b) It will decrease *[1 mark]*.

p.161 — Distance-Time Graphs
Q1 E.g.

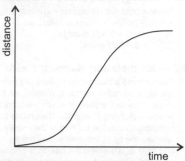

[1 mark for a continuous line that initially curves upwards, and which curves downwards at the end until it becomes horizontal, 1 mark for a straight middle section.]

p.162 — Velocity-Time Graphs
Q1 E.g.

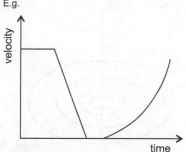

[1 mark for line which is initially horizontal, then bends to give a straight line with a negative gradient, continuing until it meets the time axis, 1 mark for showing the line then continuing horizontally along the time axis, and 1 mark for then showing the line curving upwards.]

p.163 — Forces and Free Body Force Diagrams
Q1 a)

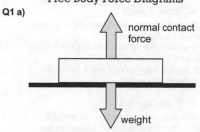

[1 mark for arrows pointing in the correct direction and labelled correctly. 1 mark for arrows being the same length.]

b)

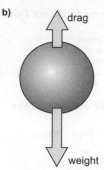

[1 mark for the arrows pointing in the right direction and being labelled correctly. 1 mark for the weight arrow being longer than the drag arrow. Allow 2 marks if no drag arrow has been shown, but the correct weight arrow has been drawn.]

p.164 — Newton's First Law of Motion
Q1 accelerating *[1 mark]*.
As the forward force is greater than the backwards force, there is a resultant force in the forward direction meaning the car accelerates.

p.165 — Newton's Second and Third Laws of Motion
Q1 $F = ma$
= 26 000 × 1.5 *[1 mark]*
= 39 000 N *[1 mark]*

p.166 — Mass, Weight and Gravity
Q1 $W = mg$, so
$m = \dfrac{W}{g}$
= 820 ÷ 10 *[1 mark]*
= 82 kg *[1 mark]*

p.167 — Mechanical Energy Stores
Q1 $PE = m \times h \times g$
= 0.80 × 1.5 × 10 *[1 mark]*
= 12 J *[1 mark]*

Q2 $KE = 0.5 \times m \times v^2$
= 0.5 × 4.9 × (2.0)² *[1 mark]*
= 9.8 J *[1 mark]*

p.168 — Work Done
Q1 20 cm = 0.2 m *[1 mark]*
$W = Fs$
= 20 × 0.2 *[1 mark]*
= 4 J *[1 mark]*

p.169 — Power
Q1 power = work done ÷ time, so
time = work done ÷ power *[1 mark]*
= 1440 ÷ 12.0
= 120 s *[1 mark]*
Convert seconds to minutes by dividing by 60:
120 s = 120 ÷ 60
= 2 mins *[1 mark]*

p.170 — Forces and Elasticity
Q1 Extension of the spring = 0.20 − 0.16
= 0.04 m *[1 mark]*
$F = x \times k$ so,
$k = \dfrac{F}{x}$
= $\dfrac{3.0}{0.04}$ *[1 mark]*
= 75 N/m *[1 mark]*

Answers

p.171 — Forces, Elasticity and Work Done

Q1 extension = 1.3 − 1.2
= 0.1 m *[1 mark]*
energy transferred in stretching
= 0.5 × spring constant × (extension)^2
= 0.5 × 54 × 0.1^2 *[1 mark]*
= 0.27 J *[1 mark]*

p.172 — Using Force-Extension Graphs

Q1 a) 3 cm *[1 mark]*

b) area of triangle = 0.5 × base × height
base = 3 cm
= 0.03 m *[1 mark]*
height = 6 N
area of triangle under graph
= 0.5 × 0.03 × 6 *[1 mark]*
= 0.09 J *[1 mark]*

p.173 — Investigating Hooke's Law

Q1 E.g. Stand up *[1 mark]* so you can get out of the way if the masses fall *[1 mark]*. / Wear safety goggles *[1 mark]* so your eyes are protected if the spring snaps *[1 mark]*.

Topic P3 — Electricity and Magnetism

p.175 — Static Electricity

Q1 E.g. hold the object near to some small scraps of paper *[1 mark]*. If the object is charged, the scraps of paper will be attracted to the object, making them 'jump' towards it *[1 mark]*.

p.176 — Current and Circuit Diagrams

Q1 charge = current × time, so
time = charge ÷ current
= 120 ÷ 2.5 *[1 mark]*
= 48 s *[1 mark]*

p.177 — Potential Difference

Q1 energy transferred
= charge × potential difference, so
potential difference
= energy transferred ÷ charge
= 360 ÷ 75 *[1 mark]*
= 4.8 V *[1 mark]*

Q2 potential difference = current × resistance, so
resistance = potential difference ÷ current
= 4.25 ÷ 0.25 *[1 mark]*
= 17 Ω *[1 mark]*

p.178 — *I-V* Characteristics

Q1 E.g.

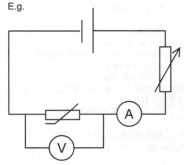

[1 mark for a complete circuit with a power supply showing a thermistor in series with a variable resistor. 1 mark for a voltmeter connected across the thermistor and an ammeter that is connected in series with the thermistor.]

p.179 — Circuit Devices

Q1 A straight line through the origin *[1 mark]*. Its current and potential difference are directly proportional *[1 mark]*.

p.180 — Series Circuits

Q1 3.6 ÷ 3 = 1.2 V *[1 mark]*

p.181 — Series and Parallel Circuits

Q1 3.5 V *[1 mark]*

p.182 — Energy and Power in Circuits

Q1 Power = potential difference × current, so
current = power ÷ potential difference
= 8.5 ÷ 2.5 *[1 mark]*
= 3.4 A *[1 mark]*

p.183 — Magnets and Magnetic Fields

Q1 Draw around a magnet on a piece of paper and put a compass next to it, marking on the piece of paper the point at which the compass needle is pointing *[1 mark]*. Then move the compass so that the tail end of the needle is where the tip of the needle was before, and mark again where the needle is pointing *[1 mark]*. Repeat this many times and then join up the markings to make a complete sketch of one field line around the magnet *[1 mark]*. Do this several times for different points around the magnet to show several field lines *[1 mark]*.

p.184 — Electromagnetism

Q1 E.g.

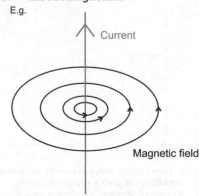

Current

Magnetic field

[1 mark for correct shape of field lines. 1 mark for correctly showing the direction of both the current and the magnetic field lines.]

Topic P4 — Waves and Radioactivity

p.186 — Wave Basics

Q1 The period is the time taken for one wave to pass a certain point.
20 waves take 40 seconds to pass a point, so one wave takes: 40 ÷ 20 = 2 s
[2 marks, otherwise 1 mark for some correct working.]

p.187 — Wave Speed

Q1 wave speed = frequency × wavelength
frequency = wave speed ÷ wavelength
= 340 ÷ 0.5 *[1 mark]*
= 680 Hz *[1 mark]*

p.188 — Measuring Waves

Q1 A cork is floated in a ripple tank *[1 mark]*. The number of bobs in a set time is recorded *[1 mark]*. The number of times the cork bobs is divided by the time taken, to obtain the frequency *[1 mark]*.

Q2 The cork bobs 30 times in 20 seconds, so in 1 second, the cork will bob 30 ÷ 20 *[1 mark]* = 1.5 bobs per second. So *f* = 1.5 Hz *[1 mark]*

p.189 — Reflection

Q1 27° *[1 mark]*

p.190 — Refraction

Q1 Refraction is when a wave changes direction at the boundary between two different materials *[1 mark]*.

p.191 — Investigation Refraction

Q1 E.g. draw around a glass block on a piece of paper and shine a light ray into the side of the glass block *[1 mark]*. Trace the incident ray and mark where the ray exits from the block. Remove the block and join up the rays that you have drawn with a straight line *[1 mark]*. Measure the angle of incidence and angle of refraction for where the light entered the block *[1 mark]*.

p.192 — Electromagnetic Waves

Q1 UV
X-rays
gamma rays
[1 mark for two correct types of wave, 1 additional mark if all three types of wave are named.]

p.193 — Uses of EM Waves

Q1 E.g. TV / radio signals *[1 mark]*

p.194 — More Uses of EM Waves

Q1 E.g. seeing broken bones *[1 mark]*, treating cancer *[1 mark]*

p.195 — Atoms and Isotopes

Q1 8 protons *[1 mark]*
16 − 8 = 8 neutrons *[1 mark]*.

p.196 — Electron Energy Levels

Q1 A positive ion is an atom that has lost one or more electrons and has a positive charge *[1 mark]*. An ion is formed when an outer electron absorbs enough energy that it leaves the atom *[1 mark]*.

p.197 — Radioactive Decay

Q1 E.g. alpha particles would not be able to pass through the packaging to sterilise the equipment *[1 mark]*.

p.198 — Decay Equations

Q1 $^{226}_{88}\text{Ra} \rightarrow \,^{222}_{86}\text{Rn} + \,^{4}_{2}\alpha$
[1 mark for correct mass number, 1 mark for correct atomic number]

p.199 — Activity and Half-Life

Q1 Activity is the number of unstable nuclei in a source that decay in a given time *[1 mark]*.

p.200 — Dangers of Radioactivity

Q1 E.g. Radiation can cause cancer *[1 mark]*. Radiation can also kill a cell completely *[1 mark]*.

Q2 Alpha particles have a short range *[1 mark]* so are unlikely to reach the scientist to irradiate her *[1 mark]*.

Answers

Topic P5 — Energy

p.202 — Energy and Energy Transfers
Q1 Mechanically *[1 mark]*

p.203 — More Energy Transfers
Q1 Energy is transferred mechanically *[1 mark]* from the kinetic energy store of the car *[1 mark]* to the thermal energy stores of the brakes and wheels *[1 mark]*.

p.204 — Efficiency
Q1 Efficiency = $\dfrac{\text{useful output energy transfer}}{\text{input energy transfer}}$

$= \dfrac{80}{500}$

$= 0.16$ *[1 mark]*

$0.16 \times 100 = 16\%$ *[1 mark]*

p.205 — Reducing Unwanted Energy Transfers
Q1 Any one from: e.g. install loft insulation / make the walls thicker / replace walls with walls that have a lower thermal conductivity *[1 mark]*.

p.206 — Mechanical Energy Transfers & Calculations
Q1 PE = *mgh*
$= 1.6 \times 10 \times 5.0$ *[1 mark]*
$= 80$ J *[1 mark]*

p.207 — Electrical Energy Transfers & Calculations
Q1 Energy transferred to bulb
$= \text{power} \times \text{time}$
$= 35 \times (2.0 \times 60)$ *[1 mark]*
$= 4200$ J *[1 mark]*

Topic P6 — Global Challenges

p.209 — Everyday Speeds and Accelerations
Q1 Increasing the time taken to slow down reduces the deceleration since $a = v \div t$ *[1 mark]* which reduces the forces involved since $F = ma$ *[1 mark]*.

p.210 — Stopping Distances and Reaction Times
Q1 If you're tired, your reaction time is likely to be longer *[1 mark]*, which would increase thinking distance and so stopping distance *[1 mark]*.

p.211 — Non-Renewable Energy Sources
Q1 Any two from: e.g. climate change / global warming / acid rain / coal mining makes a mess of the landscape *[1 mark for each correct answer]*.

p.212 — Renewable Energy Sources
Q1 Any two from: e.g. bio-fuels / wind power / the sun / solar power / hydro-electricity / the tides
[1 mark for each correct answer].
Q2 Any two from: e.g. some people think wind turbines spoil the view / wind turbines can be quite noisy / the electricity supply is unreliable / you can't generate more electricity in response to high demand.
[1 mark for each correct answer]

p.213 — More On Energy Sources
Q1 E.g. Our appliances are more energy efficient / we're trying harder to save electricity *[1 mark]*

p.214 — Electricity and the National Grid
Q1 p.d. across primary coil × current in primary coil
= p.d. across secondary coil
    × current in secondary coil
So current in secondary coil = (p.d. across primary coil × current in primary coil) ÷ p.d. across secondary coil *[1 mark]*
$= (40 \times 2) \div 10$ *[1 mark]*
$= 8$ A *[1 mark]*

p.215 — Wiring in the Home
Q1 The casing is metal so it could become live *[1 mark]*.

Index

Index

Index

Index

Index